ADVANCES IN ANALYTICAL CHEMISTRY AND INSTRUMENTATION
Volume 6

Progress in Gas Chromatography

Advances in
Analytical Chemistry and Instrumentation

EDITED BY CHARLES N. REILLEY,
Department of Chemistry, University of North Carolina, Chapel Hill, North Carolina
AND FRED W. MCLAFFERTY,
Department of Chemistry, Purdue University, Lafayette, Indiana

Progress in Gas Chromatography

OHN OWARD Edited by

J. H. PURNELL

Department of Chemistry,
University of Wales,
University College of Swansea,
Swansea, Wales

INTERSCIENCE PUBLISHERS
a division of John Wiley & Sons, New York · London · Sydney

PRINTED IN THE UNITED STATES OF AMERICA

PREFACE

The rate of publication in gas chromatography is now more or less constant at about 1800 papers a year. Obviously, it has become impossible for either the average worker or the expert to stay abreast of all developments in the field and, for this reason, we may now expect growing emphasis on the publication of review articles. Existing abstracting services provide adequately for our bibliographic needs, the main requirement being, as we see it, for critical summaries of viewpoints and findings in important, established areas and for surveys of new work which may have impact in the future.

As regards the latter, it is clearly not a simple matter to judge what may develop best and so, eventually, enter into the former category. Nevertheless, during the past few years a number of topics have shown such promise that one may feel some confidence in their future development. These are represented in this volume by articles on adsorbent modification, pressure programming, liquid surface effects, physico-chemical measurement, and theoretical "tailoring" of solvents. Well-established areas which, however, we feel have not been adequately reviewed before are also represented in articles on preparative scale methods and effluent identification. The latter is the most important single problem encountered in practice and written about in the journals, yet the information available has hitherto not been gathered together. Finally, we have in this volume a very personal and "practical" view of column theory which leads to interesting and novel comparisons of column performance and gives much original guidance on practical matters.

The contents of this volume represent an attempt by the editor to pinpoint existing needs and growth points, and in this endeavor he has been fortunate in securing the help of authors both distinguished and collaborative and who have exercised their mandate with excellent judgement. Any success this volume may have remains theirs.

July, 1967

HOWARD PURNELL

v

CONTRIBUTORS TO VOLUME 6

JOHN R. CONDER, *Department of Chemistry, University College of Swansea, Singleton Park, Swansea, Wales*

ISTVÁN HALÁSZ, *Institut für Physikalische Chemie der Universität Frankfurt/Main, Germany*

GARRARD L. HARGROVE, *Atomics International, North American Aviation, Inc., Canoga Park, California*

ERWIN HEINE, *Institut für Physikalische Chemie der Universität Frankfurt/Main, Germany*

STANLEY H. LANGER, *Department of Chemical Engineering, University of Wisconsin, Madison, Wisconsin*

DAVID A. LEATHARD, *Department of Chemistry, University College of Swansea, Singleton Park, Swansea, Wales*

DANIEL E. MARTIRE, *Department of Chemistry, Georgetown University, Washington, D.C.*

C. S. G. PHILLIPS, *Inorganic Chemistry Laboratory, Oxford University, Oxford, England*

DONALD T. SAWYER, *Department of Chemistry, University of California, Riverside, California*

C. G. SCOTT, *Research Department, Hoffman-LaRoche Inc., Nutley, N.J.*

R. P. W. SCOTT, *Unilever Research Laboratory, Colworth House, Sharnbrook, Bedford, England*

RICHARD J. SHEEHAN, *Department of Chemical Engineering, University of Wisconsin, Madison, Wisconsin*

BARRY C. SHURLOCK, *Berkeley Nuclear Laboratories, Berkeley, Gloucestershire, U.K.*

CONTENTS

Gas Chromatographic Identification

D. A. Leathard and B. C. Shurlock,
University College of Swansea, United Kingdom

1

I. INTRODUCTION

Although most aspects of gas chromatography (GC) have been extensively developed, relatively little attention has been paid to methods of peak identification—in spite of the fact that without such methods analytical GC is rendered useless. This neglect is largely due to the common practice of relying entirely upon retention coincidence methods —a situation which has undoubtedly led to much qualitative error. It is only quite recently that the limitations of retention coincidence techniques (Sec. III) have been generally appreciated, thus allowing other identification methods to receive the attention they deserve. Few review articles have, therefore, been published (1–4), and none covers the entire field.

GC is essentially a method of separating a mixture into its constituents, but at the same time three pieces of information can be obtained for each component: the retention volume (V_r), the peak width, and the peak height. In favorable cases it is possible to achieve a qualitative (and quantitative) analysis on the basis of such data alone, but generally the number of ambiguities is so large that the analyst must resort to other methods of characterization.

These methods may still involve only chromatographic information as in, say, the comparison of peak heights produced by one eluate in two detectors (Sec. IV), or determination of the change in V_r due to chemical modification of the sample (Sec. VI). Alternatively, standard analytical techniques can be adapted for continuous monitoring of the gas chromatographic effluent in order to obtain additional information about the sample (Sec. V). For example, the Beilstein test, mass spectrometry, flame photometry, and thin-layer chromatography have all been used on-stream in conjunction with GC. Indeed, provided reasonable sample sizes are available, almost any method of analyzing the

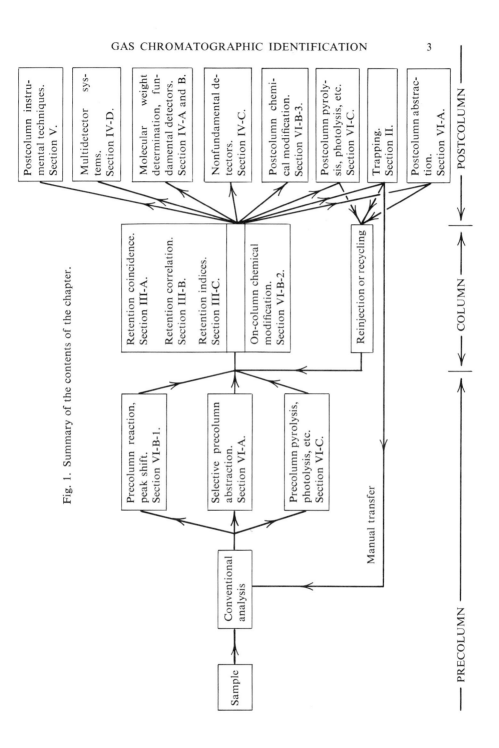

Fig. 1. Summary of the contents of the chapter.

separated components can be used if peaks are trapped individually and then transferred to conventional equipment. While this chapter is not concerned with the analysis of such trapped samples, the trapping methods themselves are discussed in the following section.

A summary of the contents of the chapter is shown in Figure 1 in terms of the precolumn, column, and postcolumn stages of GC. These stages do not, however, provide a practicable basis for arranging the material, and so a more convenient, if somewhat arbitrary, approach has been adopted in which the more familiar methods are considered first. Thus, after a discussion of trapping techniques, methods based upon the measurement of retention volume are considered. Sections then follow on detectors and the on-stream use of postcolumn instrumentation. Finally, methods which involve modification of the sample at some stage of the chromatographic identification process are considered.

The nomenclature used is conventional throughout. The separated materials of a mixed sample are referred to as solutes while they are in the column and eluates as they emerge, mixed with the carrier gas, in the effluent.

No attempt has been made to provide an exhaustive bibliography of published work, although most of the important papers published before the fall of 1966 are mentioned. Wherever possible, references have been restricted to readily available books and journals.

II. POSTCOLUMN TRAPPING TECHNIQUES

Most designs of trap rely either upon a relatively large amount of solvent or upon a very low temperature to reduce the vapor pressure of an eluate to the point where it is effectively trapped. The first type of trap (5) may suffer from the disadvantage that any subsequent treatment of the effluent is accompanied by interference from a much larger quantity of solvent. However, in certain cases such traps present no problems; for example, when the eluate is of much higher boiling point than the solvent, the latter may be removed by distillation, or when an infrared or ultraviolet spectrum is to be taken, one may allow for the bands due to the solvent. Nevertheless, for most purposes the low-temperature trap is the most convenient.

The rapid cooling needed to liquefy any reasonably volatile eluate usually results in the formation of a very fine mist which is swept straight through the trap unless precautions are taken to prevent it. In order to retain these minute droplets, it seems necessary for them to come into contact with a surface. As such droplets are frequently charged, it is possible that simple charge neutralization processes are responsible for this behavior. Indeed, electrical precipitation is often used to improve trapping efficiencies (6,7). However, it is likely that adsorption and heat transfer effects are also important.

The Volman trap (8) consists of a double-walled vessel with its inner and outer walls at different temperatures. This arrangement creates turbulence within the trap and facilitates contact of the condensed

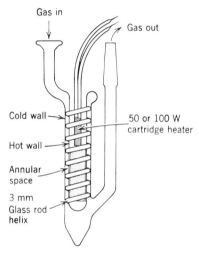

Fig. 2. A type of Volman trap suitable for preparative GC (10). By courtesy of *The Journal of Chromatography*.

droplets with the cold wall [(9,10) Fig. 2]. Simple U-shaped traps cooled in liquid air and packed with materials of high surface area, such as firebrick, have been used to trap $\sim 10^{-8}$ moles of C_5 and C_6 unsaturates with an efficiency of about 70% (11).

In an unpacked trap the droplets which are formed next to the wall stand the greatest chance of being retained. Hence, the obvious way to improve trapping efficiencies is either to increase the surface-to-volume ratio, as in packed traps, or to increase the number of times that droplet formation occurs. Each condensation will then result in retention of the "wall layer." This is the principle of the multiple temperature-gradient trap which consists of alternating hot and cold regions. Any mist which is not trapped in the first region is reevaporated and trapped in the second or the third region, etc. Daniels (12) has described a trap which employs a reflux coil condenser in this way.

Some workers have employed a different approach, in which the carrier gas and eluate are frozen down together, thus entraining the small amounts of eluate in much larger quantities of carrier gas. Swoboda (13), using this method with argon carrier gas, was able to recover 0.6–26 mg

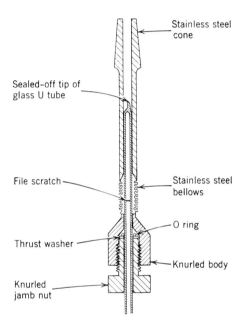

Fig. 3. Device for vacuum transfer of trapped fractions [see text for procedure, ref. 16]. By courtesy of *The Journal of Chromatography*.

samples of various organic materials with an efficiency of $100 \pm 3\%$, while Hornstein and Crowe (14) have achieved similar results with carbon dioxide as carrier gas.

Under suitable conditions, most of the methods outlined above are capable of giving recoveries in excess of 90% with the milligram quantities usually met with in preparative GC. However, they are not really suitable for analytical GC, which commonly involves submicrogram samples. Even when such samples are trapped, the recovery and handling of them is difficult, and wherever possible continuous monitoring of the effluent is desirable. Nonetheless, Amy et al. (15) have described an attractive technique for trapping very small samples ($\sim 10^{-11}$ moles) prior to introduction into a mass spectrometer. In this method the GC column is effectively extended by short, thin-walled capillaries filled with a convenient column packing. Any given part of the effluent may then be trapped in these minicolumns, which are easily sealed and stored until they can be conveniently analyzed. An ingenious method of introducing samples from such sealed glass tubes into vacuum lines, gas cells, etc., has been described by Drew and Johnson (16). The sealed tube is marked with a glass knife at one end and clamped into the device shown in Figure 3 by compression of the O-ring, thus making a vacuum-tight seal. The device is then pumped out and flexed at the metal bellows, causing the tube to break at the knife mark and the effluent to evaporate into the line.

Two trapping techniques designed especially for use with infrared analysis should be mentioned. The condensed droplets of the effluent may either be directly deposited onto KBr plates (17) or filtered out by 25μ thick cellulosic membranes, with a pore size of about 0.5μ, which are immediately ready for insertion into the spectrometer (18). These highly convenient techniques are inevitably attended by rather low trapping efficiencies and, in the case of the latter, compensation for substrate bands must be made by using a double-beam spectrometer. For complete compensation, great care must be taken to match the membranes (18).

III. IDENTIFICATION TECHNIQUES BASED UPON RETENTION BEHAVIOR

A. Coincidence Methods

The simplest method of identifying an unknown peak is to compare its retention volume with that of a standard sample. One way of doing this is to run the analysis mixture and standard separately under identical column conditions and to compare the retention volumes of standard and unknown. In practice, however, it is difficult to maintain column conditions absolutely constant and even more difficult to reproduce them from day to day. Therefore, it is better, if possible, to add the standard sample to the analysis mixture and observe whether a new peak appears or whether the shape and/or size of the unknown peak is changed. It is convenient for the standard and unknown samples to be of similar size. Then, if they have only slightly different retention volumes, this will usually be indicated by the occurrence of a shoulder on the augmented peak, or by a rounding of the peak top accompanied by an increase in the peak width and, hence, an apparent decrease in the number of theoretical plates of the column. If, on the other hand, there is no detectable change in the peak shape but an increase in the peak height, the standard and unknown have the same retention volumes, and it is probable that they are the same compound. There is, however, the distinct possibility that they are not the same, and for this reason, particularly if only one column is used, auxiliary techniques are frequently employed to supplement the retention coincidence method. The widespread use of this method is probably accounted for by its extreme simplicity rather than by its accuracy.

The uncertainties and ambiguities which arise in the use of coincidence methods are perhaps greatest when working with compounds not previously studied by GC. Under these circumstances it is helpful to carry out a brief survey of the retention behavior of a large number of standards similar to those expected in the analysis mixture. If the information obtained is then correlated in one of the ways described in Section III-B, it will be possible to predict the retention volumes of many more solutes, enabling identification of those which may not be available as standards. At the same time solutes whose similar retention volumes might lead to mistaken identification will be revealed. However, there is always some element of doubt in any assignment which is based merely upon retention data.

The certainty with which a peak can be identified depends upon the accuracy with which its retention volume can be measured and the number of closely eluted substances with which it might be confused. This intuitive observation has been expressed quantitatively by Klein and Tyler (19). They define a density of eluted peaks which may be generally expressed as (20),

$$\rho = \frac{\text{Total no. of peaks}}{\text{Total no. of divisions}} = \frac{N}{(V_2 - V_1)/\delta V}$$

where N is the number of possible eluates. If, for example, the analysis mixture is known to contain only the elements carbon and hydrogen, N would be equal to the number of all possible hydrocarbons eluted between retention volumes V_1 and V_2. δV is the smallest difference in retention volume which can be detected, and at the 95% confidence level equals 4σ, where σ is the standard error of replicate measurements of retention volume. In other words, if a chromatogram were to be taken of all possible eluates eluted between V_1 and V_2, the average number of substances which, within experimental error, were simultaneously eluted would be equal to ρ. In practice, the distribution of peaks will follow a Poisson law:

$$p_n = \frac{e^{-\rho}\rho^n}{n!}$$

where p_n is the probability of finding n solutes in a single interval δV. Hence the probability of finding either none or one solute in the interval is given by:

$$p_0 + p_1 = \frac{e^{-\rho}\rho^0}{0!} + \frac{e^{-\rho}\rho^1}{1!}$$

and p_{se}, the probability of simultaneous elution of two or more solutes in an interval by:

$$p_{se} = 1 - (p_0 + p_1)$$

Figure 4 shows calculated values of p_{se} for various values of ρ. When $p_{se} = 0.05$, i.e., a situation in which the analyst would be 95% certain

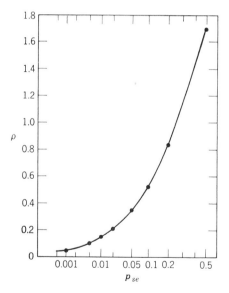

Fig. 4. Probability of simultaneous elution, p_{se}, as a function of the density of eluates, ρ, (19). By courtesy of *Analytical Chemistry*.

that there was no simultaneous elution, $\rho = 0.362$. If now V_1 is put equal to zero and it is assumed that $V_2/\delta V = 100$ (i.e., there is a 1% error in the measured retention volumes) then, $N = 100\rho = 36.2$. This is the maximum permissible number of possible eluates in an analysis mixture which in theory permits unambiguous identification in 95 cases out of 100. Of course, the treatment breaks down if the retention volumes of the eluates are biased in any way. If, for example, a mixture of 36 n-paraffins were chromatographed, the chances of mistaken identification under normal conditions would be zero.

In order to reduce mistaken identifications to the one-in-a-thousand level, no more than four eluates are allowable (Fig. 4). This means that in most practical situations identification at this level by means of retention data on a single column is impossible. The obvious way to negotiate this difficulty is to reduce ρ and hence p_{se}. This is equivalent to reducing either δV or N. The former involves improving the accuracy of routine retention measurements beyond the 1% level, which is very difficult. On the other hand, N can be reduced quite easily by making use of alternative information (19). This could, for example, be provided by elemental analysis. An alternative approach is to employ more than one column. The reasons for this are self-evident; but a semiquantitative discussion is helpful in clarifying the limitations of the statistical treatment.

The probability of multicomponent peaks being eluted from two different columns, A and B, is given by:

$$p_{se}^{A+B} = p_{se}^{A} \cdot p_{se}^{B} \qquad (1)$$

As $p_{se}^{B} < 1$, it follows that $p_{se}^{A+B} < p_{se}^{A}$, and thus the use of two columns has clearly reduced the chances of misidentification due to simultaneous elution. The extension of this approach to many columns might be expected to reduce p_{se} to a negligibly small value. However, as the statistical treatment depends upon a random distribution of eluates, eq. (1) will not be valid if the retention volume of a solute on, say, column A is related to that on column B. In the limit, when A and B are the same:

$$p_{se}^{A+B} = p_{se}^{A} = p_{se}^{B}$$

and, as the limited number of solvent types generally makes some cross-correlation inevitable, it follows that in practice:

$$p_{se}^{A} > p_{se}^{A+B} > p_{se}^{A} \cdot p_{se}^{B}$$

It is clear, therefore, that the use of several columns reduces the chances of mistaken identification, particularly if the columns are widely different. A suggested combination is shown in Table I.

TABLE I
Suggested Multicolumn Combination

Type	Column	Basis of separation
Gas–liquid	Squalane	Boiling point
	Dimethyl-sulfolane	Boiling point modified by polarity
	AgNO$_3$/glycol	Stability constant of Ag complex
Gas–solid	Activated alumina	Heat of adsorption

The use of several columns is greatly facilitated by a chromatograph which enables rapid switching from one column to another (262) or the simultaneous operation of all columns.

At the experimental level, multicolumn chromatography involves relating the peaks on one chromatogram to those on all others in order to determine the retention volumes of a given unknown on all columns. This may be done in at least two ways. First, a preliminary identification is made on column A and the retention volume of the appropriate standard is measured on column B. Then the chromatogram of the whole analysis mixture on column B is examined for a peak in the same position as the standard and of similar size, relative to other identified peaks, as the unknown. Secondly, the unknown peak on column A may be isolated and rerun on column B and its retention volume noted on both columns. This latter method has the considerable advantage that there is less likelihood of missing those solutes which are eluted in multicomponent peaks on both columns. This is illustrated in Figure 5 where it can be seen that component 3 would not be detected if both chromatograms were obtained by running the complete analysis mixture. However, if the peaks of A were rerun individually on column B, the second peak of column A would be resolved into components 2 and 3.

The rerunning of peaks is easily achieved by trapping and then reinjecting the required eluate (21–23). A simple but effective device for use in this connection is shown in Figure 6 (11). It incorporates three

3-way valves, and with these in configuration *A* the trap is isolated and the effluent detected in the usual way. By watching the detector output, the valves are switched to arrangement *B* when it is required to trap an eluate. In this mode, the eluate passes through the cold-trap, where most of it is retained; the remainder passes on to the detector. When the required peak has been trapped, the valves are returned to configuration

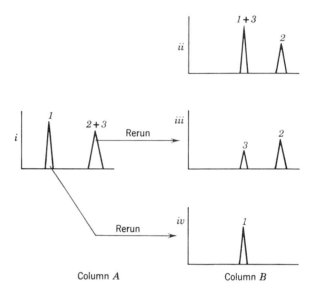

Fig. 5. A comparison of the information obtained from two dual-column retention-coincidence procedures. (*a*) comparison of measured retention data with chromatograms from both columns [(*i*) and (*ii*)]: peak *3* is masked; and (*b*) trapping the apparently individual peaks from one column, (*i*), and reinjecting them one at a time onto the other [(*iii*) and (*iv*)]: all three components detected.

A and the trap is warmed. Meanwhile the columns are switched. Finally, conversion to the arrangement *C* causes the trapped peak to be reinjected onto the new column, with the trap acting as a sample loop.

   The duration of trapping is chosen by referring to a complete chromatogram of the mixture and varies according to the width of the peak and individual requirements. Sometimes, for example, only the leading edge of a complex peak will be wanted.

   If the trap offers any significant resistance to flow, the retention volume of a material injected through the trap may differ from that injected in any other way. Care should always be taken, therefore, to

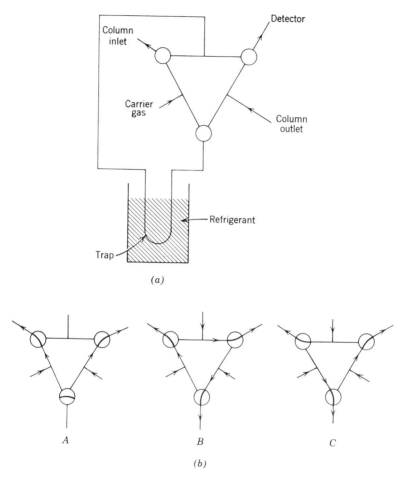

Fig. 6. Device for trapping and reinjecting eluates based upon a triangular arrangement of three 3-way valves (11). (*a*) General flow diagram; (*b*) *A*, trap isolated; *B*, trapping effluent; *C*, reinjecting trapped material.

compare retention data using the same injection system. This warning applies to all retention experiments.

Finally, it should be noted that there is no point in using several columns with stationary phrases of similar type, as the information obtained is no more of an aid to identification than that from any single one of the columns. A more detailed discussion of the various types of column is given in the next section.

B. Correlation Diagrams

Retention coincidence methods are not entirely hit or miss, since the analyst is rarely completely ignorant of the nature of the sample. Published compilations of data (24) can thus be shrewdly abstracted and a list of possibilities drawn up. This list can be further reduced by reference to retention data obtained from the actual chromatograph which is going to be used for the analysis. The arrangement, correlation, and extension of these data is considerably facilitated by making use of certain relationships which exist between the retention volumes of compounds and some of their physical parameters. The relationships referred to are easily derived from the retention volume equation (25a):

$$V_r = N_l RT / \gamma p^\circ$$

In this equation, V_r is the retention volume, measured from the air peak, of a solute with an activity coefficient γ and vapor pressure p° at $T^\circ K$, and N_l is the number of moles of liquid phase in the column. If, for the moment, it is assumed, that γ is constant for all solutes, then it follows that a linear relationship exists between V_r and $1/p^\circ$. This is illustrated in Figure 7 (25b) where V_r and p° have been plotted logarithmically for convenience. A great deal of information on the vapor pressures of many substances is available (26) along with the necessary parameters for adjusting the data to any temperature, T, by means of the Antoine equation:

$$\log p^\circ = C - A/(T + B)$$

where A, B, and C are constants.

In principle, once the retention volume of one solute has been determined, this vapor pressure data may then be used to predict the retention volumes of all others. However, the assumption that $\gamma =$ constant is not applicable to most real situations and, in practice, the prediction of retention volumes is most reliable for homologs. This is because for such compounds $\log \gamma$ and $\log p^\circ$ are approximately linearly related (27):

$$\log \gamma = a + b \log p^\circ$$

It follows that,

$$\log V_r = \log (N_l RT) - a - (b + 1) \log p^\circ \qquad (2)$$

Thus, deviations from the assumption of constant γ do not affect the linearity of log V_r/log $p°$ plots for homologs, but they do affect the slope. The slope of lines B and C in Figure 7, should be compared with the ideal value of unity shown by lines A and D.

Although the above method of correlating retention data is the most fundamental, many workers prefer to use other parameters such as the boiling point, T_b, or the number of chain atoms in a homolog, n.

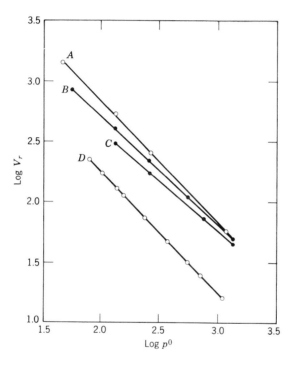

Fig. 7. Plots of log V_r against log $p°$ for: A, fluoro-, chloro-, bromo-, and iodobenzenes eluted from benzyl diphenyl at 100°C; B, n-butyl, n-propyl, ethyl and methyl benzenes, and benzene eluted from 7,8-benzoquinoline at 100°C; C, solutes as in B eluted from di-n-propyl tetrabromophthalate at 100°C; D, ethyl, n-propyl, and n-butyl alcohols eluted from medicinal paraffin each at several temperatures in the range 30–110°C (25b).

The theoretical basis of these methods is as follows. Substitution of the Trouton equation into the integrated Clausius–Clapeyron equation leads to:

$$\log p° = (10.0/R)[1 - (T_b/T)]$$

This equation, with eq. (2) then leads to:

$$\log V_r = \log (N_l RT) - a - (b + 1)(10.0/R)[1 - (T_b/T)]$$

Thus, at a fixed temperature on a given column, $\log V_r$ increases linearly with T_b. Many examples of this relationship are to be found in the literature, and it is one of the most frequently used methods of correlating retention data, as boiling points are often available when vapor pressures are not. If neither is available, retention data can often be correlated with n. It is well known (25c) that for many homologous series T_b and n are related by an expression of the form,

$$T_b = pn + q$$

where p and q are constants. Hence, since T_b is linearly related to $\log V_r$ it follows that $\log V_r$ is linearly related to n. This method of presentation has the advantage of by-passing any errors which might exist in the literature values of T_b or $p°$.

An interesting example of the use of this relationship from the work of Phillips and Timms (28) is shown in Figure 8, which illustrates the retention behavior of mixed straight-chain hydrides of silicon and germanium. Many of these compounds are not available as standard samples and are difficult to prepare in the pure state. Also, they are spontaneously inflammable in air, and hence GC is an ideal technique for studying them. The difficult problem of identification was solved by a variety of techniques, including measurement of the molecular weights of the peaks by means of a gas density balance and katharometer used as described in Section IV-A. Reference to Figure 8 shows that the resultant correlation diagram consists of a grid such that for a fixed number of silicon atoms the logarithm of the retention volume increases by 1.07 log units for the addition of each GeH_2 unit. Similarly, for a fixed number of germanium atoms, the logarithm of the retention volume increases by 0.72 log units for the addition of each SiH_2 unit. This pattern enables prediction of the retention volumes of many compounds other than those identified in the analysis mixture which had been obtained by the hydrolysis of a silicon–magnesium and/or germanium alloy.

In general, the types of correlation diagram obtained enable column substrates to be divided into those which separate solutes on the basis of vapor pressure (apolar) and those which separate on the basis of vapor pressure modified by polarity effects (polar). For the former, a plot of $\log V_r$ versus $\log p°$ (or T_b or n) consists of a single straight line

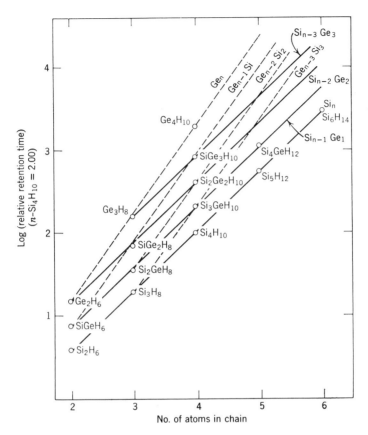

Fig. 8. Retention correlation grid for silanes, germanes, and silicogermanes eluted on Silicone 702 at 19°C (28). By courtesy of *Analytical Chemistry*.

for all solutes, whereas for the latter it consists of several lines (which may or may not be parallel), each of which defines the retention data of a certain class of compound. Thus, for example, correlation diagrams obtained for phenyl alkanes (Fig. 9) (29) comprise several parallel lines, each of which refers to a given position of substitution by the phenyl group. Similar results are found for the methyl esters of fatty acids (30). As the lines presented in Figure 9 are parallel, it follows that the log V_r's for phenyl alkanes containing the same number of carbon atoms change by a fixed increment as the position of substitution varies. This sort of relationship has been found to hold for numerous compounds and their variants [see, e.g., *n*- and iso-fatty acids and their methyl esters

(31), dimethyl acetals of fatty acid aldehydes (32)] and is the basic observation which has led to the formulation of rules governing reten- tion volumes, particularly in connection with retention indices (Sec. III-C) (33).

The various methods of using retention data for identification out- lined above may involve the comparison of chromatograms on several columns as well as the comparison of measured retention data with

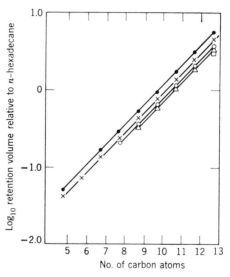

Fig. 9. Relationship between log retention volume relative to *n*-hexadecane and the number of carbon atoms in the chain of various phenyl alkanes eluted from Apiezon L at 130°C: (●) 2-phenyl isomers; (×) 3-phenyl isomers; (○) 4-phenyl isomers; (△) 5- and 6-phenyl isomers; (□) 7-phenyl isomers (29). By courtesy of *The Journal of Chromatography*.

published data. Various methods of graphical presentation facilitate these operations. One commonly used diagram is a plot of log V_r' versus log V_r'', where V_r' and V_r'' are the retention volumes of the various solutes on two columns. As log V_r' and log V_r'' each vary linearly with solute vapor pressure, then it follows that they vary linearly with each other. This sort of plot is a great aid to identification, as it summarizes the retention data on two columns and, provided that one of the column substrates is selective, various classes of compound will lie in charac- teristic regions of the diagram. Figure 10 shows a logarithmic cross-plot of the retention volumes of a large number of hydrocarbons on

tetra-amylsilane and dimethylsulfolane columns (34). Five distinct regions which enclose all members of certain classes can be discerned.
These are: (*a*) alkanes; (*b*) alkenes and cycloalkanes; (*c*) cycloalkanes;
(*d*) alkadienes, cycloalkadienes, and alkynes; and (*e*) cycloalkadienes
and alkynes. Unambiguous assignation of the class of hydrocarbon in

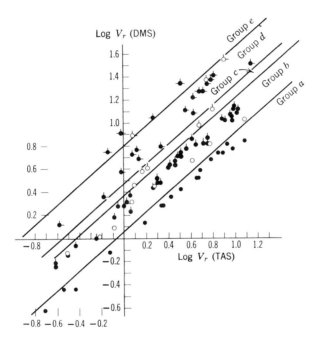

Fig. 10. A logarithmic cross-plot of the retention data of a large number of
hydrocarbons on tetra-amylsilane (TAS) and dimethylsulfolane (DMS) columns
at 25°C (34) (●) Alkanes; (●) alkenes; (●-) alkadienes; (-●-) alkynes; (○) cycloalkanes; (⟡) cycloalkenes; (⟡-) cycloalkadienes. By courtesy of *Acta Chemica
Scandinavica.*

(*b*), (*d*), and (*e*) is possible on the basis of post-column hydrogenation
experiments (35). If, for example, an unidentified eluate is known to be
in group (*b*), then, hydrogenation will only change its retention volume
if it is an alkene.

When using more than two columns, log V_r's may be plotted on
the appropriate number of vertical lines, one for each column (Fig. 11).
Then, for certain classes of compound, the line connecting the points

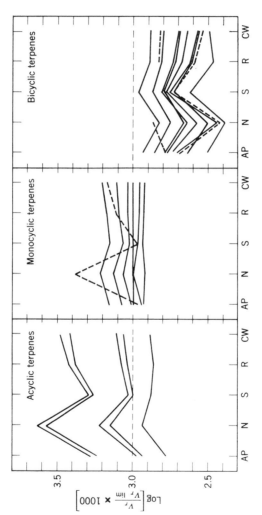

Fig. 11. The retention volumes relative to limonene (lim) of a variety of terpenes on five columns logarithmically plotted on five vertical lines to illustrate three types of connecting lines (36). Liquid phases and operating temperatures were: AP = Apiezon L, 25°; N = β, β'-oxydipropionitrile, 70°; S = silicone oil, 100°; R = Reoplex 100, 110°; CW = Carbowax 4000, 100°. By courtesy of *The Journal of Chromatography*.

for individual members may be of a characteristic shape. As Figure 11 shows, the retention data from five columns obtained by Klouwen and Ter Heide (36) exhibit significantly different shapes of connecting lines for aliphatic, monocyclic, and bicyclic terpenes.

Comparison of measured and published retention data on the same column substrate at the same temperature is facilitated by plotting the two sets of data against each other when, clearly, a straight line should be obtained (37). Any errors in measurement of retention volumes or misassignment of eluates will be revealed as deviations from this line. It must be emphasized, however, that unless all solutes have the same heat of solution this comparison must be made at the same temperature and preferably with exactly the same solvent/support ratio. The latter precaution should eliminate any anomalies due to solid support contributions to retention.

C. Retention Indices

In recent years many workers, instead of reporting retention data in a direct way as retention volumes or relative retention volumes, have relied upon one of the several available retention indices (38–43). Most of these are elaborations of the simple relative retention measurement and are obtained for a given solute by assigning to some other standard solute(s) an arbitrary retention index and then, by logarithmic comparison of retention volumes, arriving at a value for the retention index of the given solute. In this roundabout manner a number is obtained which is related to log V_r and, just as with this parameter certain rules concerning its variation with structure could be discerned, so also with retention indices. The invention of retention indices, therefore, provides nothing which is fundamentally different from straightforward retention volumes, and any discussion of their relative merits must be based upon convenience of use and accuracy of presentation of experimental results.

Recently the Institute of Petroleum Gas Chromatography Discussion Group, Data Subcommittee (45) investigated the question of the presentation of retention data and concluded that the Kovats Retention Index was the most reliable form. Consequently only this index will be considered here in any detail.

The Kovats Index (38) is based upon the retention volumes of an homologous series of n-paraffins. Starting off by defining the retention index of an n-paraffin as $I_n = 100n$, the retention index of any other substance X is then defined as:

$$I_x = 100n + 100\left[\frac{\log V_r^x - \log V_r^n}{\log V_r^{n+1} - \log V_r^n}\right]$$

where V_r^x, V_r^n, and V_r^{n+1} are the retention volumes of X and the n-paraffins with n and $n + 1$ carbon atoms chosen so that X is eluted

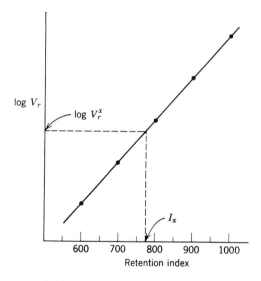

Fig. 12. Diagrammatic illustration of the derivation of the Kovats index, I_x, of a material eluted between n-heptane and n-octane.

somewhere between them. In effect, the use of these equations is equivalent to plotting $\log V_r^n$ versus I_n ($= 100n$) and reading off the appropriate value of I which places $\log V_r^x$ on the resulting straight line (Fig. 12). This procedure, for which a nomogram has been described (46), has the advantage that a single set of standards is used for presenting all retention data, thus greatly facilitating interlaboratory comparisons. Furthermore, higher accuracy results from the fact that the relative retention volume obtained does not depend upon a single standard. Also it is reported (38) that there is only a small linear variation of I values with temperature. This latter result is presumably due to the similar heats of solution of the n-paraffins and many other solutes and would be shown by any other relative retention method which used *n*-paraffins as standards.

Studies of the variation of Kovats Indices with structure (33,47) show that there is an approximately constant difference between values for a parent solute and its derivative. Swoboda (48) has called this difference the Functional Retention Index and some values due to him are shown in Table II. Many other such structural correlations have

TABLE II

Some Values of Functional Retention Indices (48)

Class of compound	Functional retention index (parent solute: *n*-paraffin)	
	Squalane, 75°C	Dinonyl phthalate, 74°C
n-Alkanol	230	402
n-Alkanal	152	288
n-Alk-2-enal	203	378
n-Alk-2,4-dienal	248	450

been observed (33,47,49,50) and it is not inconceivable that a set of rules could be found which would enable the Kovats Index of any compound to be calculated from its structure. However, it is likely that to achieve any reasonable accuracy the number of structural parameters needed would be so large as to render the scheme inoperable (51). Certain simple rules such as those referred to above can, nevertheless, provide useful guides when the necessary standards are not available.

A preliminary classification may also be possible on the basis of ΔI values, ΔI being the difference of the Kovats Index of a given solute on an apolar and a polar column. Many ΔI values have been determined (38,52) using the liquid phases Apiezon L (apolar) and Emulphor O (polar) and the results show that the members of a given class of compounds have substantially the same value of ΔI. Such relationships are restatements of the trends in retention data which are apparent from the log V_r'/log V_r'' plots mentioned above (see Fig. 10). It is apparent, therefore, that the Kovats Index does not provide anything which is not available from straightforward retention volumes. Nevertheless, if it becomes the standard way of reporting retention data a great deal will have been achieved. At present, however, its use suffers from the real disadvantage that there is a tendency to attach too much importance to

the indices themselves at the expense of obscuring the theory and practice from which they are derived. Therefore, whether retention indices
are used or not, comparison of the retention of unknown solutes with
standard samples on several columns should be used wherever possible
in preference to empirical, inexact rules and a single column. The reader
is referred to ref. 53 for a full account of the Kovats Index.

D. Variation of Retention with Temperature

All the correlation methods described above refer to GLC and have
been exhaustively studied. The corresponding methods in GSC have, in
comparison, received little attention. Early work on active charcoal
columns (54) and, very recently, graphitized carbon black columns (55)
has shown that log V_r correlates linearly with ΔH_a, the molar heat of
adsorption. The theoretical justification of this becomes apparent from
the gas–solid retention volume equation:

$$V_r = K_a A$$

where A is the surface area of the solid and $K_a = c_s/c_g$; c_g is the gas
phase and c_s is the surface phase concentration of solute. Writing,

$$K_a = \exp\left(-\Delta G_a/RT\right) = \exp\left\{(-\Delta H_a + T\,\Delta S_a)/RT\right\}$$

it follows that

$$\log V_r = (-\Delta H_a + T\,\Delta S_a)/2.303RT + \log A$$

Hence, if the entropies of adsorption of a variety of solutes are the same
or vary linearly with ΔH_a, then the observed correlation follows. Figure
13 illustrates this for the elution of a variety of terpenes on graphitized
carbon black (55). The excellent correlation of log V_r with ΔH_a should
be contrasted with its noncorrelation with T_b. The slope of the line,
4.22×10^{-4}, however, differs markedly from the theoretical value,
6.95×10^{-4}, at the temperature of the experiments, 50°C. Similarly,
the results of Greene and Pust (54) obtained for permanent gases on
charcoal at 10°C yield a slope of 3.15×10^{-4} while theory predicts a
value of 7.70×10^{-4}. These discrepancies can be reconciled if it
is assumed that

$$\Delta H_a = aT\,\Delta S_a + b$$

where a and b are constants. This assumption leads to a value for a of

1.69 in the latter instance. This is in exact agreement with the results of Barrer and Rees (56).

The use of heats of adsorption in identification is almost nonexistent, but recent advances (55) in the correlation of ΔH_a with structure and the growing interest in GSC might well catalyze this area of research. The corresponding area in GLC has been neglected, probably because there are more convenient correlation methods available.

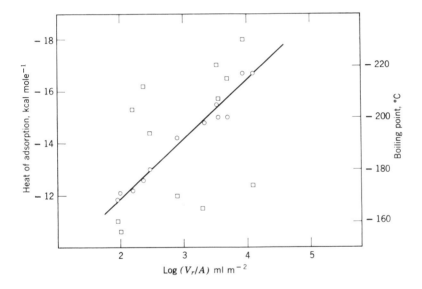

Fig. 13. Retention data for the elution of terpenes from a graphitized carbon black column at 50°C, plotted to show the good correlation of log V_r with heats of adsorption (○) and its poor correlation with boiling point (□) (55).

However, it is clear that since the GLC equivalent of the simple theory outlined above does not allow elution order to change with temperature, it cannot explain some experimental facts. For example, on a squalane column at 46°C, 2,2-dimethyl-3-ethylpentane is eluted before 2,6-dimethylheptane, whereas at 106°C the order is reversed (57). Such phenomena, which have been theoretically discussed by Hoare and Purnell (58), could be very useful in qualitative work (59,60). Therefore, the operation of a column at two widely spaced temperatures is to be advocated as an additional tool in the identification of eluates.

IV. QUALITATIVE USES OF DETECTORS

Since any molecular property can form the basis of a detection system, it is not surprising that almost 30 kinds of detector have been designed for use in gas chromatography. Although the modes of operation of these detectors vary considerably, the recorded responses all have two important features in common. In the first place, all responses are a function of some property of the effluent. Secondly, they are all also functions, preferably linear, of the eluate size. Thus, a single recorded peak is of no qualitative value unless the amount of material producing the peak is known. It is for this reason that good quantitative detectors are essential aids to identification, so that specific responses per gram or per mole of material can be found and correlated with published data, or compared with calibrated values.

Such quantitative detectors may measure either mass or moles, and a particularly appealing identification technique is to combine a gravimetric with a molar detector. The ratio of the responses for a given eluted peak gives the molecular weight of the substance concerned directly. Detectors that may usefully be employed in this way are discussed in Section IV-A. Detectors measuring properties other than mass or molar composition are conveniently classified according to the complexity of the dependence of response on effluent composition. In Section IV-B are discussed some fundamental detectors with responses that may be related to a single molecular property. Nonfundamental detectors, with responses dependent on a number of imponderables, are considered in Section IV-C.

The usefulness of combining the quantitative detectors of Section IV-A with the various detectors of Sections IV-B and C has already been mentioned. It may be more convenient, or more revealing, however, to compare the responses of two detectors, both of which measure some property other than mass or moles. The utility of such relative response techniques is illustrated in Section IV-D.

A. Detectors of Use in Molecular Weight Determination

Although knowledge of the molecular weight of an eluate gives no direct information about chemical composition, it can be of the greatest value as an aid to identification, especially if the number of possible elements in the molecule is known to be restricted to two or three. Classical methods of determining molecular weights are based on the gas laws: the number of moles, N, of a mass W of vapor with molecular weight M exerting pressure P in volume V at absolute temperature T is given by

$$N = PV/RT = W/M$$

In principle, the simplest way of obtaining M is to measure the vapor density, d_v

$$d_v = W/V = MP/RT$$

at a known pressure and temperature. The use of a detector able to measure the density of eluate alone as it emerged would thus allow M to be determined. It is difficult to conceive of a device which could achieve this in practice, however, because of the gross excess of carrier gas diluting an eluted peak.

One possible approach to this difficulty is to separate the eluate from the carrier, and then determine the density of the unknown by means of a buoyancy balance or some similar method. The practical difficulties of such a technique are immense, and it is more feasible to measure W and N separately with the aid of two detectors. W can be measured directly by removing the effluent peak in a microabstractor unit mounted on a microbalance (Sec. IV-A-1 below). N is more difficult to measure, since the eluate must be kept in the gas phase, and the only successful technique is that due to Janak (Sec. IV-A-2). The gas density detector, which is discussed in Section IV-A-3, has a response which varies jointly with W and N in a calculable manner, so that if either is known M can be determined. Alternatively, with the use of two or more carrier gases, M can be deduced from gas density responses alone. The katharometer (Sec. IV-A-4) and methods making use of the measurement of velocity of sound (Sec. IV-A-5) are also considered because they too have responses which, under suitable conditions, depend only on W and N.

1. Gravimetric Detectors

It is only recently that interest has grown in the detection of eluates by the increase in weight produced when they are absorbed after separation. The percentage changes in weight produced when conventional abstractor units (Sec. VI-A-1) are employed are very small, and miniaturization is necessary before a detector of any sensitivity can be constructed. Bevan and Thorburn (61a) were the first to describe such a gravimetric detector, which is shown diagrammatically in Figure 14. As originally reported, this detector could be used for the quantitative determination of milligram amounts of substances such as amines, alcohols, ketones, and ethers which were irreversibly adsorbed on a layer of concentrated sulfuric acid on the walls of the adsorption cell. More recently (61b) a smaller adsorption cell suitable for the detection of eluates of less than a tenth of a milligram has been described, and it

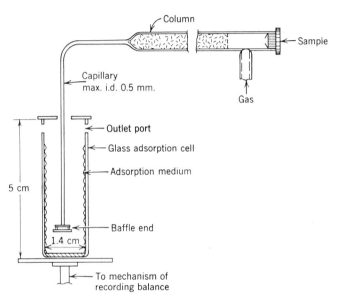

Fig. 14. A simple gravimetric detector (61a). By courtesy of *The Journal of Chromatography*.

was found that activated charcoal was suitable for the adsorbent layer. The linear dimensions of the modified cell are about half of those shown in Figure 14, but a 0.5 mm i.d. capillary is still found to be suitable.

Another gravimetric device has been described by Piel (62), who used GC support material to effect adsorption (cf., trapping techniques, Sec. II). The reported sensitivity was, however, rather low; a suitable sample size was larger than 10 mg, and the accuracy was of the order of ± 0.2 mg.

As well as allowing W to be determined as a step on the way to finding M, a gravimetric device has a great advantage in being absolute so that no internal standards are required. Now that the potentialities of gravimetric detectors are being realized they must find widespread use in all GC work except that requiring the highest sensitivity.

2. Measurement of Molar Sample Size

While the mass of an eluted sample can be measured by removing it from the gas phase (Sec. IV-A-1), the number of moles can only be measured if the pure sample can be obtained in the gaseous phase, undiluted with carrier gas. In the nitrometer technique, due to Janak (63), carbon dioxide is used as carrier gas, and is removed from the effluent gas stream by passage through a solution of caustic potash. Provided that the eluate is not absorbed in this process, its volume can be determined at a known temperature and pressure, and hence the molar sample size can be obtained. The technique can only be applied with difficulty to eluates which are not gaseous at room temperature and the sensitivity with which the volume can be measured is rather low. Nevertheless, this is the only available technique for measuring the number of moles of eluate without destroying it.

In a few special cases it is possible to estimate the number of moles of a substance eluted from a column by the use of a specific detector system employing some chemical reaction. One such example is provided by the adaptation of a Hersch cell for determining oxygen. This technique was first reported by Phillips et al. (64) after an idea of R. W. Dickinson, and there has recently been an account of its applications and an analysis of its reproducibility (65). A Hersch cell (66) consists of a silver cathode and a lead anode in contact with a dry electrolyte containing hydroxyl ions. When oxygen is reduced at the cathode the two half-cell reactions may be represented as:

$$\tfrac{1}{2}O_2 + H_2O + 2e \longrightarrow 2OH^-$$

and

$$Pb + 3OH^- \longrightarrow PbO_2H^- + H_2O + 2e$$

Monitoring the cell current allows an accurate estimate of the amount of oxygen present to be made. The technique is related to the microcoulometric post-column identification techniques discussed in Section VI-B-3, where a specific part of the unknown molecule can be determined. As an aid to identification, however, the Hersch cell is a yes/no device for oxygen detection, and would hardly be used for finding the molecular weight of oxygen!

Under certain conditions it has been found that the response of a katharometer is directly proportional to the molar size of the sample, and this is discussed further in Section IV-A-4.

3. *Gas Density Detector*

This device was first used in gas chromatography by Martin and James (67). Ideally it gives a response proportional to the difference in

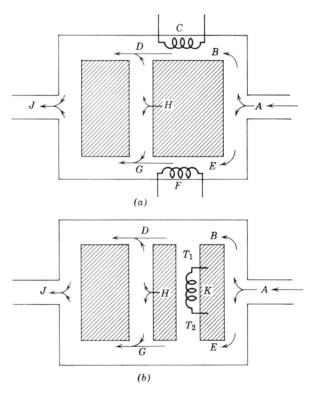

Fig. 15. Two types of gas density detector shown in vertical section. Column effluent enters at H, reference gas at A. Mixed gases leave at J. In (*a*) temperatures of filaments C and F are used to detect flow changes in channels BD and EG caused by density change in DG. In (*b*) thermocouple junctions T_1 and T_2 detect flow of gas in channel containing heater filament K.

density between the effluent gas stream and a reference stream of pure carrier gas. Two typical designs are shown in Figure 15 in a vertical section, although it is difficult to show the geometry in two dimensions. In both Figures 15*a* and 15*b* the effluent enters at H and is split into two streams *HDJ* and *HGJ*. The reference stream enters at *A*, and then passes through the channels *AB* and *AE* to join the effluent at *D* and *G*, and the mixed gases leave at *J*. If effluent and reference have identical densities, the flow rates in channels *BD* and *EG* are identical. If, however, the effluent has a greater density than the reference gas, then the flow in *EG* will tend to be restricted, and that in *BD* will be increased. The two designs of Figure 15 differ only in the means used to detect this flow change. In Figure 15*a* there is a flowmeter filament in each channel; the temperature of *F* will tend to rise and that of *C* to fall. The two filaments form part of a Wheatstone bridge, the off-balance signal from which is fed to the chromatographic recorder. In Figure 15*b* a further channel is provided through which the increased pressure at *G* can be relieved. The heater filament *K* is situated between two thermocouple junctions T_1 and T_2. The flow of gas from T_2 to T_1 causes T_2 to be cooled and T_1 to be heated, and the temperature difference can be recorded. If the effluent is of lower density than the reference stream, then *C* becomes hotter than *F*, and T_2 becomes hotter than T_1.

The change in density produced in the carrier gas by the emerging peak takes place at constant pressure, so that each molecule of unknown in a given volume has taken the place of a molecule of carrier gas. The response can therefore be taken as a measure of the *mass* of substance emerging, provided this has a much larger molecular weight than the carrier gas, for the fall in weight of carrier gas per unit volume can then be neglected. If, on the other hand, the carrier gas has a molecular weight much greater than that of the unknown, then the gas density detector signal is more a measure of the number of (heavy) carrier gas molecules displaced by the unknown, i.e., of the number of *moles* of sample in the emergent peak. According to conditions, then, the gas density detector can function either as a mass or as a mole meter. It would therefore seem to be extremely well suited for molecular weight determinations. Before considering ways in which molecular weights may be obtained with the aid of a gas density detector, it is of interest to put these intuitive ideas about the nature of the response on an algebraic footing. This is particularly useful when eluate and carrier gas have comparable densities.

Nerheim (68) has demonstrated that the electrical response of a gas density detector of the type shown in Figure 15*a* is indeed proportional to the difference in densities (and hence in molecular weights) of reference and effluent gas streams. If the carrier gas is of molecular weight M_c and the sample of molecular weight M_s is present to the extent of mole fraction X_s in the detector, then the effective molecular weight of the effluent is: $M_c + X_s(M_s - M_c)$. With pure carrier gas as reference gas, the electrical output y at any instant will be proportional to $X_s(M_s - M_c)$:

$$y = kX_s(M_s - M_c)$$

where k is a constant for a given cell, but may well alter for different carrier gases. Since n_s/n_c rarely exceeds 10^{-3}, $X_s = n_s/(n_s + n_c) \simeq n_s/n_c$ where n_s and n_c are the instantaneous number of moles of carrier gas and of sample per unit volume of effluent. It follows that:

$$y = (kn_s/n_c)(M_s - M_c)$$

and the peak area, A, is given by:

$$A = \int y \, dt = \frac{kN_s}{n_c}(M_s - M_c) \tag{3}$$

$$= KW_s\left(1 - \frac{M_c}{M_s}\right) \tag{4}$$

$$= K(W_s - N_sM_c)$$

where K is effectively constant for a given carrier gas and N_s and W_s are the total number of moles and the total weight of sample, respectively.

Equation (4) suggests that one way of visualizing the meaning of gas density peaks is to consider them as being made up of two parts. First there is a positive signal directly proportional to the mass of the separated component (the mass response). Then there is also a molar response just M_c/M_s times as large as the mass response, but acting in the opposite direction. It is also apparent from eq. (4) that if $M_s \gg M_c$ the response is directly proportional to the mass of unknown eluted, while if $M_c \gg M_s$ the response is proportional to the number of moles of sample present. These two extreme situations correspond to those discussed earlier.

With hydrogen carrier gas equal weights of substances of molecular weights 20 and 200 would give peaks differing in area by only 9% of the larger peak. With helium as carrier gas the corresponding difference would be 18%. For nitrogen carrier gas and $M_s = 20$ there will be a negative peak about half the size of the positive peak produced by $M_s = 200$, while with SF_6 carrier gas the sample of molecular weight 20 would give a negative peak more than twenty times as large as the positive peak produced by the $M_s = 200$ sample. Provided the cell constant K is known for the carrier gas in question, a knowledge of the sample size W_s and molecular weight M_s enables an accurate prediction of the peak area to be made by means of eq. (4). Conversely, however, it is only possible to make an accurate determination of the molecular weight, M_s, from the peak area and weight of sample if the carrier gas is of high molecular weight. The use of a gravimetric detector (Sec. IV-A-1), along with a gas density detector and a heavy carrier gas, provides an attractive way of finding molecular weights, and such a system employing nitrogen carrier gas has been used for determining molecular weights up to about 100 (61b).

Carrier gases such as hydrogen and helium can prove useful in molecular weight determinations, however, provided the sample size is known as a number of moles [see eq. (3)]. For a gaseous sample this can be determined by the relation $N = PV/RT$. Phillips and Timms (69) were able to measure the PV product of milligram amounts of various substances with molecular weights in the range 30–200, and they then used a gas density balance to determine the molecular weight. In order to use such a technique under normal chromatographic conditions, however, one would have to be able to separate the resolved components from the carrier gas. This is, of course, the basis of the Janak method (63) (Sec. IV-A-2), but there appears to be no record of the technique being coupled with a gas density balance, although the molecular weight of CO_2 is not too high to prevent M_s determination in this way.

An appealing technique is to use gas density information alone to determine molecular weights of eluates, an approach first employed by Liberti et al. (70). Consider again the fundamental area-response relation [eq. (4)]:

$$A_s = K(W_s/M_s)(M_s - M_c)$$

for a substance of weight W_s and molecular weight M_s in a carrier gas of molecular weight M_c. A reference substance (internal standard) of weight W_r and molecular weight M_r will give a peak of area $A_r = K(W_r/M_r)(M_r - M_c)$. If the carrier gas is replaced by a gas of molecular weight M_c', then the corresponding areas for a second sample from the *homogeneous* mixture of s and r will be:

$$A_s' = K'(W_s'/M_s)(M_s - M_c')$$

and

$$A_r' = K'(W_r'/M_r)(M_r - M_c')$$

where

$$W_s/W_s' = W_r/W_r'$$

It follows that:

$$[A_s(M_s - M_c')]/A_s'(M_s - M_c) = [A_r(M_r - M_c')]/A_r'(M_r - M_c)$$

Hence M_s can be found even if the sample sizes used in the two cases are very different, provided only that M_r, M_c, and M_c' are known. Notice in particular that the use of an internal standard removes the need to know either of the cell constants K or K'.

This sort of approach is most fruitful if the two carrier gases have very different molecular weights. Nevertheless, Liberti et al. (70) obtained values correct to within 4% using carrier gases, the molecular weights of which were more than 100 mass units less than the unknown, so that small errors in peak area measurement were likely to be much exaggerated in the extrapolation implicit in the left-hand side of the above equation.

Parsons (71) has stressed the importance of using carrier gases of higher molecular weight than the unknown in conjunction with low molecular weight gases. This enables the unknown molecular weight to be bracketed, rather than obtained by extrapolation. The use of N_2, Ar, CO_2, and $C_2H_4F_2$ to cover the range molecular weight 30–70 was typical. Parsons found that for a fixed sample size the response was directly proportional to the molecular weight of carrier gas, implying that K is independent of carrier gas. The unknown molecular weight was therefore readily obtained from a plot of response against M_c (Fig. 16) from the intercept on the M_c axis. Even when extrapolation rather than this interpolation technique was used, as in a test run with CCl_4, high accuracy was reported with the use of several rather than only two carrier gases. The molecular weight of CCl_4 was found correct to 1.4 mass units, or better than 1%.

The gas density balance has never been a very popular detector, despite earlier pleas on its behalf (72). Doubtless one reason for the lack of interest was the apparent difficulty of construction of the early models. Several workers have pointed out that the original design can be much simplified without loss of sensitivity or of predictability of response (68). Today, moreover, reliable models are available commercially and are fitted as standard equipment on several proprietary chromatographs. It is often alleged that the sensitivity of the gas density balance is inferior to that of a katharometer. Workers who use the density detector deny this, however, and find it to be an excellent device for samples as small as 10 μg. The highest sensitivity is obtained if the carrier gas has a molecular weight much larger than that of the eluate. Fluorinated hydrocarbons are becoming increasingly available, and octafluorocyclo-butane has a molecular weight more than 50 units larger than SF_6. In the opinion of the authors this detector deserves another chance, or a first chance, in many laboratories. The increasing availability of carrier

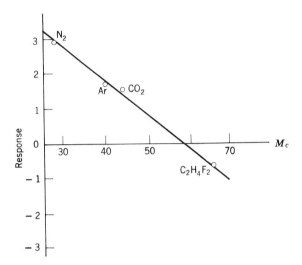

Fig. 16. Area response of a gas density detector for a fixed sample size of unknown eluate plotted against molecular weight of carrier gas, M_c. Intercept on M_c axis gives molecular weight of unknown (71). By courtesy of *Analytical Chemistry*.

gases of high molecular weight makes the molecular weight technique of Parsons (71) too good to miss.

4. *The Katharometer*

There is a certain amount of confusion in the literature which reflects the lack of firm theoretical background for the expected response characteristics of thermal conductivity detectors. In particular, there has been some discussion as to whether the relative areas of katharo-meter peaks measure weight percentage or molar compositions. These difficulties have arisen because there is no simple relation between thermal conductivity and density, for thermal conductivities of mixtures are often complex functions of those of the pure materials. Moreover, it has not proved possible to measure the conductivities of the small volumes of effluent without introducing complications from the measur-ing process itself, notably convection effects arising from the necessary introduction of a thermal gradient. Nevertheless, certain empirical correlations are possible for certain systems, although some findings are contradictory.

It has long been claimed that with helium carrier gas better agreement with the ideal mixing law is obtained if weight rather than mole percentages are used in assessing the composition of artificial mixtures (73). Grob et al. (74) found that alcohol peaks gave good measures of the weight percentage compositions of mixtures. More recently, Mecke and Zirker (75) found a theoretical justification for these findings, for light carrier gases.

Phillips and Timms, however (28), were able to find *molar* compositions of several silico-germanium hydrides from the peak areas of these materials in hydrogen carrier gas. In conjunction with a gas density balance [operated in the gravimetric mode by using hydrogen carrier (Sec. IV-A-3)] to measure peak weights, they were able to find molecular weights to better than 4% by this method. Similar reports of peak areas being related to molar composition have been made for other high molecular weight compounds in light carrier gases, but there are some anomalies (76).

No rationalization of these findings after the event can be useful, but it should be pointed out that on the simplest view (that of additivity of conductivities in the ratio of mole fractions) it is to be expected that responses will be approximately molar, since hydrogen and helium have conductivities more than ten times as large as the majority of other substances. If it transpires that katharometer response for high molecular weight eluates in hydrogen carrier gas is indeed generally molar, then the method of Phillips and Timms (28) commends itself as a simplification of the multicarrier gas density technique of Parsons (Fig. 16), if somewhat lower accuracy in molecular weight determination can be tolerated.

Smith and Bowden (77) have had some success in calculating thermal conductivity cell response *ab initio*. They consider the off-balance voltage per mole fraction of unknown, dE/dy_2, to be made up of three parts:

$$\frac{dE}{dy_2} = \frac{dE}{dT} \cdot \frac{dT}{dh} \cdot \frac{dh}{dy_2}$$

where T is the temperature of the filament and h is the surface heat transfer coefficient. They claim that dE/dT and dT/dh are instrument characteristics which could be quoted by the manufacturers. dh/dy_2 is of course directly related to dK/dy_2 where K is the thermal conductivity of gas round the filament. Here Smith and Bowden used a mixing law of the form (78)

$$K = K_1/[1 + A_{12}(y_2/y_1)] + K_2/[1 + A_{21}(y_1/y_2)]$$

whence

$$\frac{dK}{dy_2} = \frac{A_{21}K_2}{(y_2 + A_{21}y_1)^2} - \frac{A_{12}K_1}{(y_1 + A_{12}y_2)^2}$$

where y_1, y_2 are the mole fractions of carrier gas and of unknown. A_{12}, A_{21} are functions of the viscosities, conductivities, molecular weights, heat capacities, and boiling points of the pure components, but for dilute mixtures they can be considered to be independent of y_2. Equations enabling A_{12} and A_{21} to be calculated have been given (79). They were thus able to deduce theoretical response plots for sulfur dioxide, n-pentane, and benzene in helium carrier gas, which were in agreement with experiment to within 10%. Probable errors are thus no worse than those in methods requiring standardization. It appears that significant differences in signal for a given mole fraction of these substances are only obtained when the mole fraction exceeds 0.1, which is very large for a normal katharometer working on a packed column. This provides additional confirmation for the view that peak areas with low molecular weight carrier gases correspond to mole fractions, although the three test materials had molecular weights ranging only from 64 to 78.

5. Sonic Methods

Although density comparison would seem to be best studied with a gas density detector (Sec. IV-A-3), another related technique is worthy of mention. The velocity of sound, v, in a homogeneous mixture of density d, pressure p and ratio of specific heats γ is given by the well-known formula

$$v^2 = \gamma p/d$$

In a gas chromatographic effluent at constant pressure, therefore, monitoring the velocity of sound can give information about the density of the gas mixture.

Reports of the use of velocity of sound measurements for the analysis of binary mixtures of gases go back to before the turn of the century (80), but it is only recently that any serious attention has been given to acoustic methods of gas analysis. Two detectors suitable for

GC applications, in which sonic frequencies in pure carrier gas and in column effluent are compared, have been described. Robinson's device (81) compares the frequencies in resonant cavities, while Testerman and McLeod (82) have used two ultrasonic whistles, and measured the beat frequency.

A phase shift technique, first employed by Lawley (83), has recently been extended into the ultrasonic range (84) and successfully used for the detection of microgram quantities of aromatics. The sonic technique, as well as being more sensitive than the gas density method, has the added advantage that its response characteristic can be calculated for a given gas, thus eliminating the need for calibration or internal standards. At small mole fractions (below 0.01) the response is similar to that of a gas density detector. For example, with hydrogen carrier gas the observed phase shift is proportional to the density of high molecular weight eluate in the carrier. Peak areas are therefore proportional to weights, the constant of proportionality being directly calculable, and it has been shown that variations in γ can be neglected to a good first approximation.

No results have been reported for high molecular weight carrier gases, but it would be interesting to know if peak areas can then be related to the *molar* composition of effluent. Even as it stands, however, the technique should prove useful for the gravimetric determination of peaks containing microgram quantities of material, with hydrogen carrier gas.

B. Other Fundamental Detectors

1. *Dielectric Constant Measurement*

One of the major sources of difficulty in analyzing katharometer response (Sec. IV-A-4) arises because the measuring process necessarily interferes markedly with the system it is measuring. Dielectric constant techniques are akin to sonic methods (Sec. IV-A-5) in that they do not interfere with the effluent gas, but are able to distinguish between molecules on the basis of electronic configuration. Early attempts to use such detectors were disappointing (85), but recently (86,87) a much higher sensitivity has been achieved, approaching that of many flame ionization detectors ($\sim 10^{-10}$ g/sec). The effluent is passed through a small parallel-plate capacitance which forms part of the resonance circuit of a 70 mc/sec oscillator. The high sensitivity has been achieved both by the use of a small detector volume, and by using a beat technique. Although mainly used for detection of the fixed gases, and for oxides of carbon, nitrogen, and sulfur, it has been successfully employed for mixtures containing simple hydrocarbons. With the aid of a gravimetric companion detector, this device may prove useful in characterizing substances from the relative responses obtained. For example, nitro-compounds will give a much larger molar response than will most other substances.

2. *Ionization Cross-Section Detectors*

The use of chambers containing a gas and electrodes to detect ionizing radiation goes back almost 40 years. It is only fairly recently, however, that devices of this kind employing a fixed source of radiation have been used to determine the composition of gas within the chamber.

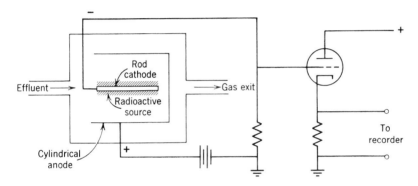

Fig. 17. Schematic diagram of a simple ionization cross-section detector and electrometer amplifier. Recently miniaturization has achieved a marked improvement in performance.

Figure 17 shows a typical experimental arrangement, with the radioactive source forming the face of one of the collecting electrodes. The measured ionization current is shown as a function of applied voltage in Figure 18. In region A there is obviously a need for accurate voltage control, because a small fluctuation in detection potential leads to a large change in the number of ion pairs that are able to reach the electrodes before recombination takes place. In region B, however, collection of ions produced by the radiation is essentially complete, and this is the most useful region in which to operate ionization cross-section detectors. At even higher applied voltages secondary ionization is produced by the accelerated ionized particles. The actual threshold voltage required to reach the response plateau at B depends on the distance of separation of the electrodes, and a cell of several cubic centimeters in volume may require 1000 V (88). Devices suitable for GC, however, have volumes requiring only about 100 V for saturation for all components, and the saturated ionization current can then be used to obtain information about the gas flowing through the cell. If, however, the inter-electrode distance were much larger than the range of the radiation, there would clearly be little change in ionization current when a more strongly absorbing gas was present. It is therefore important that the path length of the ionizing radiation should be much larger

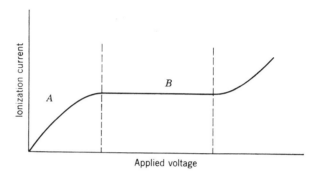

Fig. 18. Current drawn from an ionization cross-section detector as a function of applied voltage. The height of plateau B is related in a simple way to the chemical composition of the gas in the detector.

than the distance between electrodes, i.e., that the radiation should lose little energy while traversing the chamber. If this condition is satisfied, then the number of ion pairs produced per second per unit path length is given by

$$i = kcQ$$

where c is the concentration in molecules per unit volume, Q is the ionization cross section, and k is a cell constant (for a fixed source of radiation). For a gaseous mixture, then

$$i = (kP/RT) \sum_j x_j Q_j$$

where x_j is a mole fraction. In GC the area of a peak measures the extra number of ion pairs collected from the eluate peak mixed with the carrier gas, and is therefore proportional to the difference in cross sections of eluate and carrier, ΔQ, and to the number of moles of eluate, m:

$$A = k'm \cdot \Delta Q$$

where k' is a function of flow, temperature, and pressure. The noise level is determined to a large extent by pressure and temperature fluctuations.

Deisler et al. (88) were among the first to discuss gas analysis with such a device, and using an α-particle source they were able to calibrate the detector to allow determination of three component mixtures. They found that a threshold voltage of 400 V was required for nitrogen, and 70 V for hydrogen. A little earlier, Pompeo and Otvos had patented a similar device which used the potentially hazardous $^{90}Sr/^{90}Y$ source (89) and this system was applied specifically to GC by Deal et al. (90). Although α-particles have higher specific ionizations, the use of high energy β sources was preferred because they could be shielded from the carrier gas, thus avoiding possible contamination of the atmosphere. Also, because the device of Deal et al. (90) had a large active volume (~ 5 cc), and because it is important that the radiation particles lose little energy in the gas (see above), a high energy source was necessary. Despite the rather large volume, however, 100 V was found to be sufficient to achieve saturation for all substances tested, including nitrogen.

As chromatographic techniques have improved, the need for very small detector volumes has increased so that response time can be compatible with the improved efficiencies obtainable. In 1963, Lovelock et al. (91) reported that they had successfully designed a cross-section detector with an effective volume of about 0.1 ml with parallel-plate electrodes. Since the ionizing radiation now had to travel only 1 mm, lower energies could be used for a given degree of attenuation, and so the use of a weak β source became possible. Using tritium occluded in Ti or Zr and coated on steel electrodes, they were able to achieve a 50-fold increase in ionization efficiency and minimum mass detectability (10^{-9} g/sec) compared with typical cross-section detectors then in use. In 1964 the same authors (92) achieved a further reduction in volume to 8 µl, suitable for capillary column use. The sensitivity of this device, quoted as 3×10^{-11} g/sec, is comparable with flame ionization techniques. At about the same time, Abel (93) reported the design features of a 12 µl micro-ionization cross-section detector that would withstand a pressure of 1 atm without leakage.

Because of the high sensitivity and lack of radiation hazard now possible with cross-section detectors, there is no doubt that they will prove increasingly popular. They should find particular use in qualitative work, because it has been shown that ionization cross sections are functions only of chemical composition, and can be computed by addition of the relevant values for the individual atoms. Otvos and Stephenson (94) confirmed this experimentally for a number of molecules, both for slow single electrons at low pressures, and for processes due to high-energy β particles at atmospheric pressure. Boer (95) found empirical confirmation from chromatograms of various hydrocarbons, where Q for a carbon atom was 4.16 relative to a value of 1.00 for a hydrogen atom.

3. *Photoionization Detectors*

The main attraction of a photoionization device is that the exciting energy can, in principle, be nicely controlled. Lovelock (96) was the first to report the application of this technique to GC, and has since

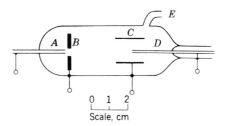

Fig. 19. A simple photoionization detector (108). Discharge gas enters at A, carrier gas at D, and gases are pumped out at E. Discharge is applied between A and B, and detection takes place at electrodes C and D (anode). If a dc discharge is used, A is the cathode, and B the anode. By courtesy of *Analytical Chemistry*.

used it as a concentration detector (97). A diagrammatic representation of a photoionization detector is shown in Figure 19. Helium, argon, nitrogen, and hydrogen are suitable gases for the UV source and, if a d.c. discharge is used, the pressure of gas should be below 100 mm Hg. It is, however, possible to use a helium source at atmospheric pressure if an rf discharge is employed. Unless scrupulous precautions are taken to obtain pure gas for the discharge, the high-energy photons are removed by impurities, so that materials with the highest ionization potentials (e.g., CO_2 and H_2O) do not give a response. In practice, therefore, the device is only suitable for detecting those substances which give a response on a flame ionization detector. A detailed study by Locke and Meloan of the characteristics of a photoionization detector has shown that the device is inherently selective, because substances with the lowest ionization potentials tend to give the highest response on a molar basis (98) (see Fig. 20). Photoionization efficiencies of about 10^{-4} were found (98) and 2×10^{-10} g of low molecular weight

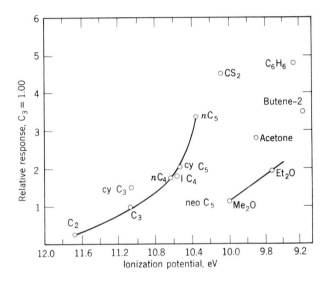

Fig. 20. Observed photoionization molar response in an argon discharge as a function of ionization potential (98). By courtesy of *Analytical Chemistry*.

compounds could be detected. All studies with photoionization detectors reported to date (96–99) have used an internal source, as shown in Figure 19, where the discharge gas and effluent come into intimate contact. It would obviously be desirable to use an external source, and to use a monochromator to provide monoenergetic photons.

C. Nonfundamental Detectors

1. *Flame-Ionization Detector*

Measurement of the ionization produced when certain molecules are burnt in a hydrogen flame is frequently used as a means of detection. There has been some measure of success in relating response of flame-ionization detectors to effluent composition, especially for organic compounds, where the extent of ionization reflects the number of combustible carbon atoms in the molecule (100,101). Except for hydrocarbons, however, correlation is probably not good enough to give qualitative information about an unknown effluent.

Karmen and Giuffrida (102) noticed an interesting effect which should prove useful in routine tests for the presence of halogens or phosphorus in eluted peaks. They coated an annular electrode with sodium hydroxide and, when used in the conventional manner, normal flame-ionization behavior was noticed. The larger flame produced by increasing the hydrogen flow rate, however, enveloped the electrode and caused it to glow red. This brought about a slight decrease in response to most substances, but halogen-containing material (especially bromides) and phosphorus insecticides gave greatly enhanced signals. This behavior may be related to the finding that the addition of halogen to flames containing alkali metals can greatly increase the extent of ionization (103). Karmen (104) has described a modification of the technique, in which the sodium is liberated from a grid held in one flame, and its presence detected in a secondary hydrogen flame. The sensitivity of this specific detection system is excellent, being in the nanogram region. A detailed study has been reported recently (105) of the response characteristics of a similar coupled sodium flame-ionization system, in which the two flames were very close together. It was found that the polarities of the two jets had a profound influence on the relative responses obtained in the sodium and sodium-free flames. In particular, if both jets were cathodes, there was an enormous increase in the normal flame ionization response to halides and organic phosphorus compounds. Conversely, the sodium flame system had the least influence on the normal flame-ionization current when both jets acted as anodes; under these conditions the ratio of flame ionization to sodium flame response was a maximum.

2. Argon β-Ray Ionization Detector

This device is essentially a modified ionization cross-section detector (Sec. IV-B-2), in which the energy of the bombarding radiation is stored in metastable argon atoms promoted to the first resonance level. Since these species have a long life compared with the normal transit time of a β particle through the detector, an increase in sensitivity is achieved by increasing the extent of ionization. The detector differs markedly from the cross-section device in that its response shows no marked variation for different eluates. In fact, provided the ionization potential of the substance concerned is below the excitation energy of the argon (about 11.6 eV) there is a high molar response which differs only slightly for substances with ionization potentials from 6 to 11 eV (106). The detector is thus unlikely to be helpful in qualitative investigations, although substances with ionization potentials greater than 11.6 eV produce no response, and this is a possible basis for their identification.

3. *Electron-Capture Detectors*

This detector is one of the few devices which have been developed with the deliberate aim of achieving a highly selective response. A diagram of a typical electron-capture detector is shown in Figure 21,

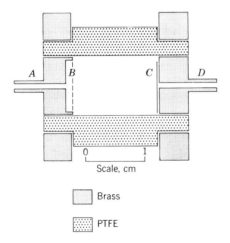

Scale, cm

Brass

PTFE

Fig. 21. An electron capture detector (108). Carrier gas enters at *A* and passes through the brass gauze diffuser *B* before leaving at *D*. The source of ionizing radiation is at *C*. *A* acts as detector anode, and *D* as cathode, so that carrier gas moves against flow of negative particles. By courtesy of *Analytical Chemistry*.

and there is an obvious resemblance to a cross-section detector (Sec. IV-B-2, Fig. 17). Indeed, at high applied voltages the device acts as such a detector, and the passage of an eluate *E* through the detector is then accompanied by an increase in current due to ionization by the radioactive particles:

$$\beta + E \rightarrow E^+ + e + \beta$$

At lower applied voltages, however, the ions and electrons produced recombine more readily, and so the current falls toward the standing value arising from carrier gas ionization:

$$\beta + C \rightarrow C^+ + e + \beta$$

(region A of Fig. 18). If, however, the eluate has a high electron affinity, the process

$$E + e \rightarrow E^-$$

becomes important. Since the drift velocity of E^- is much less than that of an electron, the process

$$E^- + C^+ \rightarrow E + C$$

is more likely than

$$e + C^+ \rightarrow C$$

so that the standing current is reduced, giving rise to a *negative* peak.

While most molecules can be ionized with comparable ease, the ability to *capture* electrons varies considerably, and is principally determined by the predominant functional group in the molecule. Lovelock and Lipsky (107) found that the applied voltage at which the transition from positive to negative response occurred was characteristic of the class to which the compound belonged. They coined the name "electron affinity spectroscopy" for the process of finding that voltage. For qualitative GC work, it was more convenient to work at a fixed, low voltage so that no cross-section effects would be present. Any persistent field, however low, is liable to cause undesirable electron acceleration, and so a pulse-sampling technique was introduced in which a collecting voltage of 50 V was applied for only about 1 in 20 μsec (97). It was found that significant electron capture negative peaks were obtained with many halogenated materials, as well as with organic compounds containing oxygen (108,109). With inert substances such as alkanes, no signal was produced.

Lovelock and co-workers have also used the pulsed detector to measure actual electron affinities. They employed a dual detector arrangement with a photoionization device (Sec. IV-B-3) to determine the vapor concentrations (110), and phenyl chloride as internal standard. These workers were particularly interested in relating the measured affinity for thermal electrons to biological and carcinogenic activity. In a further attempt to ensure that the electrons really were thermal, the collecting voltage was reduced to 30 V and the sampling time reduced to 0.5 every 50 μsec. Furthermore, 5% methane was added to the argon carrier gas to remove any electrons that might become excited above the thermal level.

Electron affinities of atoms are notoriously difficult to determine experimentally, and it now appears that the same is proving true for molecules. Stockdale, Hurst, and Christophorou (111) have attempted to study electron capture and related processes using carefully controlled electron energy distributions. They conclude that under the conditions used by Lovelock et al. almost the whole effect observed for the reference substance (phenyl chloride) was due to dissociative capture caused by electron acceleration during the short collecting pulse (i.e., $AB + e \rightarrow A^- + B$ rather than $AB + e \rightarrow AB^-$). They go so far as to suggest that in many cases the results obtained with electron capture detectors have little to do with electron affinities.

It is possible that these contradictions arise from differences in detector design (112). Barney, Stanley, and Cook (113), for example, found that pulsed operation would not always remove ionization effects for some substances, and that it was important to have the electrons moving against the carrier stream, as in Figure 21. This parallel plate design is to be preferred to a cylindrical arrangement of the type sometimes used in cross-section detectors (Fig. 17). It seems unlikely that the detector geometry affects the efficiency of recombinations involving electrons, but negative ion combination rates may be expected to be significantly increased if the ions are drifting in the direction opposite to the flow of carrier gas.

Despite the uncertainty about the mode of operation of the detector, it has been successfully used in numerous qualitative analyses. In particular, it is frequently employed in pesticide analysis, where the early studies of halogenated materials (114) have been extended to phosphates, and there has been some success in correlating the structure of phosphate pesticides with EC response (115–117). Another application is in the analysis of lead alkyls from petrol, and in connection with this work Dawson (118) has pointed out that EC detectors are temperature sensitive, and with temperature programming it is essential to provide efficient thermostatting for the detector.

Landowne and Lipsky appear to have been the first to suggest the usefulness of preparing derivatives of materials which themselves give no EC response (109). Thus, they found that monochloroacetates of sterols (119) gave markedly larger responses than did pure sterols. It has long been known that tri- and hexa-fluoroacetyl acetones form stable but very volatile transition metal complexes (120), and these have recently been much used for quantitative inorganic GC analysis (121,122). Ross has made a study of the chromium and aluminium complexes with these fluorinated ligands, as well as with acetylacetone, and concludes that the metal atom has a significant effect on the observed EC response (123,124).

A number of other studies using electron capture detectors are discussed in Section IV-D.

4. *Piezoelectric Sorption Detector*

An unusual device, based on the fact that the output from a piezoelectric material is influenced by the presence of adsorbed substances on its surface, has recently been described by King (125). He points out that such devices are already available commercially for use in detecting traces of water vapor, and sensitivity towards, for example, xylene can be as high as 1 ppm of carrier gas. Of particular interest is the fact that one can modify the selectivity at will by altering the adsorbent layer. GC stationary phases are useful here, because of their low volatility, and it is found that relative responses correlate well with retention results from conventional GC. For example, if the relative response of benzene to that of cyclohexane is taken as unity with a layer of silicone oil on the piezoelectric, the corresponding value for an adsorbent layer of 1,2,3-tris(2-cyanoethoxy)propane is 8.06. The possibility therefore arises of being able, in effect, to use the detector as a second column.

An attractive dual detector system might well be provided by two piezoelectric detectors in parallel, one of which is coated with a boiling point stationary phase, and the other with a selective stationary phase. By analogy with retention coincidence methods (Sec. III-A), it would be as well to have several such detectors, including some coated with highly selective liquid phases, to avoid possible ambiguities.

5. $^{85}Krypton$ *Clathrate Detector*

Gudzinowicz and Smith (126) have described an interesting specific arrangement for detecting strongly oxidizing inorganic gases, such as OF_2, Cl_2, and NO_2Cl. The effluent stream is passed into a ^{85}Kr quinol clathrate, and any oxidant present releases radioactive Kr atoms which are then detected with a Geiger counter. The Geiger trace is compared with that from a conventional detector, to find accurate retention times, since the response time of the clathrate system is long, due to its rather large volume.

D. Dual Detector Systems

It is not usually possible to characterize a peak from the information provided by one chromatogram alone, because almost all detectors give responses which are functions of sample size as well as of some molecular property. The gravimetric devices of Section IV-A-1 are an extreme case where the response is a function of sample size alone, and their usefulness in identification work arises because they enable the signal given by the same sample on a second detector to be reduced to a response per unit mass. In Section IV-A-3 mention was made of a successful combination of such a gravimetric detector with a gas density balance, using nitrogen as a heavy carrier gas, which enabled molecular weights to be determined (61b). Similarly, with a light carrier gas (hydrogen), the molar response of a katharometer has been used in conjunction with a gas density balance to find molecular weights (28) (Sec. IV-A-4).

These recent molecular weight dual detector systems are special examples of the technique of characterizing eluates by the *relative responses* given by two detectors. The pioneer in this field was Grant, who compared the peak heights obtained with his flame emissivity detector and with a katharometer (127). Applications of the technique have not been numerous until recently, possibly because the available detector systems did not measure sufficiently different properties of the eluate. At the moment, however, there is a growing interest in emission photometric techniques of a more sophisticated kind than that used by Grant. These techniques are inherently selective, and so different chemical types give very different relative responses to the flame photometric and to a conventional detector. An example of such a combination has recently been reported (128) by Braman, who used a flame photometric detector of the type developed by Juvet and Durbin (129), which is discussed further in Section V-E. Braman used a flame-ionization detector as a reference, to achieve comparable sensitivity, but pointed out that a katharometer would give a more universal response.

The majority of applications of relative response techniques have involved electron capture detectors, however, because of the large degree of specificity shown by such detectors. Mention has already been made (Sec. IV-C-3) of the use of a photoionization detector in a dual arrangement with the early electron capture detector (97), and the argon β-ionization detector has also been used as a reference (108). Of all the double systems that have been used, however, the combination of EC with flame-ionization detector is by far the most popular as a means of achieving simultaneous qualitative and quantitative analysis. Dawson (130) used a series arrangement to detect polynuclear aromatics (which frequently give marked EC responses) in peaks much overlapped in the FID chromatogram. Oaks, Hartmann, and Dimick (131) used FID and EC in parallel to make a detailed study of the volatile sulfides in garlic, with the aid of numerous sulfide standards. They noticed that the trisulfides in particular had a very high relative response (Table III) the

TABLE III

Relative EC and FID Responses for Organic Sulfur Compounds[a]

Compound type	Range of ϕ[b]
Monosulfides	0.01–0.10
Mercaptans	0.10–0.50
Saturated disulfides	0.6–4.0
Unsaturated disulfides	8.0–20.0
Trisulfides	150–400

[a] Ref. 131.
[b] ϕ = Electron capture response/flame ionization response.

EC response being about 250 times as large as that of the FID. It was thus possible to readily distinguish the trisulfides from the mono- and disulfides, and Oaks et al. were able to identify 11 of the 21 observed FID peaks (Table IV).

Clemons and Altshuller (132) have recently studied the relative EC and FID responses of a number of low molecular weight halogenated substances, and have found that the relative responses varied over seven orders of magnitude. While fluorinated alkanes had low EC responses, C_6F_6 gave a high response. In general, however, iodinated substances gave the highest EC responses, and there was a marked increase in relative response as the number of halogen atoms in the molecule increased. In general, one iodine atom was equivalent to three chlorine atoms.

Teitelbaum (133) has warned of possible errors arising in the interpretation of dual chromatograms if a parallel arrangement is used. He gives examples where two similar peaks from the same column have apparent retention times that differ for two detectors by several seconds. Such effects are most likely to be observed, however, with detectors of

TABLE IV

Identification of Sulfur Compounds in Garlic[a]

Observed ϕ[b]	Expected type of compound	Observed relative retention time	Assignment	Standard relative retention time
0.4	Mercaptan	0.04	Methyl mercaptan	0.04
0.01	Monosulfide	0.06	Dimethyl sulfide	0.06
2.4	Disulfide	0.15	Dimethyl disulfide	0.16
0.09	Monosulfide	0.21	Diallyl sulfide	0.18
10.0	Unsaturated disulfide	0.39	Methyl allyl disulfide	0.46
300.0	Trisulfide	0.65	Dimethyl trisulfide	0.76
20.0	Unsaturated disulfide	1.00	Diallyl disulfide	1.00
200.0	Trisulfide	1.68	Methyl allyl trisulfide	1.63
320.0	Trisulfide	3.42	Diallyl trisulfide	3.42

[a] Ref. 131.

[b] ϕ = Electron capture response/flame ionization response.

relatively large effective volume and for retention times of the order of minutes. Under such conditions it would be as well to take precautions against possible misinterpretations arising from this cause.

V. POSTCOLUMN INSTRUMENTAL METHODS

The concept of an analytical machine which is capable of separating a complex mixture as well as identifying the separated components is an attractive one which has only been partially realized. Such a machine could rely upon GC for resolution of the analysis mixture and upon a variety of other instrumental techniques for continuous identification of the separated materials. This may be done either with conventional GC using fast-scan instrumentation or with interrupted elution GC (I-EGC) using slow-scan equipment. In the latter technique, which has recently been automated by Scott et al. (134), the analysis time scale is expanded by interrupting elution while a peak is instrumentally analyzed. This procedure enables conventional slow-scan instruments to be used and hence results in a large financial saving. It is evident from Table V

TABLE V

The Cost of Various Instrumental Arrangements[a]

Objective	Instruments	Cost in the UK, 1966 (£)
Speed	Normal GC, fast-scan IR and MS	23,500
Economy	I-EGC, normal low resolution IR and MS	8,000
Resolution	I-EGC, high resolution IR and MS	34,250

[a] Ref. 134.

that the use of I-EGC makes possible an enormous reduction in capital outlay at the expense of increasing the analysis time. Since in many situations qualitative work forms only a relatively small part of the total work, this disadvantage is probably not very important.

The most important postcolumn instrument and the most studied in conjunction with GC is the mass spectrometer.

A. Mass Spectrometry

The mass spectrometer (MS) is one of the few detectors which simultaneously provides both qualitative and quantitative information about effluents. For the analyst faced with a poorly characterized sample (135) it can save months of labor as well as giving identifications which are more accurate than those obtainable from less sophisticated methods. It is the most general GC detector in the sense that it is readily applicable to any conceivable molecule within the practical mass range. For this reason it is perhaps more useful than either IR or UV and yet shares with these techniques the tremendous advantage that its spectra lend themselves to interpretation and cataloging. Thus it is not necessary to hold a vast stock of standard chemicals to cover all possible eventualities, and the results of one worker may be confidently used by another. This practice bypasses the notorious difficulties introduced by the irreproducibility of GC retention data and removes much of the duplication of experimental work which is apparent in the literature.

Most types of commercial spectrometer have been used (136) ranging from the simple, inexpensive, nonmagnetic, radio-frequency device used by Varadi and Ettre (137,138) to complex high-resolution instruments. The former is essentially an electronic valve and is therefore much cheaper than conventional spectrometers. It has not, however, gained widespread popularity, probably because of its limited mass range. Varadi and Ettre claim that this extends up to 250 amu, though Ryhage (139) has stated that the device cannot resolve masses higher than about 50.

The main requirements of MS-GC are that the emergent peak is scanned in a time which is small compared with the time of emergence of the peak from the chromatograph and that the sampling system is capable of maintaining a low pressure ($\sim 10^{-5}$ torr) in the ionization chamber of the spectrometer. The latter requirement may be achieved by leaking only a small fraction of the effluent into the spectrometer via some sort of reduction system, preferably constructed in glass to minimize memory effects. A simple design is shown in Figure 22 (140).

The use of helium carrier gas, and the choice of a low enough electron energy to prevent its ionization, ensures that a conventional GC trace is conveniently provided by monitoring the total ionization current and that the spectra observed will be those of the effluent alone. These spectra will sometimes show a persistent background due to solvent bleeding (141) and for this reason gas–liquid columns should be operated at as low a temperature as possible. Gas–solid columns, which are not, of course, liable to the same restriction, would seem to be ideally suited for use with mass spectrometry.

Scan times of a few seconds in the mass range 20–200 amu are adequate for many purposes and are readily available. As McFadden and Day have pointed out (142), the limitation on the scan rate resides in the ancillary equipment (amplifiers, recorders, etc.) rather than in the spectrometer itself.

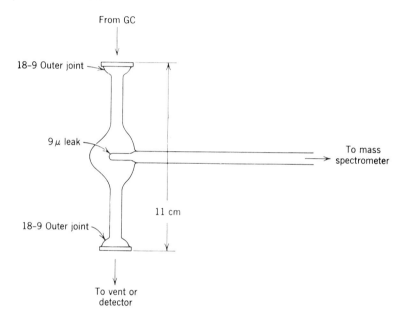

Fig. 22. A simple, all-glass leak for use with MS-GC (140).

The detection limit of conventional low-resolution equipment is about 10^{-8} to 10^{-9} g, although the effective sensitivity has been greatly increased by Ryhage and co-workers (139,143,144) by concentrating the effluent a hundred times, thereby allowing a much larger sample to be taken while still maintaining the ionization chamber at the required low pressure. They used two molecular separators in series in order to preferentially remove the helium carrier gas. Such separators rely upon the high diffusion coefficient of helium and a simple all-glass design is shown in Figure 23 [145 (see also ref. 146)]. On the basis of work on the methyl esters of C_{18} acids, Ryhage et al. conclude (144) that 0.5 ng of effluent are detectable using this method, while a molecular ion is obtainable with 2 ng and complete identification with 20 ng. Therefore, the detection limits of mass spectrometry are somewhat lower than those of the hydrogen flame-ionization detector, while the amount of information concerning the effluent which can be obtained from the mass spectrometer is much larger.

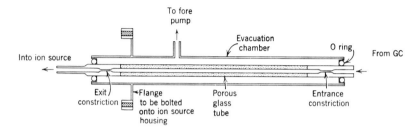

Fig. 23. All-glass molecular separator which enables helium carrier gas to be preferentially removed from the column effluent thereby increasing the concentration of eluate sampled (145). By courtesy of *Analytical Chemistry*.

When a large number of mass ambiguities exist, the use of high resolution mass spectrometry is to be advocated (145). Inevitably the gain in resolution is accompanied by a loss in sensitivity, but mass integration by the use of a photographic plate in the Mattauch-Herzog focal plane type of instrument compensates to some extent for this as well as eliminating the need for scanning. The recording of several consecutive spectra involves moving the photographic plate between scans. This takes only a matter of seconds and is no bar to the use of this system on moderately fast chromatograms.

Mass spectrometry is particularly useful when it is difficult to completely separate two components of a mixture. Under these circumstances the leading edge of the composite peak will have a very different composition from its trailing edge. This is clearly seen with low resolution spectrometers from serial spectra taken as the peak emerges from the chromatograph or with high resolution spectrometers from the time-resolved spectrum obtained by continuously moving the photographic plate (147). In this connection it is appropriate to mention that Sweeley et al. have recently described a system which enables two m/e values to be recorded continuously by rapid alternation of the accelerating voltage (148).

An excellent example of the uses of MS-GC is provided by the work of Dorsey, Hunt, and O'Neal (149). They employed a 100-cm capillary leak of 0.45 ml/min from a total flow rate of 1 ml/min, scanning the mass range 20–200 amu in 1 sec with a cycloidal focusing spectrometer. They studied a mixture of C_9 paraffins, many of which are difficult to separate by GC. For example, a given peak could, on the grounds of boiling point, be assigned equally as well to one of seven C_9 paraffins. The occurrence of a mass peak at 85 amu uniquely indicated the presence of 4,4-dimethylheptane. On subtracting the spectrum

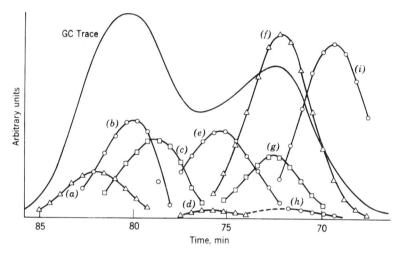

Fig. 24. Illustration of the ability of MS to dissect a complex multicomponent peak (150). The identified components and the m/e values monitored are as follows: (a) n-heptane, $m/e = 114$; (b) 1, trans-2-dimethylcyclopentane, $m/e = 112$; (c) 1,- cis- and trans-3-dimethylcyclopentane; (d) 1,1-dimethylcyclopentane; (e) 3-methylhexane; (f) cyclohexane, $m/e = 84$; (g) 2-methylhexane, $m/e = 85$; (h) 2,3-dimethylpentane; (i) benzene, $m/e = 78$. By courtesy of Analytical Chemistry.

of this compound from the total spectrum, the spectrum of another C_9 paraffin, 2,6-dimethylheptane, was revealed. In another case a given peak could be assigned to nine C_9 isomers! By taking 28 serial spectra as the peak emerged, it was identified as a mixture of 4-ethylheptane and 3,4-dimethylheptane. The evolution of a complex peak is shown in Figure 24 (150).

The work of Dorsey et al., as well as illustrating the considerable power of MS-GC, spotlights some of its defects. Thus 2,5-dimethylheptane has the same boiling point and cracking pattern as 3,5-dimethylheptane. Similarly, propyne and allene have identical mass spectra, although the difference in their boiling points is sufficient to enable them to be resolved chromatographically with little difficulty. Furthermore, it is only rarely that MS can distinguish between *cis* and *trans* isomers, whereas in most cases this is readily achieved by GC (151).

Nevertheless, even allowing for these fundamental limitations, there is little doubt that MS-GC is the most versatile all-purpose qualitative analytical system available. This versatility is, however, obtained at great cost and, even though this may be considerably reduced by using Interrupted Elution Chromatography, the particular requirements of a given project can often be met in other much cheaper ways.

B. Infrared Spectroscopy

Almost since the beginning of GC, infrared spectroscopy has been used as a means of identification. In early work the eluate was trapped and transferred to a conventional spectrometer. Special techniques for use in this connection have been described in Section II (17,18). The continuous monitoring by IR of GC effluents is, however, a relatively recent development.

Bartz and Ruhl (152) have been able to obtain good IR spectra (see Fig. 25) by simultaneously scanning the ranges 2.5–7.0 and 6.5–16 μ in 16 sec. They passed IR radiation through a rectangular light pipe (volume 12 ml, optical path length 40 cm) fitted to the end of the GC column and, by chopping the emergent beam, applied it alternately to two spectrometers, each of which was locked on to one or the other of the ranges. A system of solenoid-operated valves enabled the operator to select which peaks were scanned and to retain such peaks in the cell for further scans if necessary. After each peak had been scanned the cell was purged with nitrogen. The system was capable of dealing with peaks separated by more than 32 sec. Another system which scans the range 2.5–15 μ in 45 sec has been described (153) and successfully used in the identification of some constituents of cigarette smoke (154). More recently, Low (155) has used computer-averaged multiple scan infrared interferometry to obtain spectra over the region 4–40 μ in 1 sec with a resolution of about 20 cm^{-1}.

The principal disadvantage of the above systems is that relatively large samples are needed (10^{-3} to 10^{-4} g peak load) to obtain a good spectrum. This can be overcome to some extent by using long-path cells; a system involving an optical path length of 240 cm has been described

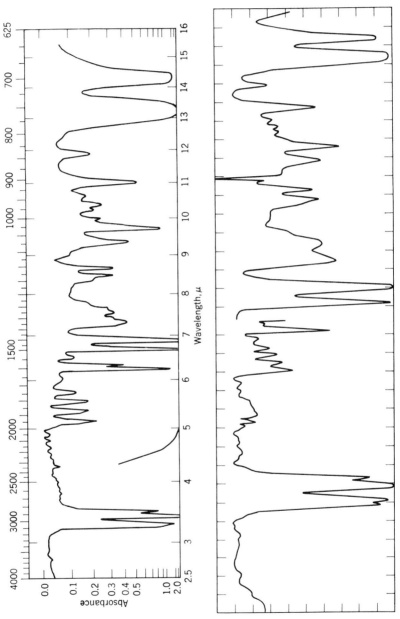

Fig. 25. Comparison of slow scan infrared spectrum of a polystyrene film (top) with the equivalent spectrum obtained in 16 sec (152). By courtesy of *Analytical Chemistry*.

(156). It was designed so that any given peak could be diverted into the cell and scanned *ad infinitum*; the exact moment at which to divert the gas stream was indicated by a hydrogen flame-ionization detector operating on 5% of the effluent. In favorable cases 3×10^{-5} g of effluent gave a good spectrum. However, the volume of the cell (130 ml) would be prohibitively large in many analyses.

C. Ultraviolet Spectroscopy

Kaye and Waska (157) have modified a Beckman far UV DK-2 spectrophotometer to scan 1600–2100 Å in 6 sec with a resolution of better than one angstrom. Using this machine, they were able to distinguish all the alkyl iodides containing less than six carbon atoms. The sensitivity of the latest machine is not quoted, but the sensitivity of an earlier design (158) for representative substances was intermediate between that of thermal conductivity and hydrogen flame-ionization detectors. For example, the detection limit for naphthalene ($\epsilon = 1.25 \times 10^5$ liter mole^{-1} cm^{-1}) at 2108 Å was 10^{-8} g.

D. Nuclear Magnetic Resonance

NMR has, to date, only been used as a post-trapping technique and is limited by the relatively large samples needed (~ 1 mg) (159). Recent work (160) has greatly increased the available sensitivity by computer averaging multiple scans of very weak resonances, and good spectra have been obtained with as little as 0.2 μmoles of hydrogen by scanning over a weekend.

E. Emission Spectroscopy

Observations of the light emitted by excited species in flames form the basis of many methods of elemental analysis, among which the simplest are those commonly used in qualitative analysis. One of these, the Beilstein test, has been successfully adapted for use with GC (161), and as a simple, sensitive method of detecting halogen or CN-containing compounds, it has much to commend it. However, any more general method must rely upon an accurate spectroscopic analysis of the emitted light. By this means, phosphorus and sulfur have been detected at the parts per billion and parts per million levels, respectively (162).

Juvet and Durbin (129) have recently described a flame photometer for the analysis of both organic and inorganic materials. For the latter

it is highly specific and can thus be used to identify the elemental constituents of unresolved peaks. In favorable cases it can detect as little as
10^{-11} moles and should find wide application in inorganic GC. Zado
and Juvet (163) have described a similar detector which, although a
factor of ten less sensitive, can be constructed for less than 500 dollars.
The emission spectrum is excited in an oxyhydrogen flame and analyzed
by a diffraction spectroscope with photomultiplier detection. The
spectroscope covers the range 355–625 mµ and has a half-intensity bandwidth of 6 mµ. Provision is made for operation in a nonselective mode
such that all emitted light (with the exception of certain OH bands which

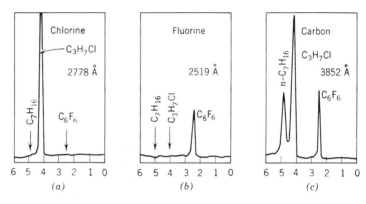

Fig. 26. Three chromatograms of a mixture of *n*-heptane, propyl chloride,
and hexafluorobenzene using spectroscopic detection (165). By courtesy of
Analytical Chemistry.

are filtered out) is detected. This arrangement is very similar to that
used by Grant (127,164) in the very first use of flame photometry and
GC. In this work the responses of photometer and katharometer were
compared and significant variations were found between different
homologous series. An account of other useful dual detector systems
will be found in Section IV-D.

McCormack, Tong, and Cooke (165) have used 2450-mc microwave
excitation to obtain emission spectra. They were able to detect bands due
to C_2, P, CS, CCl, etc., and in certain cases could relate the occurrence
of these to the structure of the eluate. However, they point out that care
should be taken in the interpretation of these experiments, since flame
reactions may produce atomic groupings which do not exist in the parent
material. Figure 26 illustrates the high specificity of the system (165).

Recently Bache and Lisk have used the method successfully for the study of phosphorus and iodine-containing insecticides and herbicides (166,167). These workers have also shown (168) that higher sensitivity and selectivity may be obtained by operating with the effluent at reduced pressure. The relationship between sensitivity and pressure is, however, not simple. For example, the response of the system toward the 2535.65-Å atomic phosphorus line rises to a maximum at around 200 torr, at which pressure the sensitivity is about an order of magnitude higher than that at atmospheric pressure. In contrast, although the response to the 2062-Å atomic iodine line is also maximized at a similar pressure, the response is then only some 40% larger than that at atmospheric pressure.

VI. SAMPLE MODIFICATION AS AN AID TO IDENTIFICATION

The limitations attending the use of retention data for identification purposes have been discussed in Section III. The detectors considered in Section IV are usually unselective in the sense that they respond to the presence of molecules of a wide variety of chemical types, although useful qualitative information can be provided by dual detector arrangements. The instrumental techniques of Section V are able to provide direct information about chemical composition, and are the most desirable means of identification under almost all circumstances. They are, however, expensive and not a little complicated, so that capital expenditure and maintenance costs can be high. In many laboratories, therefore, modification of the sample before, during, or after separation will play a large part in purely chromatographic identifications. Indeed, in the analysis of large molecules these techniques appear to provide one of the few acceptable approaches.

Three alternative methods may be adopted: one or more components may be completely or partially *removed*, *converted* by means of chemical reagents, or *degraded* by pyrolysis or other techniques.

A. Abstraction Techniques

1. *Complete Removal of Certain Components*

Any rapid selective physical or chemical abstraction process can be used, but it is obvious that one must have a fairly clear idea of the

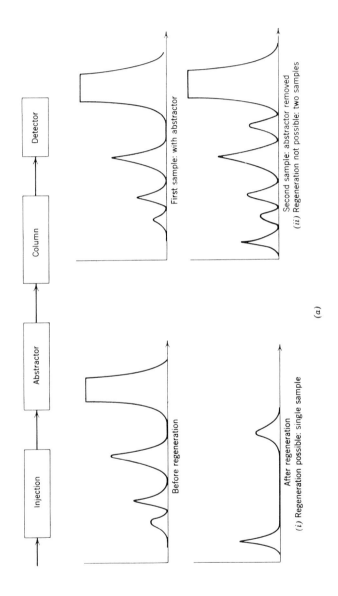

(a)

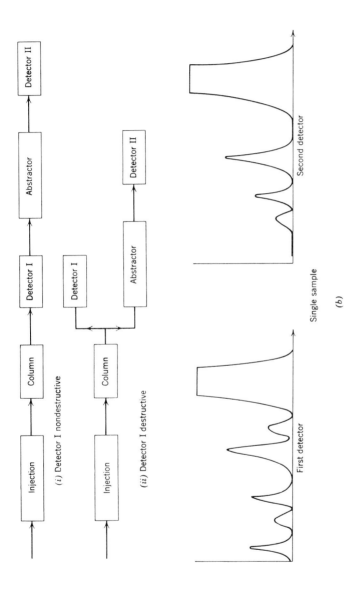

Fig. 27. Various experimental arrangements for use with an abstractor unit. (a) If regeneration is possible case (i) applies, and only a single sample is required. Otherwise, two samples with a single detector (ii) or one sample with two detectors (b) are needed. For the examples shown the abstractor removes two peaks. (b) In case (ii) peak areas will be reduced according to the stream splitting ratio.

sort of components present so that a suitable abstractor can be tried. Thus, although it is placed first here, in practice this technique might well be one of the last to be adopted.

The abstraction process may either be carried out conventionally prior to injection, or it may take place on stream. The latter approach, which usually involves placing the abstractor before the analytical column, is particularly useful when it enables the abstracted components to be regenerated and subsequently chromatographed. Each peak in the second chromatogram, which is usually very simple, is then known to belong to a certain class of compound, while in the first chromatogram each peak is known *not* to belong to that class. A schematic arrangement is shown in Figure 27a. Only a single sample is required in such a regeneration technique, although it is of course essential to have an efficient precolumn abstractor of effective volume much smaller than that of the analytical column.

In the majority of cases reported, however, regeneration is not possible, and it becomes necessary to use two samples, the second to be run without abstraction so that it is known which peaks were removed in the first sample (169). An alternative approach when removal is irreversible is to use two detectors rather than two samples, and to put the abstractor *after* the column. Two possible arrangements are shown in Figure 27b. Provided that the sample spends much longer in the analytical column than in the abstractor, chromatograms obtained by this postcolumn and the precolumn methods will be identical.

Two kinds of abstractor are commonly employed. The first makes use of selective physical solution and sorption processes of the type responsible for GLC and GSC separations. The second kind makes use of chemical reactions which convert the normally volatile compound to an involatile derivative which the carrier gas is not able to convey to the column. One example of this approach is the sulfuric acid absorption of unsaturated hydrocarbons in a precolumn (170). Another is the removal of carbonyl compounds from aqueous mixtures, prior to injection, by the formation of bisulfite addition compounds (171).

Physical Removal. A normal chromatographic column may well effectively absorb higher boiling compounds while allowing low boiling components to be eluted. Column material of the diatomaceous earth type held at very low temperatures has been used to completely abstract trace components from large volumes of air (172,173). Of course, on warming the column to normal temperatures all absorbed material is recovered, and hence such columns are of no use for selective sorptions. It is possible, however, to achieve a certain amount of selectivity by the use of suitable stationary phases. For instance, Martin (174) used a coating of β,β'-thiodipropionitrile, and was able to hold back benzene while allowing C_{11} saturates and olefins to be eluted. Such examples employing a liquid coating are, however, rare—a reflection of the notorious nonselectivity of conventional liquid phases. Increased selectivity is made possible by the use of packing loaded with complexing agents such as silver nitrate in glycol (175) or tetrahalophthalate esters (176), and increasing attention is being paid to such columns. At the moment we are also witnessing accelerating growth of interest in the use of gas–solid columns (177) including those of organic composition (178), and there can be little doubt that some interesting materials for selective removal of compounds will soon become available. Until now, however, the only substances that have been at all widely used for selective sorption are the crystalline alumino-silicates or zeolites.

Barrer (179) has reviewed early work on "molecular sieves" of various kinds, including the zeolites. A recent account of progress in the understanding of these compounds has been given by Breck (180), who pays particular attention to synthetic zeolites in which the diameter of the pores can be tailor-made by ionic substitution. The most frequently used synthetic material is the 5A sieve, which selectively retains straight chain molecules while allowing branched isomers to be eluted. Although this property is commonly employed in alkane separations (181–183) it can be equally valuable in analyses involving olefins or alcohols (184). Other interesting separations reported (184) include those of aldehydes (retained) from ketones, and of acids (retained) from esters. With such systems it may be desirable to work at high temperatures, so that high molecular weight ketones and esters which are strongly but not irreversibly held can be eluted in reasonably short times.

By raising the temperature, however, it is possible to desorb even the n-alkanes from 5A sieves. Such desorption occurs readily near the critical temperature (185) which for C_{15} hydrocarbons is about 400°C. Eggertsen and Groennings (186) were the first to report the analysis of n-paraffins from petroleum fractions by regeneration from a molecular sieve. During the first chromatogram the precolumn was at 200°C, at which temperature they found C_6 to C_{10} n-alkanes to be completely persorbed by 5A sieves, so that the branched isomers could be chromatographed. The precolumn was then heated to about 400°C to elute the n-paraffins. Albert (183) has reported similar work in which he found that at 160°C some C_{10} and C_{11} iso-paraffins were partially absorbed by the precolumn. Although this anomaly did not occur at 210°C, it was replaced by another because n-pentane, and presumably lower n-paraffins, were not then retained. A chromatogram of the abstracted higher n-alkanes was obtained by warming the precolumn to 400°C. At such temperatures, pyrolysis will take place at a reasonable rate and the method does not therefore commend itself for accurate quantitative work. It should be useful for qualitative identification provided extents of pyrolytic conversion are low, as would be the case with normal flow rates and short precolumns. Precolumns used in work of this kind are commonly only about six inches long.

Brunnock (187) has described a drastic alternative, which avoids any complications due to pyrolysis during regeneration. He destroys the lattice of a 5A abstractor with hydrofluoric acid solution (taking care to avoid excessive heat generation) in order to liberate n-paraffins, which are apparently unaffected by the treatment.

It is clear that factors other than working temperature affect the behavior of these molecular sieves, notably the previous history of a particular batch, and the water content. It is therefore not very surprising to find that conflicting reports of abstraction behavior of particular sieves have arisen. Even less surprising is the finding (172) that after treating the molecular sieve with hexamethyl disilazane, a substantially different separating ability was obtained to that observed with the untreated material.

5A molecular sieve can effect the most certain separations for small paraffins, where the n- and branched molecules have substantially different cross sections, only the smaller of which is able to pass inside the zeolite framework. For larger molecules, where the size differential between straight and branched isomers is not so marked, it is advisable to vary the operating temperature and the extent to which the sieve is dried, in order to find the optimum conditions for separation.

Although molecular sieves are proving useful, their possible applications are limited compared with those of selective chemical treatments.

Chemical Removal. Difficulties are encountered when liquid reagents are used, principally because with reasonable flow rates it is difficult to achieve efficient absorption of the sample simply by bubbling it through the reagent. It is possible to carry out reaction before injection (188) but the advantage of complete reaction is then often outweighed by complications arising from deposition of the reagent at the head of the column. It is for these reasons that interest has grown in the use of precolumns containing chromatographic support material coated with reactive chemicals. Such devices expose a large surface area of reagent to the sample so that, provided reaction itself is rapid, a short precolumn can ensure complete abstraction with normal flow rates. Use has been made of two such abstractors (189) in the analysis of petroleum fractions. A mixture of 20% mercuric sulfate in 20% sulfuric acid was found to completely absorb the alkenes and alkynes, while a 4% silver sulfate in 95% sulfuric acid coating gave very efficient removal of aromatics as well as the unsaturates. On the other hand, it was found (189) that bromine water on a firebrick column was useless—a result presumably due to the rather high volatility of alkyl bromides.

An interesting abstractor was discovered accidently by Ikeda, Simmons, and Grossman (190). They noticed that chromatograms obtained for certain samples after the column had been used to analyze a hydroboration reaction mixture were deficient in peaks due to alcohols definitely known to be present. They showed that peak removal was due to a layer of boric acid (or a polymer thereof) on the surface of the solid support, and this finding enabled them to make efficient abstractors for the selective removal of alcohols from complex mixtures.

Care must be taken in the interpretation of chromatograms obtained with and without abstraction, as may be exemplified from the above work. Boric acid will dehydrate rather than retain certain alcohols. If, then, the abstractor is placed before the column, such an alcohol will produce a peak with the retention time of the corresponding unsaturated compound. If the abstractor is now placed after the analytical column, although the offending alcohol will still be dehydrated and proceed to the detector as an unsaturate, it will have the retention time characteristic of the alcohol itself. By this means, Ikeda et al. (190) were able to avoid erroneously labeling the compound responsible as non-alcoholic. It would clearly be as well to confirm the validity of conclusions based on any abstraction experiment by this expedient of placing the abstractor in turn at either end of the column. A device which enables this to be done without the need for any dismantling has been described in Section III (Fig. 6) in connection with trapping and reinjecting procedures. In this device the trap which is usually at the column outlet is transferred by manipulation of three valves to the column inlet, where it acts as a sample loop. The extension of this arrangement for use with precolumns is obvious.

An abstractor that will selectively absorb aldehydes from mixtures of aldehydes, ketones, alcohols, and hydrocarbons has recently been discovered (191), again by accident. The material used is a commercial, general purpose packing known as FFAP, so the substance responsible for the abstraction is not yet known. Reaction is rather slow, so that a column several feet long, rather than the usual precolumn lengths of a few inches, must be used. It has also been found that the abstraction process is accompanied by the formation of water, and that with continued use the abstraction ability is impaired.

Another example of the use of chemical abstraction was described some years ago (192), making use of the fact that neutral silver nitrate will react with secondary alkyl bromides, but not with primary compounds:

$$RCHBrCH_2R' + AgNO_3 \longrightarrow AgBr + RCH{=}CHR' + HNO_3$$

For example, 2-bromobutane could be removed from a mixture with 1-bromo-2-methylpropane. Three firebrick precolumns were necessary in this work. One was coated with the silver nitrate reagent, the second contained sulfuric acid to remove the olefins, and the third had a coating of disodium phosphate to remove the nitric acid. Experiments showed that above 30°C both secondary and tertiary alkyl bromides reacted, and were thus removed completely while primary isomers were unaffected. The primary components of a complex mixture containing 13 monobromoalkanes could thus be identified.

Maleic anhydride on silica gel has been used to remove butadiene by a Diels–Alder reaction (193), and this technique has been extended in a novel approach to identification in which the extent of abstraction is studied as a function of flow rate (194) (see Sec. VI-B-2).

2. Precolumn Partition

While complete removal of components on a precolumn makes use of more or less irreversible processes, another approach to effluent identification involves only partial removal by equilibration of the sample between two immiscible solvents. Suffis and Dean (195) were among the first to try this method, but their technique was cumbersome and required gram quantities of sample. More recently, a refinement of the technique, which is applicable to nanogram quantities of unknown, has been reported by Beroza and Bowman (196). The first stage in their method is to take a chromatogram of one aliquot of a solution of the sample in a suitable solvent. A second aliquot is then shaken with an immiscible solvent of greater density, so that each of the unknown substances is independently distributed between the two solvents. The upper layer is then chromatographed, and the chromatogram compared with that obtained from the first aliquot. The diminution in peak height is related to the distribution coefficient for the unknown concerned. The method has been particularly useful for nanogram quantities of pesticide residues, and by using an electron capture detector the relatively large quantities of chosen solvent involved do not obscure the chromatogram obtained.

Recently the partition technique has been extended to the identification of a wide variety of organic compounds, by means of seven binary solvent systems (197). Using a suitable solvent system it is possible to characterize even very closely related compounds from the distribution coefficients determined by GC. Deviations from ideality due to molecular association are avoided by the use of low solute concentrations. As originally reported, this method depends for its accuracy on the use of identical sample sizes before and after partition. The technique could readily be made independent of sample size by the use of an internal standard which is insoluble in, or of known solubility in, the second layer.

There is no reason why the method should not be applied to traces of gaseous as well as to liquid effluents. It is also interesting to note that this technique is essentially an extension of the use of multiple column systems, but that the requirements of a suitable partitioning liquid are not so great, particularly with respect to volatility. The use of complexing agents should prove particularly useful for inorganic analysis, and identification of both ligands and ions should be possible from stability constant comparisons.

3. Abstraction Followed by Displacement

A novel use of an abstraction column has been described by Scott and Phillips (198) for the determination of traces of alkenes in alkanes. Traces of 1-hexene and 1-heptene (about 1 in 10^8) were added to purified n-heptane which was forced as a liquid down an alumina/silver nitrate column at room temperature. When all the liquid had passed through, the temperature was raised to 75°C and nitrogen was passed through the column to remove all traces of heptane. The alkenes, which had been totally adsorbed during the passage of the liquid, remained firmly attached to the column packing. A stream of nitrogen saturated with

1-octene was then forced through the column displacing the adsorbed hexene and heptene.

Although displacement chromatography is out of favor at the moment, the dual use of a single column for both abstraction and analysis appears to be most attractive, especially for trace amounts of material which are often completely masked by much larger peaks. When it is reported in the literature that a compound is chromatographically pure, it usually means that a large sample has given only one, albeit very broad, peak. Under these circumstances it is not surprising that contaminants which may be chemically similar are not detected.

B. Chemical Conversion

It will be convenient to divide the available methods of chemical modification into three types: precolumn, postcolumn and on-column. Techniques using precolumn conversion are concerned primarily with the chromatographic behavior of the derivatives so produced, while postcolumn techniques require actual separation of components before they can usefully be applied. In contrast, on-column methods use reactive stationary phases in the analytical column itself.

1. Peak Shift Techniques

A standard method of identification, especially in organic chemistry, is the preparation of characteristic derivatives. If such derivatives are to be suitable for gas chromatographic analysis they must be volatile, and much of the early work in this field was concerned with the preparation of volatile derivatives of compounds which were themselves involatile, or which decomposed on moderate heating. The drive to find derivatives suitable for the gas chromatography of amino acids is particularly notable. One solution to this problem was to convert the amino acid to an aldehyde by reaction with ninhydrin (199), a technique which was adapted so that it could be carried out on a precolumn (200,201). In other fields some workers were concerned with preparing volatile derivatives from carbohydrates (202), while others sought ways of improving the chromatography of blood alcohol (203–205). Thus, three methods of modifying alcohols in aqueous solutions immediately ahead of the column were devised. One technique was to inject samples onto sodium nitrite to yield nitrite esters, which have good chromatographic properties. Another approach was to pass the sample, with hydrogen carrier gas, through a heated precolumn reactor which contained Raney nickel, and to chromatograph the resulting hydrocarbon mixture. The most satisfactory quantitative method was to dehydrate the alcohols by spraying upwards of 5 μl of sample onto phosphorous pentoxide or phosphoric acid on firebrick at about 200°C in the carrier stream. The olefins which were formed from C_2 to C_5 alcohols enabled very accurate assessment of the alcohol concentrations to be made (203).

All these early methods were adopted because of some failing in the available GC technique for the pure substances concerned. It appears to have been Langer and Pantages (206) who first pointed out that a knowledge of the chromatographic behavior of volatile derivatives *per se* should be useful when attempting to identify substances which would chromatograph perfectly well by themselves. Earlier, these workers, together with Wender, had shown that an improvement in the chromatographic results obtained with phenols could be gained if the phenols were converted to their more volatile silyl ether derivatives (207). Langer and Pantages (206) now prepared the trimethylsilyl derivatives of alcohols, and studied the characteristic peak shifts produced by reaction.

At about the same time, other workers applied a similar peak shift technique when studying sulfur-containing compounds present in petroleum (208). Chromatograms were obtained before and after desulfurization, and the retention times of product hydrocarbons were used as aids to identification. The method has since been extended to removal of oxygen (209), nitrogen (210), and halogens (211). Various other modifications of petroleum fractions have frequently been reported, notably hydrogenation of olefins and/or aromatics, and dehydrogenation of naphthenes (181,212). Such work is generally regarded as part and parcel of the abstraction techniques discussed in Section VI-A-1, and little attention has been paid to the systematic study of the changes in retention times produced by reaction. Franc and Kolouskova (213) have, however, recently undertaken a study of the changes in retention time brought about by hydrogenation of compounds containing different numbers of double bonds.

As the molecular weight of a derivative produced by a reaction such as hydrogenation is similar to that of the parent, the observed peak shift is due almost entirely to changes in polarity, and it is desirable to use a polar stationary phase. On the other hand, the production of silyl derivatives is associated with a large change in molecular weight so that large peak shifts can be observed even with boiling point

columns. Fales and Luukkainen (214) have stressed the need for volatile derivatives to have molecular weights significantly different to those
of the parent compounds, and for this reason they prefer O-methyl-
oximes to O-methyl hydroxylamines when attempting peak shift
identification of carbonyls. The classical oxime derivatives are unsuitable
because they dehydrate to nitriles under chromatographic conditions.

In certain cases it is convenient to prepare derivatives of *lower*
molecular weight than the parent compound. For example, the identification of carboxylic acid groupings in large molecules is much simplified if they are transesterified, thus converting any esters to simple
methyl esters. In a recent study (215) a mixture of methanol, sodium
methoxide, and methyl acetate was used to study the groupings present
in polymers. Free acids are, of course, not themselves converted to
methyl esters.

The work so far described has depended on the conventional
preparation of derivatives from macro samples of the unknown prior to
introduction to the chromatographic column. Anders and Mannering
(216) have devised a neat technique in which esterification of alcohols,
phenols, and primary and secondary amines is carried out on the column
itself. This is achieved by injecting an anhydride a few seconds after the
sample. It is essential that retention times are of the order of tens of
minutes, so that the time between sample injection and reaction does
not become critical. Two new peaks normally result if the anhydride is
in excess, but if, for example, two esterifiable groups are present, it is
possible to observe four peaks. By using a simultaneous injection of two
different anhydrides, a further aid to identification is achieved by the
formation of two product esters from a single functional group (Fig. 28).
By this technique (216) a number of alkaloids and steroids have been
characterized. More recently, the same method with a mixed injection
of acetic and propionic anhydrides has been used to aid work on the
identification of narcotic analgesics (217).

Frequently, of course, retention times are so short, or reaction
times so long that this approach would be useless. For example, it was
found that trimethylsilyl ethers could not be prepared by this technique
(216) unless the carrier gas supply was stopped for five minutes after
the injection of hexamethyldisilazane. In such circumstances it is
obviously simpler to carry out reaction before injection, and Hoff and
Feit (187,188) have made a rather detailed study of the potentialities of
a technique in which chemical reaction is brought about in the injection
syringe. They worked with eight functional groups, and devised means

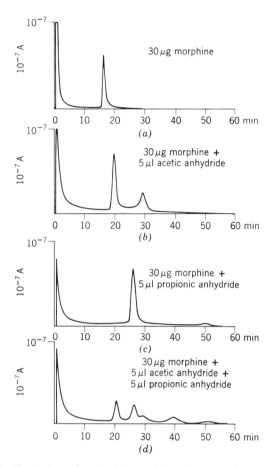

Fig. 28. Illustration of peak shift resulting from precolumn reaction (216). The anhydrides are added in large excess. The new peak near 40 min in (*d*) is probably due to a mixed ester (morphine contains two hydroxyl groups). By courtesy of *Analytical Chemistry*.

by which 13 reagents could be used in the syringe to aid identification. It seems probable that the method could be extended to gas analysis, in which case it would be possible to inject the remaining gas without allowing any liquid reagent to enter the column.

Little work has been reported in which chemical modification is carried out in reactive precolumns. This is in marked contrast to the situation with respect to abstractor techniques (Sec. VI-A-1) where some sort of precolumn is almost invariably employed. An obvious reason for this is that it is difficult to find involatile reactive substances which will yield volatile derivatives. Nevertheless, small concentrations of water in gases have been detected by passing the damp gas through a reactive precolumn of calcium carbide or hydride (218). Unfortunately, although in theory the acetylene (or hydrogen) evolved should give a direct measure of the water content, it was found that in practice the method worked only qualitatively. This was due to the fact that some water was absorbed by chalk impurities in the reactive bed.

2. On-Column Reactions

Few identification studies have been made with systems in which the sample is allowed to react chemically while undergoing separation on an analytical column. If the sample and the column reagent react to give a volatile product or products, then it becomes possible for two or more peaks to be observed for a single component from the unknown sample. This situation should be distinguished from that produced by the double injection method of Anders and Mannering (216) (Sec. VI-B-1). In that approach care is taken to ensure that reaction is completed within the first few plates of the column, whereas we are here concerned with the possibility of reaction taking place continuously, as a sample peak progresses, with a steady accumulation of the volatile reaction product. Such a situation is hard to achieve in practice (just as the use of reactive precolumns yielding volatile derivatives is uncommon) but has been discussed in some detail by Kallen and Heilbronner (219).

If the products of reaction are involatile, then a diminution in height and possibly complete removal of a sample peak is possible. The process is also associated with peak broadening, the magnitude of which depends upon the reactant loading and on the flow rate (220). Gil-Av and Herzberg-Minzley (194) coined the name of partial subtraction chromatography for this use of reactive stationary phases, and they pointed out that a study of relative peak sizes as a function of flow rate would give a measure of the reactivity of the component concerned toward the stationary phase. By way of illustration they presented results obtained for a variety of conjugated dienes chromatographed on a dienophilic stationary phase, chloromaleic anhydride (Fig. 29). There is no reason why the stationary phase itself need be reactive, and greater flexibility might well ensue if conventional liquid phases were used as solvents for more interesting reagents. The study of chemical reactions

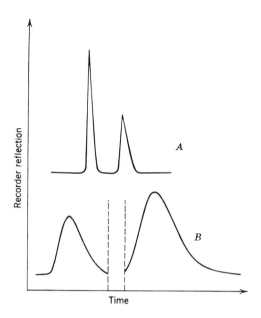

Fig. 29. Example of on-column reaction affecting chromatogram of commercial 1,3-pentadiene when stationary phase contains chloromaleic anhydride (194). A: fast flow rate (77 ml/min); B: low flow rate (11.4 ml/min). The first peak in each case is of the *trans* isomer. By courtesy of *The Journal of Chromatography*.

on chromatographic columns is, however, still in its infancy and so one cannot reasonably hope for any significant contributions from this field for several years.

3. *Postcolumn Reactions*

All modification methods discussed so far have been concerned with bringing about changes in the chromatogram of the unmodified sample. The abstraction technique removes some peaks, either partially or totally (Sec. VI-A); the precolumn peak shift method (Sec. VI-B-1) aims at replacing certain peaks by those due to the chemical derivatives; the on-column approach can use both of these modifications (Sec. VI-B-2), but usually concentrates on partial abstraction. The techniques to be discussed in this section are not concerned with such chromatographic modifications, but use the chromatographic process to achieve separation, and then operate chemically on the separated peaks.

Several such techniques were adopted during the period before highly selective detectors became available, and were concerned with increasing the detectability limits. For example, a copper oxide furnace was used to convert the carbon content of the separated peaks to carbon dioxide, which was determined by microtitration (221,222) or by coulometry (223). At the same time, the hydrogen content was converted to water. Oxidation has been used to increase katharometer sensitivity toward small impurities (224), and use has been made of the added expedient of converting the water to hydrogen (225). A similar increase in sensitivity was achieved by conversion of the carbon content to methane (200,226).

It is unlikely that the use of these chemical reactors to increase the sensitivity of thermal conductivity cells can be useful from the qualitative point of view, since the relationship between response and chemical composition is far from straightforward. The microtitration approach seems to be more promising, since it allows a direct measure of the carbon content of the separated component. Empirical information about the molecular formula is then obtained provided the total weight of that component can be determined. This could be achieved simply, even in a complex mixture, with the aid of a gravimetric detector (Sec. IV-A) and a device of known stream-splitting ratio. Similarly, the weight percentage of sulfur in a peak can be determined by passing it through a combustion tube, and subjecting the sulfur dioxide so produced to coulometric titration with bromine or iodine (227,228). The gravimetric detector provides the limiting sensitivity, for the coulometer can accurately measure the sulfur dioxide from as little as 10^{-8} g of sulfur. It may still be useful to know that sulfur is present in a particular peak, however, even if the percentage composition cannot be determined.

Following the recent technical improvements in automatic titration systems, particularly the possibility of working with small volumes, a number of other sensitive coulometric techniques have been used in conjunction with GC. A recent example has been given, again using catalytic conversion to produce a simple gaseous substance which can conveniently be titrated (229). The effluent is passed in hydrogen carrier gas over a nickel/magnesium oxide catalyst which converts nitrogen-containing materials to ammonia, which is titrated with coulometrically generated hydrogen ions. The sensitivity limit is 10^{-9} g of nitrogen, which is approaching flame-ionization standards. Coulometry has also been used for halide determination (230). In a few cases it is possible to use the coulometric technique without any conversion of the eluate.

For example, thiols present in samples to the extent of less than 1 ppm can be titrated with electrically generated silver ions (231).

A novel coulometric method has recently been described (232) in which oxidation of the eluate is achieved by mixing the effluent carrier gas with a second carrier gas stream containing coulometrically generated oxygen. The mixed gases then flow through a reactor containing a hot platinum surface, and thence to a Hersch cell (66). The technique relies, in principle, on following the *fall* in concentration of the oxygen leaving the reactor, rather than the production of an oxidized product. In practice, the oxygen concentration is maintained almost constant by means of a negative feedback loop containing the Hersch cell, an amplifier, and the oxygen generator. As an eluate emerges and is oxidized, the concentration of oxygen in the Hersch cell tends to fall, causing a decrease in the input to the amplifier, and hence an *increased* output current, which is fed to the oxygen generator. A recorder displays the integrated generating current, which gives an exact measure of the amount of oxygen consumed by the eluate; thus there is no need for standardization. Sensitivity is comparable with that of an ionization detector. Provided that the sample size is known, and that oxidation is complete, the technique should give useful information about the formulas of hydrocarbons or even of molecules containing C, H, and O.

The usefulness of most postcolumn reaction techniques lies in the fact that it is possible to convert unknown peaks into compounds which are more readily identifiable. In the titrimetric methods, these latter substances are usually simple oxides or hydrides of the elements, whereas in conventional qualitative analysis it is usual to achieve identification by forming rather complex products having very characteristic properties (e.g., melting point or color). Walsh and Merritt (233) devised a simple method of carrying out such conventional qualitative analysis on the column effluent, placing great emphasis on color change reactions. A multiway stream splitter was attached to the column outlet, and each branch of the effluent was bubbled through a qualitative reagent contained in a vial. After a color change had taken place with a particular reagent, the vial could be replaced in a few seconds so that virtually continuous monitoring of all but the fastest chromatograms was possible. Walsh and Merritt used a five-way stream splitter, and with the aid of about a dozen reagents were able to classify peaks containing any one of 11 functional groups in (at most) two runs. The simplicity and wide applicability of the method make it worthwhile to outline the classification scheme (Table VI). Having classified peaks by

TABLE VI

Postcolumn Qualitative Analysis[a]

No.	Reagent	Color after reaction	Functional group indicated	Minimum detectable amount of eluate, μg	Other reagents to help classification
1	Ceric nitrate	Yellow-amber	Primary, secondary, or tertiary alcohol	100	8
2	2,4 DNPH	Yellow ppt.	Aldehyde or ketone	20	9
3	Ferric hydroxamate in propylene glycol	Red	Ester or nitrile	40	10
4	Sodium nitroprusside	Red	Mercaptan, sulfide, disulfide, or primary amine	50	11,12
					7
		Blue	Secondary amine	50	7
5	Formaldehyde and sulfuric acid	Wine-red	Aromatic nuclei or unsaturated aliphatics	20	Distinguish by retention data
				40	
6	Alcoholic silver nitrate	White ppt.	Alkyl halide	20	13
7	Hinsberg's	Orange	Primary or secondary amine	100	4
8	Nitrochromic acid	Yellow to blue-grey	Primary or secondary alcohol	20	1
9	Schiff's	Pink	Aldehyde	50	2
10	Ferric hydroxamate	Red	Ester	40	3
11	Isatin	Green	Mercaptan or disulfide	100	4,12
12	Lead acetate	Yellow ppt.	Mercaptan	100	4,11
13	Mercurous nitrate	Yellow to orange ppt.	Iodide	20	6
		White or grey ppt.	Bromide or chloride		

[a] Ref. 233.

functional groups, the use of retention time/carbon number correlation plots (Sec. III-B) becomes more reliable.

In a similar way, Casu and Cavalotti (234) have made use of the oft forgotten ability of gas chromatography to separate in space the components of a complex mixture. They positioned a horizontally advancing strip, of the type used in thin-layer chromatography, under the exit tube of their chromatograph. The strip moved at the same rate as the recorder chart so that the physical position of a component could be pinpointed on the strip directly from a peak on the chart. The strip was then developed with the aid of reagents of the type used by Walsh and Merritt. An interesting point was made by Casu and Cavalotti concerning large peaks and the possibility of obscuring minor components. They found that some large recorder peaks corresponded to very light color spots, a fact which they attributed to the overlap of a minor component containing the relevant functional group by a major component without that group. Very few detection systems, apart from spectroscopic arrangements (Sec. V) and abstraction/displacement techniques (Sec. VI-A-3), share this ability to reveal overlapped peaks.

More recently Janák (235) has used the moving strip technique to obtain a one-dimensional separation of components, and has then employed thin-layer methods to achieve a two-dimensional separation. Such a device has been automated (236). Janák (237) has also used a servomechanism to make the strip move at a rate determined by the magnitude of the detector signal. He was thus able to concentrate the eluate on a few grains of silica adsorbent, and could detect as little as 1 ng of biphenyl or 50 pg of phenanthrene from the color produced with a suitable developer.

Several post-column techniques have been described in which individual separated components are trapped down before chemical reaction is brought about, and such techniques offer certain advantages over the precolumn reaction procedures of Section VI-B-1. In the latter approach, two complete chromatograms are obtained, the second being run after bulk chemical treatment of a second sample. It is then often difficult to decide which peaks have moved to produce new peaks, especially with complex mixtures. Moreover, only one or two peaks in the first chromatogram may be in doubt, and it is then desirable to be able to isolate them rather than to modify them along with several known peaks. For example, the trapped individual eluates from mixtures of unsaturated hydrocarbons have been rechromatographed after hydrogenation (35). The retention time for the hydrogenated compound provided an additional clue to the identity of the unsaturated molecule, and was especially useful for some dienes and alkynes, for which there is a lack of published retention data. The first chromatogram is in effect a purification run, or clean-up procedure. These post-column chemical modifications can thus be thought of as precolumn modifications carried out on pure substances. One of the most frequently employed techniques of this kind is pyrolysis. This, together with other degradative methods proving to be useful in GC identification, is discussed in the next section.

C. Degradative Methods

It should be possible to arrive at definite conclusions about the nature of most small molecules by use of the techniques already described. Large molecules (say molecular weights greater than 150) present difficulties on two counts: (*1*) their chemical composition is more complex, and (*2*) they cannot readily be chromatographed. The obvious technique to employ in order to overcome these difficulties is pyrolysis, whereby smaller and simpler molecules are produced.

1. *Pyrolysis*

The great attraction of pyrolysis as an identification tool is that molecules tend to give characteristic product distributions. The technique is in some ways analogous to mass spectrometry (Sec. V-4) but as with that technique it is often difficult to interpret the cracking patterns. The major criterion for a successful pyrolysis method is that conditions must be very closely controlled so that they can be readily reproduced. There is still some doubt as to the feasibility of having a standard pyrolytic method which can be reproduced in any laboratory, but much progress has been made in improving the basic technique. In particular, it is now standard practice to carry out the pyrolysis in the chromatographic system itself, and microgram quantities of material can therefore be used.

In early work, e.g., ref. 238, the products of pyrolysis of high polymers were frozen down, and the low-boiling material was then chromatographed quite separately. Even with this rather crude technique it was easy to distinguish between, say, methyl and ethyl acrylate polymers by comparison of the resulting chromatograms (Fig. 30). Radell and Strutz (239) came near to combining pyrolysis with GC when they used a pyrolysis loop of metal tubing held in a bath of molten Wood's

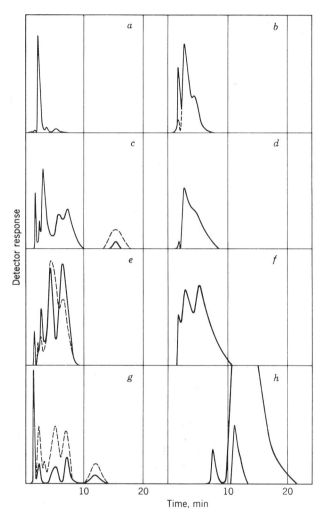

Fig. 30. An early illustration of the usefulness of pyrolysis-GC for polymer identification (238). (*a*) Natural rubber; (*b*) Hycar 4021 (polyacrylate); (*c*) poly(butadiene/styrene); (*d*) poly(ethyl acrylate); (*e*) poly(butadiene/acrylonitrile); (*f*) poly(methyl acrylate); (*g*) polyisobutene; (*h*) poly(vinyl acetate). By courtesy of W. H. T. Davison, S. Slaney, and A. L. Wragg.

metal. The products of pyrolysis were subsequently transferred to the column with a stream of helium. It was Janák (240), however, who first reported the successful pyrolysis of material on a heated platinum wire held in the carrier gas stream. He used heating times of from 0.1 to 5 sec and reported surprisingly good reproducibilities for a variety of test materials. Franc and Blaha (241) used this technique for a number of nonpolymeric aromatic compounds and were able to relate yields of hydrogen, carbon monoxide, methane, and carbon dioxide in a semi-quantitative way to the functional groups present. For example, they found that phenols gave a substantial yield of methane, while nitro compounds gave none. Dhont (242), too, has applied the technique to volatile compounds, and has been able to distinguish normal from iso-alcohols. Nelson and Kirk (243) studied the products of pyrolysis of various substituted barbituric acids and found one persistent peak which they tentatively identified as being due to the long-awaited HNC molecule. Another interesting study of organic pyrolysis products is that of some indole alkaloids by Van Binst and co-workers (244) who preferred to revert to a system in which pyrolysis and GC were carried out separately, so that chromatographic conditions should not affect the product distribution.

Most pyrolytic work continues to be carried out with high poly-mers and it is in this field that most attention has been paid to the im-portant question of reproducibility, without which it is impossible to obtain reliable fingerprint chromatograms (sometimes known as pyrograms). It has become clear (245) that the smaller the sample, the more reproducible is the product distribution. It is also important to carry out pyrolysis quickly; this means reaching temperatures upwards of 500°C in a fraction of a second. Jones and Moyles (246) have de-scribed a neat device for achieving this, in which the sample, in a suitable solvent, is painted as a thin film on the center of the heater filament. Before "firing," the film is dried under an infrared lamp. These workers paid particular attention to destroying *all* the sample (247), but this is a matter for some controversy, since it is often claimed that a clean pyrolysis can be achieved only if a small fraction of the sample is degraded. The reader is referred to references (245) and (248) and to the informal paper on the pyrolysis technique by Keulemans and Cramers (249), including the ensuing discussion. Quite recently, the pyrolysis/GC approach has been used for identification of bacterial macromolecules (250), and when the technical difficulties have been overcome this method will doubtless prove even more rewarding.

It is noteworthy that there is an increasing interest in the mechan-isms by which pyrolysis of polymers occurs. Lehrle and Robb (251) were among the first to use pyrolysis/GC to study the breakdown mechanism of polymers and copolymers. More recently, the effect of monomer distribution on the pyrolysis of acrylate copolymers has been investigated (252), and the products of polybutene pyrolysis have been studied from a semimechanistic viewpoint (253). Such work is still hampered by the lack of theoretical background for pyrolysis mechanisms which might be expected to be able to relate products to structure. It is not until there is greater understanding in this field that any significant progress can be made in the interpretation of polymer fingerprints.

Apart from pyrolysis, oxidative degradation (254) of polymers has also been studied by GC. Recently there has been a report (255) of fragmentation brought about by an on-stream electric discharge. At the moment, however, the most widely applied nonpyrolytic approach for small molecules is that known as carbon skeleton chromatography.

2. Carbon Skeleton Chromatography

This technique depends on the catalytic removal of functional groups, so that only simple hydrocarbons need to be separated and identified (although this in itself is often far from easy). The method first developed a few years ago (256) has since been considerably improved (mainly by the use of new catalysts) by Beroza and Sarmiento (257). A measure of the potential of this technique is given by the fact that the device is now a standard fitting on some commercial chromatographs. It can work at the microgram level, and can eliminate functional groups containing oxygen, nitrogen, sulfur, or the halogens, although the carbon skeleton remaining depends on the nature of the group that has been removed. For example, alcohols and aldehydes are degraded to the alkane with one less carbon atom, while halides and sulfides suffer no such carbon loss.

3. Photolysis

Another development which may prove popular is the use of closely controlled mercury-sensitized photolysis. Juvet and Turner (258), who have recently adopted this approach for liquid alcohols and esters, found that consistent photolysis patterns were obtained within a given homologous series (with the usual exception of the early members) (see Fig. 31). Work is in progress on other substances (259) and it has been reported (260) that almost all organic materials have solubilities for mercury large enough to make the method feasible. As with pyrolysis, it is absolutely essential that all traces of oxygen are absent from the

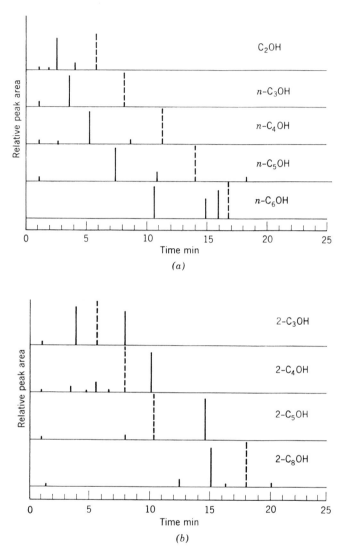

Fig. 31. Programmed temperature chromatographic "spectra" of products of mercury-photosensitized decomposition of (a) primary alcohols, and (b) methyl secondary alcohols. Initial temperature 60°C, rising by 5.7°C/min. Separation achieved on a Carbowax 20M column with flow rate 42.2 ml min⁻¹. Irradiation time: (a) 10 min, (b) 3 min. Parent peaks are dotted (258). By courtesy of *Analytical Chemistry*.

system, but it is claimed that in other respects the method is superior to pyrolysis. In particular, standardization is easily achieved, and the breakdown patterns are simple. Juvet and Turner foresee no difficulty in standardizing the 2537-Å source, which in their experiments accounted for 97% of the total light output. Moreover, the reproducible results are obtained at very low conversions, and this is claimed to avoid the problems associated with a changing matrix that beset early pyrolysis work. Partly because of these low conversions, however, milligram samples had to be used. These are about a hundred times as large as the present limiting size for pyrolysis methods. Moreover, photolysis times were rather long, typically 3–10 min.

Juvet and Turner suggest that a universal table of photolysis chromatography fingerprints could be compiled in the form of programmed temperature retention indices for the various product peaks. It is already clear (261) that a given functional group gives rise to homologous peaks, with a characteristic shift in retention index relative to the parent peak. At the same time common peaks are formed by some functional groups (notably by esters and ethers) and have characteristic absolute values of retention index (261). It would be interesting if other workers were to carry out similar work to check the expected reproducibility between laboratories. If this can be established, the method could well replace more conventional techniques for some materials. In particular, photochemical degradation has some advantages over infrared spectroscopy. It can be used, for example, to identify both acid and alcohol groupings in an ester (259).

References

1. H. Boer, in *Gas Chromatography 1962*, M. van Swaay, Ed., Butterworths, London, 1962, p. 318.
2. R. C. Crippen and C. E. Smith, *J. Gas. Chromatog.*, **3**, 37 (1965).
3. T. Gaumann, *Ann. Rev. Phys. Chem.*, **16**, 125 (1965).
4. G. Schomburg, *Z. Anal. Chem.*, **200**, 360 (1964).
5. H. S. Kroman and S. R. Bender, *J. Chromatog.*, **13**, 242 (1964).
6. A. E. Thompson, *J. Chromatog.*, **6**, 454 (1961).
7. P. Kratz, M. Jacobs, and B. M. Mitzner, *Analyst*, **84**, 671 (1959).
8. D. H. Volman, *J. Chem. Phys.*, **14**, 707 (1946).
9. R. K. Stevens and J. D. Mold, *J. Chromatog.*, **10**, 398 (1963).
10. R. Teranishi, J. W. Corse, J. C. Day, and W. G. Jennings, *J. Chromatog.*, **9**, 244 (1962).
11. B. C. Shurlock, unpublished work.
12. N. W. R. Daniels, *Chem. Ind. (London)*, **1963**, 1078.

13. P. A. T. Swoboda, *Nature*, **199**, 31 (1963).
14. I. Hornstein and P. Crowe, *Anal. Chem.*, **37**, 170 (1965).
15. J. W. Amy, E. M. Chait, W. E. Baitinger, and F. W. McLafferty, *Anal. Chem.*, **37**, 1265 (1965).
16. C. M. Drew and J. H. Johnson, *J. Chromatog.*, **9**, 264 (1962).
17. L. Giuffrida, *J. Assoc. Offic. Agr. Chemists*, **48**, 354 (1965).
18. P. J. Thomas and J. L. Dwyer, *J. Chromatog.*, **13**, 366 (1964).
19. P. D. Klein and S. A. Tyler, *Anal. Chem.*, **37**, 1280 (1965).
20. P. D. Klein, private communication.
21. L. Pypker in *Gas Chromatography 1960*, M. van Swaay, Ed., Butterworths, London, 1960, p. 284.
22. W. Kemp and O. Rogne, *Chem. Ind.* (*London*), **1965**, 418.
23. H. T. Badings and J. G. Wassink, *J. Chromatog.*, **18**, 159 (1965).
24. J. S. Lewis, *Compilation of Gas Chromatographic Data*, ASTM, 1963.
25. H. Purnell, *Gas Chromatography*, Wiley, New York, 1962; (a) p. 207; (b) p. 209; (c) p. 39 ff.
26. T. E. Jordan, *Vapour Pressures of Organic Compounds*, Interscience, New York, 1954.
27. G. J. Pierotti, C. H. Deal, E. L. Derr, and P. E. Porter, *J. Am. Chem. Soc.*, **78**, 2989 (1956).
28. C. S. G. Phillips and P. L. Timms, *Anal. Chem.*, **35**, 505 (1963).
29. J. M. Blakeway and D. B. Thomas, *J. Chromatog.*, **6**, 74 (1961).
30. J. C. Hawke, R. P. Hansen, and F. B. Shorland, *J. Chromatog.*, **2**, 547 (1959).
31. H. Brandenberger and S. Muller, *J. Chromatog.*, **7**, 137 (1962).
32. G. M. Gray, *J. Chromatog.*, **4**, 52 (1960).
33. J. Zulaica and G. Guiochon, *Bull. Soc. Chim. France*, **1963**, 1242.
34. B. Smith, R. Ohlson, and G. Larson, *Acta Chem. Scand.*, **17**, 436 (1963).
35. B. Smith and R. Ohlson, *Acta Chem. Scand.*, **14**, 1317 (1960).
36. M. H. Klouwen and R. Ter Heide, *J. Chromatog.*, **7**, 297 (1962).
37. G. Valkanas and N. Iconomou, *J. Chromatog.*, **12**, 536 (1963).
38. E. Kovats, *Helv. Chim. Acta*, **41**, 1915 (1958).
39. J. F. Smith, *Chem. Ind.* (*London*), **1960**, 1024.
40. M. B. Evans and J. F. Smith, *J. Chromatog.*, **6**, 293 (1961).
41. W. J. A. Vanden Heuvel, W. L. Gardiner, and E. C. Horning, *Anal. Chem.*, **36**, 1550 (1964).
42. W. J. A. Vanden Heuvel and E. C. Horning, *Biochem. Biophys. Acta*, **64**, 416 (1962).
43. H. von Van den Dool and P. D. Kratz, *J. Chromatog.*, **11**, 463 (1963).
44. See *Gas Chromatography 1964*, A. Goldup, Ed., Institute of Petroleum, London, 1965, p. 348.
45. See *J. Gas Chromatog.*, **3**, 298 (1965).
46. K. P. Hupe, *J. Gas Chromatog.*, **3**, 12 (1965).
47. C. Baron and B. Maume, *Bull. Soc. Chim. France*, **1962**, 1113.
48. P. A. T. Swoboda, in *Gas Chromatography 1962*, M. van Swaay, Ed., Butterworths, London, 1962, p. 273.
49. C. Merritt, J. T. Walsh, D. H. Robertson, and A. I. McCarthy, *J. Gas Chromatog.*, **2**, 125 (1964).

50. A. I. McCarthy, H. Wyman, and J. K. Palmer, *J. Gas Chromatog.*, **2**, 121 (1964).
51. P. G. Dodsworth, in *Gas Chromatography 1962*, M. van Swaay, Ed., Butterworths, London, 1962, p. 287.
52. A. Wehrli and E. Kovats, *Helv. Chim. Acta*, **42**, 2709 (1959).
53. E. Kovats, in *Advances in Chromatography*, J. C. Giddings and R. A. Keller, Eds., M. Dekker Inc., N.Y., 1965.
54. S. A. Green and H. Pust, *J. Phys. Chem.*, **62**, 55 (1958).
55. G. M. Petrov and K. D. Shcherbakova, in *Gas Chromatography 1966*, A. B. Littlewood, Ed., Institute of Petroleum, London, 1967, p. 50.
56. R. M. Barrer and L. V. C. Rees, *Trans. Faraday Soc.*, **57**, 999 (1961).
57. M. C. Simons, D. B. Richardson, and I. Dvoretzky, in *Gas Chromatography 1960*, R. P. W. Scott, Ed., Butterworths, London, 1960, p. 211.
58. M. R. Hoare and J. H. Purnell, *Trans. Faraday Soc.*, **52**, 222 (1956).
59. B. D. Blaustein, C. Zahn, and G. Pantages, *J. Chromatog.*, **12**, 104 (1963).
60. J. Bricteux and G. Duyckaerts, *J. Chromatog.*, **22**, 221 (1966).
61. (a) S. C. Bevan and S. Thorburn, *J. Chromatog.*, **11**, 301 (1963); (b) S. C. Bevan and S. Thorburn, *Chem. Brit.*, **1**, 206 (1965).
62. E. V. Piel, *Anal. Chem.*, **36**, 696 (1964).
63. J. Janák, in *Vapour Phase Chromatography*, D. H. Desty, Ed., Butterworths, London, 1957, p. 247.
64. T. R. Phillips, E. G. Johnson, and H. Woodward, *Anal. Chem.*, **36**, 450 (1964).
65. G. E. Hillman and J. Lightwood, *Anal. Chem.*, **38**, 1430 (1966).
66. P. A. Hersch, in *Advances in Analytical Chemistry and Instrumentation*, Vol. 3, C. N. Reilley, Ed., Interscience, New York, 1964.
67. A. J. P. Martin and A. T. James, *Biochem. J.*, **63**, 138 (1956).
68. A. G. Nerheim, *Anal. Chem.*, **35**, 1640 (1963).
69. C. S. G. Phillips and P. L. Timms, *J. Chromatog.*, **5**, 131 (1961).
70. A. Liberti, L. Conti, and V. Crescenzi, *Nature*, **178**, 1067 (1956).
71. J. S. Parsons, *Anal. Chem.*, **36**, 1849 (1964).
72. E. A. Johnson, D. G. Childs, and G. H. Beavan, *J. Chromatog.*, **4**, 429 (1960).
73. D. H. Rosie and R. L. Grob, *Anal. Chem.*, **29**, 1263 (1957).
74. R. L. Grob, D. Mercer, T. Gribben, and J. Wells, *J. Chromatog.*, **3**, 545 (1960).
75. R. Mecke and K. Zirker, *J. Chromatog.*, **7**, 1 (1962).
76. Discussion in *Gas Chromatography 1964*, A. Goldup, Ed., Institute of Petroleum, London, 1965, p. 332.
77. B. D. Smith and W. W. Bowden, *Anal. Chem.*, **36**, 82 (1964).
78. A. L. Lindsay and L. A. Bromley, *Ind. Eng. Chem.*, **42**, 1508 (1950).
79. R. C. Reid and T. K. Sherwood, *Properties of Gases and Liquids*, McGraw-Hill, New York, 1958.
80. E. Hardy, *Compt. Rend.*, **121**, 1116 (1895).
81. C. F. Robinson, U.S. Pat. 2,952,153 (1960).
82. M. K. Testerman and P. C. McLeod, in *Gas Chromatography*, N. Brenner, J. E. Callen, and D. Weiss, Eds., Academic Press, New York, 1962, p. 183.
83. L. E. Lawley, *Chem. Ind. (London)*, **1954**, 200.
84. F. W. Noble, K. Abel, and P. W. Cook, *Anal. Chem.*, **36**, 1421 (1964).

85. (a) D. W. Turner, *Nature*, **181**, 1265 (1958); (b) J. H. Griffiths, D. James, and C. Phillips, *Analyst.*, **77**, 897 (1952).
86. J. D. Winefordner and D. Steinbrecher, *Anal. Chem.*, **33**, 515 (1961).
87. J. D. Winefordner, H. P. Williams, and C. D. Miller, *Anal. Chem.*, **37**, 161 (1965).
88. P. F. Deisler, K. W. McHenry, and R. H. Wilhelm, *Anal. Chem.*, **27**, 1366 (1955).
89. D. J. Pompeo and J. W. Otvos, U.S. Pat. 2,641,710 (1953).
90. C. H. Deal, J. W. Otvos, V. N. Smith, and P. S. Zucco, *Anal. Chem.*, **28**, 1958 (1956).
91. J. E. Lovelock, G. R. Shoemake, and A. Zlatkis, *Anal. Chem.*, **35**, 460 (1963).
92. J. E. Lovelake, G. E. Shoemake, and A. Zlatkis, *Anal. Chem.*, **36**, 1410 (1964).
93. K. Abel, *Anal. Chem.*, **36**, 954 (1964).
94. J. W. Otvos and D. P. Stevenson, *J. Am. Chem. Soc.*, **78**, 546 (1956).
95. H. Boer, in *Vapour Phase Chromatography*, D. H. Desty, Ed., Butterworths, London, 1957, p. 169.
96. J. E. Lovelock, *Nature*, **188**, 401 (1960).
97. J. E. Lovelock and A. Zlatkis, *Anal. Chem.*, **33**, 1958 (1961).
98. D. C. Locke and C. E. Meloan, *Anal. Chem.*, **37**, 389 (1965).
99. J. F. Roesler, *Anal. Chem.*, **36**, 1900 (1964).
100. H. Purnell, *Gas Chromatography*, Wiley, New York, 1962, pp. 302–304.
101. E. M. Bulewicz, *Nature*, **211**, 961 (1966).
102. A. Karmen and L. Giuffrida, *Nature*, **201**, 1204 (1964).
103. P. J. Padley, F. M. Page, and T. M. Sugden, *Trans. Faraday Soc.*, **57**, 1552 (1961).
104. A. Karmen, *Anal. Chem.*, **36**, 1416 (1964).
105. J. Janák and V. Svojanovsky, in *Gas Chromatography 1966*, A. B. Littlewood, Ed., Institute of Petroleum, London, 1967, p. 166.
106. J. E. Lovelock, *J. Chromatog.*, **1**, 35 (1958).
107. J. E. Lovelock and S. R. Lipsky, *J. Am. Chem. Soc.*, **82**, 431 (1960).
108. J. E. Lovelock, *Anal. Chem.*, **33**, 162 (1961).
109. R. A. Landowne and S. R. Lipsky, *Anal. Chem.*, **34**, 726 (1962).
110. J. E. Lovelock, *Nature*, **189**, 729 (1961).
111. J. A. Stockdale, G. S. Hurst, and L. G. Christophorou, *Nature*, **202**, 459 (1964).
112. J. E. Lovelock, *Anal. Chem.*, **35**, 474 (1963).
113. J. E. Barney, C. W. Stanley, and C. E. Cook, *Anal. Chem.*, **35**, 2206 (1963).
114. E. S. Goodwin, R. Goulden, A. Richardson, and J. G. Reynolds, *Chem. Ind. (London)*, **1960**, 1220.
115. C. E. Cook, C. W. Stanley, and J. E. Barney, *Anal. Chem.*, **36**, 2354 (1964).
116. M. J. de F. Maunder, H. Egen, and J. Roburn, *Analyst*, **89**, 157 (1964).
117. H. Egan, E. W. Hammond, and J. Thomson, *Analyst*, **89**, 175 (1964).
118. H. J. Dawson, *Anal. Chem.*, **35**, 542 (1963).
119. R. A. Landowne, and S. R. Lipsky, *Anal. Chem.*, **35**, 532 (1963).
120. A. L. Henne, M. S. Newman, L. L. Quill, and R. A. Staniforth, *J. Am. Chem. Soc.*, **69**, 1819 (1947).
121. R. E. Sievers, B. W. Ponder, M. L. Morris, and R. W. Moshier, *Inorg. Chem.* **2**, 693 (1963).

122. R. W. Moshier and R. E. Sievers, *Gas Chromatography of Metal Chelates*, Pergamon Press, Oxford, 1965.
123. W. D. Ross, *Anal. Chem.*, **35**, 1596 (1963).
124. W. D. Ross and G. Wheeler, *Anal. Chem.*, **36**, 266 (1964).
125. W. H. King, *Anal. Chem.*, **36**, 1735 (1964).
126. B. J. Gudzinowicz and W. R. Smith, *Anal. Chem.*, **35**, 465 (1963).
127. D. W. Grant, in *Gas Chromatography 1958*, D. H. Desty, Ed., Butterworths, London, 1958.
128. R. S. Braman, *Anal. Chem.*, **38**, 734 (1966).
129. R. S. Juvet and R. P. Durbin, *Anal. Chem.*, **38**, 565 (1966).
130. H. J. Dawson, *Anal. Chem.*, **36**, 1852 (1964).
131. D. M. Oaks, H. Hartmann, and K. P. Dimick, *Anal. Chem.*, **36**, 1560 (1964).
132. C. A. Clemons and A. P. Altshuller, *Anal. Chem.*, **38**, 133 (1966).
133. C. L. Teitelbaum, *Anal. Chem.*, **37**, 309 (1965).
134. R. P. W. Scott, I. A. Fowlis, D. Welti, and T. Wilkins, in *Gas Chromatography 1966*, A. B. Littlewood, Ed., Institute of Petroleum, London, 1967, p. 318.
135. R. G. Buttery, D. R. Black, and M. P. Kealy, *J. Chromatog.*, **18**, 399 (1965).
136. A. E. Banner, R. M. Elliott, and W. Kelly, in *Gas Chromatography 1964*, A. Goldup, Ed., Institute of Petroleum, London, 1965, p. 180.
137. P. F. Varadi and K. Ettre, *Anal. Chem.*, **34**, 1417 (1962).
138. P. F. Varadi and K. Ettre, *Anal. Chem.*, **35**, 410 (1963).
139. R. Ryhage, *Anal. Chem.*, **36**, 759 (1964).
140. E. J. Levy, E. D. Miller, and W. S. Beggs, *Anal. Chem.*, **35**, 946 (1963).
141. R. Teranishi, R. G. Buttery, W. H. McFadden, T. R. Mon, and J. Wasserman, *Anal. Chem.*, **36**, 1509 (1964).
142. W. H. McFadden and E. A. Day, *Anal. Chem.*, **36**, 2362 (1964).
143. R. Ryhage and E. von Sydow, *Acta Chem. Scand.*, **17**, 2025 (1963).
144. R. Ryhage, S. Wilkstrom, and G. R. Waller, *Anal. Chem.*, **37**, 435 (1965).
145. J. T. Watson and K. Biemann, *Anal. Chem.*, **37**, 844 (1965).
146. J. T. Watson and K. Biemann, *Anal. Chem.*, **36**, 1136 (1964).
147. D. Henneberg, *Anal. Chem.*, **38**, 495 (1966).
148. C. C. Sweeley, W. H. Elliott, I. Fries, and R. Ryhage, *Anal. Chem.*, **38**, 1549 (1966).
149. J. A. Dorsey, R. H. Hunt, and M. J. O'Neal, *Anal. Chem.*, **35**, 511 (1963).
150. L. P. Lindeman and J. L. Annis, *Anal. Chem.*, **32**, 1742 (1960).
151. R. A. Hively, *Anal. Chem.*, **35**, 1921 (1963).
152. A. M. Bartz and H. D. Ruhl, *Anal. Chem.*, **36**, 1892 (1964).
153. P. A. Wilks and R. A. Brown, *Anal. Chem.*, **36**, 1896 (1964).
154. I. Schmeltz, R. L. Stedman, C. D. Stills, and W. J. Chamberlain, *Anal. Chem.*, **37**, 1614 (1965).
155. M. J. D. Low, *Chem. Comm.*, 1966, p. 371.
156. M. St. C. Flett and J. Hughes, *J. Chromatog.*, **11**, 434 (1963).
157. W. Kaye and F. Waska, *Anal. Chem.*, **36**, 2380 (1964).
158. W. I. Kaye, *Anal. Chem.*, **34**, 287 (1962).
159. E. G. Brame, *Anal. Chem.*, **37**, 1183 (1965).
160. R. E. Lundin, R. H. Elsken, R. A. Flath, N. Henderson, T. R. Mon, and R. Teranishi, *Anal. Chem.*, **38**, 291 (1966).
161. F. A. Gunther, R. C. Blinn, and D. E. Ott, *Anal. Chem.*, **34**, 302 (1962).

162. S. S. Brody and J. E. Chaney, *J. Gas Chromatog.*, **4**, 42 (1966).
163. F. M. Zado and R. S. Juvet, *Anal. Chem.*, **38**, 569 (1966).
164. D. W. Grant and G. A. Vaughan, in *Vapour Phase Chromatography*, D. H. Desty, Ed., Butterworths, London, 1957, p. 420.
165. A. J. McCormack, S. C. Tong, and W. D. Cooke, *Anal. Chem.*, **37**, 1470 (1965).
166. C. A. Bache and D. J. Lisk, *Anal. Chem.*, **37**, 1477 (1965).
167. C. A. Bache and D. J. Lisk, *Anal. Chem.*, **38**, 783 (1966).
168. C. A. Bache and D. J. Lisk, *Anal. Chem.*, **38**, 1757 (1966).
169. N. Brenner and V. J. Coates, *Nature*, **181**, 1401 (1958).
170. R. L. Martin, *Anal. Chem.*, **32**, 336 (1960).
171. R. Bassette and C. H. Whitnah, *Anal. Chem.*, **32**, 1098 (1960).
172. I. H. Williams, *Anal. Chem.*, **37**, 1723 (1965).
173. P. S. Farrington, R. L. Pecsok, R. L. Meeker, and T. J. Olson, *Anal. Chem.*, **31**, 1512 (1959).
174. R. L. Martin, *Anal. Chem.*, **34**, 896 (1962).
175. M. A. Muhs and F. T. Weiss, *J. Am. Chem. Soc.*, **84**, 4697 (1962).
176. S. H. Langer, C. Zahn, and G. Pantazoplos, *J. Chromatog.*, **3**, 154 (1960).
177. Papers in *Gas Chromatography 1964*, A. Goldup, Ed., Institute of Petroleum, London, 1965, pp. 219–300.
178. S. D. Nogare, *Anal. Chem.*, **37**, 1450 (1965).
179. R. M. Barrer, *Quart. Rev. (London)*, **3**, 293 (1949).
180. D. W. Breck, *J. Chem. Ed.*, **41**, 678 (1964).
181. R. Rowan, *Anal. Chem.*, **33**, 658 (1961).
182. P. A. Schenck and E. Eisma, *Nature*, **199**, 170 (1963).
183. D. K. Albert, *Anal. Chem.*, **35**, 1918 (1963).
184. N. Brenner, E. Cieplinski, L. S. Ettre, and V. J. Coates, *J. Chromatog.*, **3**, 230 (1960).
185. W. P. Ballard, S. P. Dickens, and B. F. Smith, U.S. Pat. 2,818,455 (1957); quoted in ref. 186.
186. F. T. Eggertsen and S. Groennings, *Anal. Chem.*, **33**, 1147 (1961).
187. J. V. Brunnock, *Anal. Chem.*, **38**, 1648 (1966).
188. (a) J. E. Hoff and E. D. Feit, *Anal. Chem.*, **35**, 1298 (1963); (b) J. E. Hoff and E. D. Feit, *Anal. Chem.*, **36**, 1002 (1964).
189. W. B. Innes, W. E. Bambrick, and A. J. Andreatch, *Anal. Chem.*, **35**, 1198 (1963).
190. R. M. Ikeda, D. E. Simmons, and J. D. Grossman, *Anal. Chem.*, **36**, 2188 (1964).
191. R. R. Allen, *Anal. Chem.*, **38**, 1287 (1966).
192. W. E. Harris and W. H. McFadden, *Anal. Chem.*, **31**, 114 (1959).
193. J. Janák and J. Novak, *Chem. Listy.*, **51**, 1832 (1957).
194. E. Gil-Av and Y. Herzberg-Minzly, *J. Chromatog.*, **13**, 1 (1964).
195. R. Suffis and D. E. Dean, *Anal. Chem.*, **34**, 480 (1962).
196. M. Beroza and M. C. Bowman, *Anal. Chem.*, **37**, 291 (1965).
197. M. C. Bowman and M. Beroza, *Anal. Chem.*, **38**, 1544 (1966).
198. C. G. Scott and C. S. G. Phillips, *Nature*, **199**, 66 (1963).
199. I. R. Hunter, K. P. Dimick, and J. W. Corse, *Chem. Ind. (London)*, **1956**, 294.
200. A. Zlatkis and J. F. Oró, *Anal. Chem.*, **30** 1156 (1958).

201. A. Zlatkis, J. F. Oró, and A. P. Kimball, *Anal. Chem.*, **32**, 162 (1960).
202. A. G. McInnes, D. H. Ball, F. P. Cooper, and C. T. Bishop, *J. Chromatog.*, **1**, 556 (1958).
203. F. Drawert, R. Felgenhauer, and G. Kupfer, *Angew. Chem.*, **72**, 555 (1960).
204. F. Drawert and K. H. Reuther, *Chem. Ber.*, **93**, 3066 (1960).
205. F. Drawert, in *Gas Chromatography 1962*, M. van Swaay, Ed., Butterworths, London, 1962, p. 353.
206. S. H. Langer and P. Pantages, *Nature*, **191**, 141 (1961).
207. S. H. Langer, P. Pantages, and I. Wender, *Chem. Ind. (London)*, **1958**, 1664.
208. C. J. Thompson, H. J. Coleman, C. C. Ward, and H. T. Rall, *Anal. Chem.*, **32**, 424 (1960).
209. C. J. Thompson, H. T. Coleman, R. L. Hopkins, C. C. Ward, and H. T. Rall, *Anal. Chem.*, **32**, 1762 (1960).
210. C. J. Thompson, H. T. Coleman, C. C. Ward, and H. T. Rall, *Anal. Chem.*, **34**, 151 (1962).
211. C. J. Thompson, H. T. Coleman, C. C. Ward, and H. T. Rall, *Anal. Chem.*, **34**, 154 (1962).
212. K. H. Nelson, W. J. Hines, M. D. Grimes, and D. E. Smith, *Anal. Chem.*, **32**, 1110 (1960).
213. J. Franc and V. Kolouskova, *J. Chromatog.*, **17**, 221 (1965).
214. H. M. Fales and T. Luukkainen, *Anal. Chem.*, **37**, 955 (1965).
215. S. J. Jankowski and P. Garner, *Anal. Chem.*, **37**, 1709 (1965).
216. M. W. Anders and G. J. Mannering, *Anal. Chem.*, **34**, 730 (1962).
217. S. J. Mulé, *Anal. Chem.*, **36**, 1907 (1964).
218. R. Aubeau, L. Champeix, and J. Reiss, *J. Chromatog.*, **16**, 7 (1964).
219. J. Kallen and E. Heilbronner, *Helv. Chim. Acta*, **43**, 489 (1960).
220. A. Klinkenberg, *Chem. Eng. Sci.*, **15**, 255 (1961).
221. L. Blom and L. Edelhausen, *Anal. Chim. Acta*, **13**, 120 (1955).
222. L. Blom and L. Edelhausen, *Anal. Chim. Acta*, **15**, 559 (1956).
223. A. Liberti and G. P. Cartoni, in *Gas Chromatography 1958*, D. H. Desty, Ed., Butterworths, London, 1958, p. 321.
224. A. E. Martin and J. Smart, *Nature*, **175**, 422 (1955).
225. G. E. Green, *Nature*, **180**, 295 (1957).
226. A. Zlatkis and J. A. Ridgway, *Nature*, **182**, 130 (1958).
227. P. J. Klaas, *Anal. Chem.*, **33**, 1851 (1961).
228. R. L. Martin and J. A. Grant, *Anal. Chem.*, **37**, 644 (1965).
229. R. L. Martin, *Anal. Chem.*, **38**, 1209 (1966).
230. D. M. Coulson, *J. Agric. Food Chemists*, **8**, 399 (1960); through *Chem. Abstr.* **55**, 17997f (1961).
231. E. M. Fredericks and G. A. Harlow, *Anal. Chem.*, **36**, 263 (1964).
232. G. Burton, A. B. Littlewood, and W. A. Wiseman, in *Gas Chromatography 1966*, A. B. Littlewood, Ed., Institute of Petroleum, London, 1967, p. 193.
233. J. T. Walsh and C. M. Merritt, *Anal. Chem.*, **32**, 1378 (1960).
234. B. Casu and L. Cavallotti, *Anal. Chem.*, **34**, 1514 (1962).
235. J. Janák, *J. Chromatog.*, **15**, 5 (1964).
236. R. Kaiser, *Z. Anal. Chem.*, **205**, 284 (1964).
237. J. Janák, in *Gas Chromatography 1964*, A. Goldup, Ed., Institute of Petroleum, London, 1965, p. 333.

92   D. A. LEATHARD AND B. C. SHURLOCK

238. W. H. T. Davison, S. Slaney, and A. L. Wragg, *Chem. Ind.* (*London*), **1954**, 1356.
239. E. A. Radell and H. C. Strutz, *Anal. Chem.*, **31**, 1890 (1959).
240. J. Janák, *Nature*, **185**, 684 (1960).
241. J. Franc and J. Blaha, *J. Chromatog.*, **6**, 396 (1961).
242. J. H. Dhont, *Nature*, **192**, 747 (1961).
243. D. F. Nelson and P. L. Kirk, *Anal. Chem.*, **36**, 875 (1964).
244. G. Van Binst, L. Denolin-Dewaerseggler, and R. H. Martin, *J. Chromatog.*, **16**, 34 (1964).
245. A. I. M. Keulemans and S. G. Perry, in *Gas Chromatography 1962*, M. van Swaay, Ed., Butterworths, London, 1962, p. 356.
246. C. E. R. Jones and A. F. Moyles, *Nature*, **191**, 663 (1961).
247. C. E. R. Jones and A. F. Moyles, *Nature*, **189**, 222 (1961).
248. S. G. Perry, *J. Gas Chromatog.*, **2**, 54 (1964).
249. A. I. M. Keulemans and C. A. M. G. Cramers, in *Gas Chromatography 1964*, A. Goldup, Ed., Institute of Petroleum, London, 1965, p. 154.
250. E. Reiner, *Nature*, **206**, 1273 (1965).
251. R. S. Lehrle and J. C. Robb, *Nature*, **183**, 1671 (1959).
252. K. J. Bombaugh, C. E. Cook, and B. H. Clampitt, *Anal. Chem.*, **35**, 1834 (1963).
253. E. M. Barrall, R. S. Porter, and J. F. Johnson, *J. Chromatog.*, **11**, 177 (1963).
254. R. G. Scholz, J. Bednarczyk, and T. Yamauchi, *Anal. Chem.*, **38**, 331 (1966).
255. J. C. Sternberg, I. H. Krull, and G. D. Friedel, *Anal. Chem.*, **38**, 1639 (1966).
256. M. Beroza, *Anal. Chem.*, **34**, 1801 (1962).
257. (a) M. Beroza and R. Sarmiento, *Anal. Chem.*, **37**, 1040 (1965); (b) M. Beroza and R. Sarmiento, *Anal. Chem.*, **36**, 1744 (1964).
258. R. S. Juvet and L. P. Turner, *Anal. Chem.*, **37**, 1464 (1965).
259. R. S. Juvet, private communication.
260. R. R. Kuntz and G. J. Mains, *J. Phys. Chem.*, **68**, 408 (1964).
261. R. S. Juvet, R. L. Tanner, and J. C. Y. Tsao, *J. Gas Chromatog.*, **5**, 15 (1967).
262. B. C. Shurlock and J. H. Purnell, *Talanta*, **14**, 1191 (1967).

Liquid Surface Effects in Gas–Liquid
Chromatography (GLC)*

DANIEL E. MARTIRE, *Department of Chemistry,*
Georgetown University, Washington D.C.

I. INTRODUCTION

For a long time now, GLC workers have been aware of the ability
of chromatographic support materials to adsorb certain solute species.
Solid support adsorption has hindered the assignment of meaningful
retention times and the identification of solute peaks, particularly when
columns of low liquid loading are used.

In 1961 the suggestion was made that solute adsorption at the gas–
liquid interface, i.e., on the liquid surface, might also play an important
role in determining solute retention behavior. This hypothesis has since

*Supported in part by the American Chemical Society Petroleum Research
Fund, and by the National Science Foundation, Grant GP 5320.

been substantiated by direct evidence from independent, static thermo-dynamic measurements. Accordingly, the GLC partitioning process for low-loaded columns, which has always been a source of puzzlement, is more complex than previously imagined.

This chapter reviews the historical development of the liquid-surface adsorption phenomenon in GLC and examines its many important implications.

II. GAS–LIQUID CHROMATOGRAPHIC EVIDENCE FOR SOLUTE ADSORPTION AT THE GAS–LIQUID INTERFACE

In 1961 Martin (1) reported the unusual finding that the elution order of nonpolar hydrocarbon solutes from GLC columns containing polar liquid phases changed with the weight ratio of liquid phase to solid support. He attributed the likely cause of these changes to adsorption of solute molecules at the gas–liquid interface, and suggested that this previously overlooked factor was an important contributor to the retention volume.

The retention behavior was studied for three liquid phases of different polarity: n-hexadecane, 1-chloronaphthalene, and β,β' thiodipropionitrile (TDPN); these were chosen as a representative cross-section of liquids normally used in GLC. For the nonpolar n-hexadecane the observed changes in elution order with varying liquid-phase percentage were quite small and were attributed to adsorption on the solid support. However, very large changes were observed with the highly polar TDPN, and changes of intermediate magnitude with the moderately polar 1-chloronaphthalene.

The following considerations led Martin to conclude that the change in elution order with the polar liquid phases was not explainable by adsorption of solute on the solid support:

1. The retention volumes were not affected when the support was made less adsorptive by treatment with dimethyldichlorosilane.

2. The extrapolated values of the measured retention volumes, obtained by extending the line for a given solute to 0% liquid phase, differed widely from one liquid phase to another.

3. These extrapolated retention volumes were not equal to the values observed with measurements on bare support alone.

Martin points out that adsorption of nonpolar molecules on polar liquid surfaces is not an uncommon phenomenon and that it leads to a surface excess concentration of solute. In bulk solutions one is usually justified in ignoring the contribution of the surface layer to the thermodynamic properties of the system. However, when a liquid is spread upon a support material of high surface area, the surface-to-volume ratio becomes large, and any difference between the bulk liquid and surface concentrations of the solute could be significant. (A typical liquid coating, 20% by weight, on 40–60 mesh Chromosorb P has a surface-to-volume ratio approximately 10^5 times larger than a bulk sample of 1 cc and 1 cm².)

Therefore, based on the assumption that solute retention depends upon adsorption on the liquid surface, as well as upon solution in the bulk liquid, Martin proposed a new chromatographic retention volume equation:

$$V_{Rg}^0 = K_s V_L + K_a A_L \qquad (1)$$

where V_{Rg}^0 equals the corrected net retention volume per gram of packing*; K_s is the bulk partition coefficient equal to the concentration of the solute in the liquid phase/concentration of the solute in the gas phase; K_a is the surface partition coefficient equal to the concentration the solute on the surface in excess of that in the bulk/concentration of the solute in the gas phase; V_L is the volume of liquid phase per gram of packing; and A_L is the available surface area of liquid per gram of packing. Note that K_s and K_a, as used here, will refer strictly to infinite dilution values unless otherwise stated.

To test this novel equation, Martin measured retention times on various columns containing from 1.5 to 24.9% by weight liquid phase, and computed V_{Rg}^0 values. For each liquid phase, columns with Chromosorb P and Chromosorb W, both 35–48 mesh, were prepared and

* The specific retention volume, V_g^0 (in cubic centimeters per gram of liquid phase), is defined by

$$V_g^0 \equiv 273.2 V_R^0 / (W_L T)$$

where V_R^0 is the corrected net retention volume in cc, W_L is the weight of the liquid phase, and T is the column temperature.

According to Martin (1),

$$V_{Rg}^0 \equiv V_R^0 / \text{g packing} = V_R^0 / W_L(\%)$$

where (%) represents the weight per cent of liquid phase in the packing. Therefore,

$$V_{Rg}^0 = V_g^0 \ (\%) \ T/(273.2)$$

studied. Surface areas of the column packings were determined by a
continuous flow method (2). The liquid surface areas of the P packing
were 5–3 times those of the W (range of 3.9–0.9 m^2/g for the P, and
0.8–0.3 m^2/g for the W), with the areas for both decreasing with increasing liquid load in the range of 0–25%.

By rearranging eq. (1),

$$V^0_{Rg}/A_L = [K_s(V_L/A_L)] + K_a \tag{2}$$

and then making plots of V^0_{Rg}/A_L against V_L/A_L, Martin attempted
to test the reasonableness of his hypothesis. All of these plots, based
on the results for thirteen solutes in the two polar liquids, yielded
straight lines and values for K_s (from the slopes) and K_a (from the
intercepts).

In Table I computed values are listed for the relative contributions
of solution and adsorption at 25°C to the retention volumes of 2,2,4-
trimethylpentane (TMP) in TDPN ($K_s = 12.8$, $K_a = 2.97 \times 10^{-4}$ cm)
and in 1-chloronaphthalene ($K_s = 516$, $K_a = 7.16 \times 10^{-4}$ cm). It was
now evident that if liquid surface adsorption did exist, its relative
magnitude could be very significant in many cases.

Hence, eq. (1) accounted for the changes in elution order with polar
liquid phases, because the solution contribution (K_sV_L) increases
linearly with the liquid percentage, while the adsorption contribution
(K_aA_L) decreases (due to the decrease of A_L with increasing loading).
Therefore, in theory at least, different elution orders should be
obtainable by varying the relative contributions of solution and adsorption.

Martin further explained that, for high A_L/V_L, the polarity of the
liquid phase should largely determine whether solute will adsorb preferentially on the liquid surface or on the solid support. According to
his analysis, adsorption on the liquid should be more important with
polar phases, especially for nonpolar solutes, while adsorption on the
solid should be more important with nonpolar phases, especially for
polar solutes.

In view of the important and controversial nature of these findings,
Pecsok et al. (3) extended and amplified the types of measurements made
by Martin to cover a wider range of solutes and even lower loaded
columns (0.30–14.90%). Twenty-two representative solutes, including
oxygenated compounds of diverse polarities, were studied on n-hexa-
decane and TDPN. Both Chromosorb P (42–60 mesh, A_L: 3.9–2.0 m^2/g)
and Chromosorb W (60–80 mesh, A_L: 1.4–0.7 m^2/g) were employed. The

TABLE I

Contributions of Solution and Adsorption to the Retention Volume of 2,2,4-Trimethylpentane[a,b]

Per cent of liquid phase on Chromosorb P	V_L, cc	$A_L \times 10^{-4}$, cm²	Solution, $K_s V_L$	Adsorption $K_a A_L$	Total V_{Rg}^0	Percentage of adsorption
		β,β' Thiodipropionitrile, TDPN				
1.5	0.0135	2.71	0.17	8.05	8.22	97.9
3.0	0.0268	2.50	0.34	7.43	7.77	95.6
5.0	0.0450	2.29	0.58	6.80	7.38	92.1
8.0	0.0721	2.03	0.92	6.03	6.95	86.8
12.0	0.1085	1.69	1.39	5.02	6.41	78.3
16.0	0.145	1.42	1.86	4.22	6.08	69.4
20.0	0.181	1.17	2.32	3.48	5.80	60.0
25.0	0.226	0.89	2.89	2.64	5.53	47.7
		1-Chloronaphthalene				
2.0	0.0167	2.75	8.6	19.7	28.3	69.6
4.0	0.0330	2.44	17.0	17.5	34.5	50.7
7.0	0.0587	2.08	30.3	14.9	45.2	33.0
10.0	0.0840	1.85	43.3	13.2	56.5	23.4
17.0	0.143	1.57	73.8	11.2	85.0	13.2
25.0	0.210	1.38	108.3	9.9	118.2	8.4

a Calculations based on Table 1 of ref. 1.
b All data per gram of packing.

surface areas were determined by pressure–volume measurements in a static system, because the continuous flow method was deemed to be unsatisfactory. For the same support it was found that, within experimental error, both n-hexadecane and TDPN had the same values for surface area.

Comparing their results with Martin's, they found that (*1*) they generally agreed on all values of K_s, usually within $\pm 10\%$ of each other, and (*2*) their K_a values were about 75% of his values, indicating a smaller effect due to liquid surface adsorption.

Pecsok suggested that the differences in the two sets of values were probably due to differing purities of the TDPN. However, as we shall see later, the differences could also be explained, in part, by the use of differing sample sizes or by the use of erroneous surface areas.

The highlights of Pecsok's (3) work, with respect to its bearing on Martin's hypothesis, were:

1. The nonpolar solutes exhibited no liquid surface or solid surface adsorption effects on n-hexadecane.

2. The polar solutes gave skewed peaks and nonreproducible retention times on low-loaded n-hexadecane columns. (This was presumed to be due to solid support effects.)

3. Liquid surface effects were not completely negligible for the polar oxy compounds on TDPN.

4. The nonpolar solutes on TDPN behaved in the same manner as observed by Martin, i.e., adsorption on the liquid surface was the main factor contributing to their retention at low loadings.

5. The values determined for K_a were independent of the solid support material employed. (In view of this, an explanation based solely on solid support adsorption seemed unreasonable since Chromosorb P and Chromosorb W have widely differing solid surface activities.)

6. Treated (hexamethyldisilazane) and untreated columns of 9.3% TDPN on Chromosorb P produced the same retention volumes and similar peak shapes for all solutes, thus verifying the absence of solid support effects.

Despite this wealth of experimental information, the liquid–surface adsorption hypothesis did not meet with immediate acceptance by workers in gas chromatography. This lack of acceptance was partially justified because the evidence offered to substantiate the hypothesis was not entirely conclusive.

III. CONFIRMATION OF THE EXISTENCE OF SOLUTE ADSORPTION AT THE GAS–LIQUID INTERFACE BY INDEPENDENT STATIC MEASUREMENTS

To corroborate the measurements made by gas chromatography, Martin (4) made static measurements of solution surface tensions for a number of nonpolar solute, polar solvent (liquid phase) systems. The Gibbs adsorption equation, which describes solute concentrations at the gas–liquid interface, provided the corroborating means. If ideal bulk solution behavior is assumed, the equation takes the form (5),

$$\Gamma_2^{(1)} = \frac{-x_2}{RT} \left(\frac{\partial \gamma}{\partial x_2} \right)^{\infty} \tag{3}$$

where $\Gamma_2^{(1)}$ is the excess concentration of the solute on the surface (moles/cm^2) over that in a system in which the liquid retains the bulk composition up to a sharp interface; x_2 is the mole fraction of solute in the bulk liquid; R is the gas constant; T is the temperature; and $(\partial \gamma / \partial x_2)^{\infty}$ is the limiting value (infinite dilution) for the change of solution surface tension with solute mole fraction.

It was a simple matter to show that the Gibbs equation was related to the partition coefficients, K_s and K_a, by the following expression (4)

$$\Gamma_2^{(1)} = (K_a/K_s)x_2 n_L \tag{4}$$

where n_L = moles of liquid phase per unit volume = ζ_L/M_L, where ζ_L is the density of the liquid phase and M_L is its formula weight.

Combining eqs. (3) and (4), he obtained

$$\left(\frac{\partial \gamma}{\partial x_2} \right)^{\infty} = -\frac{K_a}{K_s} RTn_L \tag{5}$$

To evaluate $(\partial \gamma / \partial x_2)^{\infty}$, the pure solvent surface tension and the solution surface tensions at a single solute mole fraction, $x_2 = 0.01$, were measured with a du Nouy tensiometer (6) for 13 hydrocarbon solutes in 1-chloronaphthalene. Then, by arbitrarily taking the observed value of the surface tension lowering as the true limiting value, $(\partial \gamma / \partial x_2)^{\infty}$, he obtained reasonably good agreement with the value computed from the GLC results through eq. (5).

However, because of the assumptions employed, the large error in the surface tension determinations (probably due to solute volatility), the possible error in the GLC results, and the failure to determine K_s

independently by a static method, the offered evidence was still not entirely conclusive, but, nevertheless, was convincing enough to spur further investigation.

Accordingly, to avoid the ambiguities inherent in the chromatographic approach, Martire, Pecsok, and Purnell (7,8) decided to examine both surface and bulk liquid behavior in a static apparatus, where all the parameters could be controlled, and where the area-to-volume ratio was that of the bulk liquid. A completely closed system containing a McBain balance (9) and a du Nouy tensiometer (6) enclosed in a single well-thermostatted chamber was constructed for the measurement of solute activity coefficients and solution surface tensions. With this apparatus, solutions of concentrations as low as 0.005 mole fraction of solute could be studied with reasonable accuracy. The systems chosen for investigation were: (*a*) benzene-TDPN, and (*b*) cyclohexane-TDPN. This choice was made, first, because chromatographic information was available, and, secondly, because the activity coefficients differed by about an order of magnitude.

The measured solute activity coefficients (f_2) displayed the following dependence at 30.00°C on mole fraction (8); benzene: $\log f_2 = 0.5289 - 0.498x_2$; cyclohexane: $\log f_2 = 1.6076 - 3.692x_2$. Hence, the infinite dilution values ($x_2 \to 0$) were: $f_2^\infty = 3.38$ (benzene), $f_2^\infty = 40.5$ (cyclohexane). These latter values were converted to bulk partition coefficients through the well-known relation

$$K_s = RTn_L/(f_2^\infty p_2^0) \qquad (6)$$

where p_2^0 is the saturated vapor pressure of the pure solute. The computed K_s values are listed in Table II.

TABLE II

Comparison of Static and Chromatographic Values for K_a and K_s[a,b]

	$10^6 K_a$, cm			K_s		
	Chromatographic		Static	Chromatographic		Static
Solute	Ref. 1	Ref. 3	Ref. 8	Ref. 1	Ref. 3	Ref. 8
Benzene	136	67	161	391	366	370
Cyclohexane	59	46	98.3	29.1	29.0	30.3

[a] Taken from Table 5 of ref. 8.
[b] TDPN at 30°C.

The solution surface tensions were measured, and the slope of the plot of γ against x_2 as $x_2 \to 0$ gave $(\partial \gamma / \partial x_2)^\infty$. The results were: for benzene, $(\partial \gamma / \partial x_2)^\infty = -86.4$ dynes/cm; for cyclohexane, $(\partial \gamma / \partial x_2)^\infty = -644$ dynes/cm. The computation of K_a was performed by first considering the more complete form of the Gibbs equation (5)

$$\Gamma_2^{(1)} = -\frac{1}{RT} \left(\frac{\partial \gamma}{\partial \ln a_2} \right) \tag{7}$$

where a_2 = activity of the solute = $x_2 f_2$. Note that $a_2 \to 1$ (or $f_2 \to 1$) as $x_2 \to 1$, according to the usual convention used for GLC solutions. Therefore, it follows from eq. (7) that

$$\Gamma_2^{(1)} = -\frac{1}{RT} \left(\frac{\partial \gamma}{\partial x_2} \right) \left(\frac{1}{x_2} + \frac{\partial \ln f_2}{\partial x_2} \right)^{-1} \tag{8}$$

In some instances, depending on the functional form of $\ln f_2$, eq. (8) might not reduce to eq. (3) as infinite dilution is approached. In this particular situation, since $(\partial \ln f_2 / \partial x_2) = c$, a constant, it follows from eqs. (4) and (8) that

$$\frac{K_a}{K_s} x_2 n_L = -\frac{x_2}{RT} \left(\frac{\partial \gamma}{\partial x_2} \right) (1 + c x_2)^{-1} \tag{9}$$

Then, by letting $x_2 \to 0$, they (8) obtained the same result as eq. (5), i.e.,

$$K_a = \frac{K_s}{n_L RT} \left(\frac{\partial \gamma}{\partial x_2} \right)^\infty \tag{10}$$

Finally, by utilizing eq. (6), they found

$$K_a = -\frac{1}{f_2^\infty p_2^0} \left(\frac{\partial \gamma}{\partial x_2} \right)^\infty \tag{11}$$

The K_a values determined from the above relation are also listed in Table II.

These data then permitted an unbiased direct comparison between the values obtained chromatographically [corrected to 30°C by interpolation from the published values (1,3)] and those obtained by the static measurements. The agreement (within about 5%) between the corresponding K_s values was as good as could have been expected, particularly since the TDPN used in the various investigations came from different sources. The values of K_a, however, showed considerable disagreement. It has been suggested (7,8) that the discrepancy arises largely through the use of erroneous surface areas in the chromatographic calculations. However, the question has not yet been raised whether one should expect any correlation at all between surface data from planar interfaces and similar data from curved interfaces (as in GLC). More about these points later.

Nevertheless, the work of Martire, Pecsok, and Purnell served unequivocally to substantiate the hypothesis that the excess surface concentration (i.e., solute adsorption at the gas–liquid interface) plays an important role in determining the magnitude of the retention volume.

IV. RECENT (1966) GLC PAPERS ON THE SUBJECT

It has been established so far that liquid surface adsorption can take place with nonpolar and, to a lesser extent, polar solutes on polar stationary liquid phases.

Recently, Martire (10) considered systems containing a polar solute component, which had both a large dipole moment and a strong hydrogen bonding propensity, and which, it was thought, should exhibit appreciable solute orientation and adsorption on polar liquid surfaces. The systems studied were the normal alcohols (C_1 to C_4) on the liquid phases, glycerol and β,β'-oxydipropionitrile (ODPN). The following evidence suggested that solid support adsorption effects were negligible: the support material (Chromosorb W) was completely treated, the liquid phases were polar, the elution peaks were symmetric, and the retention times were reproducible.

For the methanol systems, a systematic variation in the specific retention volume (V_g^0) with weight per cent liquid was observed for both stationary phases. Analysis via eq. (2) indicated that liquid surface effects were present. However, for the ethanol, propanol, and butanol systems, only small random variations in V_g^0 were observed, denoting the absence of liquid surface effects.

In an attempt to find a common characteristic for systems which exhibit adsorption at the gas–liquid interface, Martire (10) posed the question, "Is there any general correlation between some thermodynamic property of the solution and the relative magnitude of the liquid adsorption effect?" A partial answer was found by plotting K_a/K_s (taking this ratio as the gauge for the relative magnitude of adsorption) against the solute activity coefficient at infinite dilution (f_2^∞). The data for the graph were computed from Pecsok's results (3) with the help of eq. (6).

Figure 1 illustrates that K_a/K_s increases more or less linearly with increasing nonideality of the bulk solution. A rationale follows.

All of the solutions in TDPN exhibit positive deviations from Raoult's law ($f_2^\infty > 1$). Large positive deviations from ideality reflect the squeezing of solute molecules out of the bulk liquid and onto the surface phase or into the vapor phase, primarily because the solvent–solvent interactions are so much stronger than the solute–solvent interactions that the solute molecule cannot compete with a solvent molecule

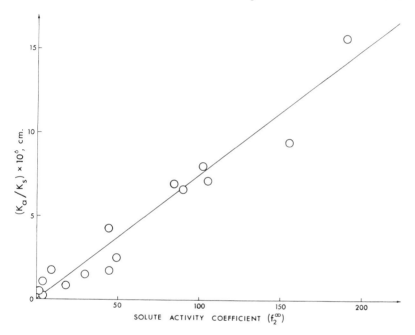

Fig. 1. (K_a/K_s) vs. f_2^∞ in TDPN at 25°C.

for the interaction of another solvent molecule. Thus, the solute has minimal solubility in the bulk liquid, i.e., the solvent is a poor solvent; the poorer the solvent, the higher the activity coefficient and the larger the value of K_a/K_s.

This implies that, if f_2^∞ data were available for a particular liquid phase, then on the basis of a few measurements one should be able to predict the relative magnitude of solute adsorption on that liquid. This would be accomplished by constructing a plot similar to Figure 1.

Unfortunately, published f_2^∞ data are very scarce. Furthermore, as we will discuss later, no *general* method exists for accurately predicting $(\partial\gamma/\partial x_2)^\infty$, and hence K_a through eq. (11), for a binary solution from the pure component bulk or surface properties.

Martire (10) then attempted to rationalize the behavior of his alcohol systems according to the scheme presented above. It turned out, however, that all the f_2^∞ values were low (in glycerol, 1.63–11.4, and in ODPN, 2.61–6.41, for C_1 through C_4, respectively), which would indicate small or negligible K_a values. The discrepancy between the observed and predicted behavior of methanol was eventually attributed to its preferential adsorption, via hydrogen bonding, by the liquid phases. He concluded his discussion by distinguishing between two classes of adsorption at the gas–liquid interface.

1. The first type is characterized by large solute activity coefficients, i.e., the bulk liquid is a poor solvent. Here, the less polar the solute is with respect to the solvent and the less soluble it is in the bulk liquid, the larger the solute surface excess concentration.

2. The second type is characterized by relatively low solute activity coefficients, significant solute solubility in the bulk liquid, and a solute and solvent molecule of comparable high polarity. Here, the solute molecules are preferentially adsorbed because of strong dipole–dipole interactions or hydrogen bonding between the solute and the liquid surface.

Indications were that the first type produced, by far, the larger surface effects. However, a large grey area has not yet been explored. What about polar–polar systems, with intermediate activity coefficients, which could conceivably exhibit small amounts of both types of adsorption? [An example might be the oxy-TDPN systems studied by Pecsok (3).] The nature of liquid phase adsorption in GLC systems must eventually be considered in more detail.

Urone and Parcher (11) have studied the GLC behavior of polar solutes on columns with deactivated and nondeactivated acid-washed Chromosorb P as support materials, and squalane and tri-*o*-tolyl phosphate (TTP) as liquid phases. In accord with the earlier workers (1,3), they found that liquid surface effects were absent on both the squalane and TTP. Also, they ascertained that surface area shows little dependence on the treatment of support.

They have discussed the nature of the partitioning process for low-loaded columns ($< 2\%$). They point out that a more complicated mechanism probably exists than that of simple liquid phase or solid support adsorption. Their feelings are that adsorption partition coefficients are very complex functions, and that the assumption of additivity of surface and bulk liquid contributions is, in general, an oversimplification. They propose a more realistic model which considers a modified layer whose partitioning properties are affected by the support to varying degrees depending on the surface activity of the support and the amount of liquid phase. Intuitively, one would expect the structure of the liquid layers nearest to the solid–liquid interface to be modified due to their partial orientation on the support. This is especially true for polar liquid phases. In fact, at very low loadings it is conceivable that the entire liquid phase could be quite unlike a normal bulk liquid. This merely points out the necessity for a more definitive examination of the liquid structure on chromatographic support materials.

In work recently published Pecsok and Gump (12) have considered polar solute–nonpolar solvent systems to determine whether liquid surface adsorption were an important feature of these systems. They employed a completely static method using a bulk liquid sample because of the possibility of polar solute–solid support interactions with GLC. Two experimental systems were used: (a) the McBain balance–du Nouy tensiometer (8), and (b) a Cahn electrobalance. Some results are given in Table III. One can see that, for comparable values of the activity coefficient, the solute–squalane systems exhibit much larger values for $(\partial\gamma/\partial x_2)^\infty$ than those determined by Martire et al. (8).

TABLE III

Values of f_2^∞, $(\partial\gamma/\partial x_2)^\infty$, K_s, and K_a for Solutions in Squalane at 30°C[a]

	Methanol	Ethanol	Acetone	Diethyl-amine
f_2^∞	24.4	19.9	2.85	0.757
$(\partial\gamma/\partial x_2)^\infty$	−2460	−1250	−209	−249
K_s	9.15	23.0	44.0	158
$10^6 K_a$, cm	473	603	195	999

[a] Taken from Table 2 of ref. 12.

The significance of these findings is not yet clear to this writer. How can one reconcile these results with the GLC results (3,11) which indicate the absence of liquid surface effects for polar solute–nonpolar solvent systems? Why hasn't anyone observed this immense effect chromatographically? (Even with high liquid loads, where solid support adsorption is negligible, liquid surface adsorption should still be quite large for these systems, according to Table III.)

Furthermore, these systems resist classification. Diethylamine, for example, exhibits a negative deviation from Raoult's law. Thus, if there is a unique property which governs the likelihood that a small amount of solute will drastically reduce the surface tension of the solvent, then it is apparently not the solute activity coefficient.

Thus far we have considered three recent studies, each of which has shown us that the mechanism of solute adsorption at the gas–liquid interface is complicated indeed. The last paper, fortunately, does not un-cover any additional discrepancies or inconsistencies. Instead, it repre-sents the first conscious attempt to utilize the extra measure of selec-tivity, provided by liquid surface adsorption, for improving an actual GLC separation. Rogozinski and Kaufman (13) have demonstrated that reduction in the surface area-to-volume ratio for a highly polar liquid phase improves aromatic–aliphatic separations. Since aliphatics are retained primarily by adsorption on the liquid surface and aromatics primarily by solubility in the bulk liquid (1,3), then aliphatic retention can be reduced, while aromatic retention is increased, simply by de-creasing A_L/V_L, i.e., increasing the weight per cent liquid. Maximum selectivity was achieved with a column packing containing 38% TDPN which gave the minimum surface-to-volume ratio without exceeding the liquid-holding capacity of the support (Chromosorb P, 60–80 mesh).

They also examined the effect of using a surface active agent (cetyl alcohol) on the liquid phase surface to reduce the adsorption of the aliphatics (hence their retention) and found it to be negligible. Finally, they evaluated Martin's proposition that the use of capillary columns should further reduce surface adsorption effects because of the lower surface-to-volume ratios attainable. In studying the selectivity of capil-lary columns, they found no marked advantage over the highly loaded packed columns for their particular separation. They computed that a packing containing 40% liquid phase had an average film thickness of $1\ \mu$, which compared favorably with the quoted values of 0.5–2.5 μ for capillary columns. This work on capillary columns serves as additional GLC evidence for Martin's adsorption hypothesis.

V. SURFACE AREAS AND FILM THICKNESS IN GLC

It has been suggested (7,8) that the discrepancy (close to a factor of two) between the K_a values determined chromatographically and those determined statically (see Table II) arises mainly from the use of erroneous surface areas in the chromatographic investigations.

Both the continuous flow method used by Martin (1) and the static pressure-volume method used by Pecsok (3) are based on the Brunauer-Emmett-Teller (BET) approach for determining surface areas, and both employ an inert gas as the adsorbate. However, the small pore size of the chromatographic support makes it likely that, when dealing with the larger molecules normally encountered in GLC, the effective area is less than that "seen" by the smaller inert gas molecules. Supporting evidence is that measurements on bare Chromosorb P based on the BET method using an inert gas gave values of about 4 m^2/g, whereas when using acetone vapor a value of about 2 m^2/g was found (15).

Martin (1) and Pecsok (3) have reported plots of liquid surface area against percent TDPN for columns containing Chromosorb W and Chromosorb P solid supports. These areas have been recalculated (8) from the original GLC data using the static K_a values in Table II. Remarkably, the recalculated values for the specific surface areas for uncoated Chromosorb P were found to be approximately 2 m^2/g. Therefore, it appears that the static and GLC data can be reconciled on this basis.

An accurate knowledge of the surface areas possessed by finely divided solids is important not only in physical adsorption phenomena, but also in heterogeneous reactions involving solid catalysts. Direct determination of area is, of course, impossible with these highly irregular and porous solids. The BET method is undoubtedly the most widely used technique for indirect determination of area. Surface areas estimated in this manner can be accepted as generally reliable but approximate. The method is realistic in the sense that multilayer adsorption is provided for. However, it contains many rough approximations, including the necessity to estimate the cross-sectional area of the adsorbate (e.g., that of nitrogen is taken to be 16.2 $Å^2$). Furthermore, there are many subtleties connected with the surface that lead, at times, to puzzling area values. The presence of fine pores or capillaries may be such as to allow one gas to penetrate, whereas another gas with larger molecules finds the pores inaccessible (15).

Accordingly, it would be enlightening to obtain accurate and meaningful measurements of available surface areas for chromatographic supports. Determination of the retention volume dependence upon weight per cent liquid phase for a solute eluted from a series of otherwise identical columns would allow evaluation of $K_a A_L$ for the solute. Then, a study of the solubility and surface tension characteristics of the solute in the chosen liquid [by means of the combined McBain balance and du Nouy tensiometer apparatus (8)], in turn, would allow unequivocal evaluation of K_a and hence A_L. Of particular interest would be a comparison of surface areas as "seen" by various organic solute molecules.

The scheme described above has been used (8) to explicitly evaluate the apparent liquid film thickness, d_f (the dominant term in the expression for liquid phase mass transfer), for Chromosorb P and Chromosorb W packings. It was found that the ratio of d_f values (d_f on Chromosorb W/d_f on Chromosorb P) for fixed per cent TDPN on the two supports was effectively constant (3.75 ± 0.15) over the whole range of liquid loadings. This was taken to imply a similar mode of liquid distribution. Since in the mass transfer term of the chromatographic rate equation the film thickness appears as its square, the considerably greater column efficiency attainable with Chromosorb P than with Chromosorb W can now be clearly accounted for. It was further deduced that as liquid phase is added to support it first forms a monolayer and then, progressively, uniformly fills capillaries which have approximately cylindrical geometry.

VI. THERMODYNAMICS OF BULK SOLUTIONS STUDIED BY GLC

Gas–liquid chromatography has proved useful in measuring physicochemical properties of bulk liquid solutions where the solute component approaches infinite dilution (16). If GLC is regarded as a partitioning process between two bulk phases, then, according to theory, the specific retention volume (V_g^0) should be a unique property of the nature of the solute and solvent at a given temperature. For the liquid loadings (20–30%) normally used in these studies, it has usually been assumed that the partition coefficient and the related activity coefficient at infinite dilution (f_2^∞) are independent of the area-to-volume ratio of the solvent. This enabled thermodynamicists to compute f_2^∞ values directly from the expression (17),

$$f_2^\infty = 273.2R/p_2^0 M_L V_g^0 \qquad (12)$$

However, it is now apparent that, even with liquid loadings as high as 25%, the model of a two-phase partitioning system will, in many cases, be highly inexact. Bulk liquid activity coefficients determined by GLC can be in serious error unless corrected for solute adsorption at the gas–liquid interface.

Considerable caution is thus necessary in the interpretation of chromatographic data for the study of solution thermodynamics. The significant quantity is the bulk partition coefficient, K_s, which must now be determined by the graphical method suggested by Martin (1) [see eq. (2)] to ensure that all surface contributions to the retention volume are corrected for. Once K_s is found, f_2^∞ may be computed from eq. (6). If the temperature dependence of f_2^∞ is also determined, then the partial molar excess quantities may be obtained as well.

VII. REPORTING OF GLC RETENTION DATA

It is also apparent that, when liquid surface effects are significant, a marked variation in the specific retention volume with weight percent of liquid phase occurs. This, of course, would not concern the analyst, who usually relies on relative retention times or Kováts retention indices for identification purposes. It might be erroneously argued that one can ignore surface effects when dealing with relative retention data because of some fortuitous "cancelling-out" of surface terms. However, as Martin's (1) work first illustrated, normal paraffins, branched paraffins, cycloparaffins, olefins, etc., behave differently with a change in liquid phase percentage because they have widely different values of K_s and K_a. This implies that the cataloging of all forms of retention data must be handled with more concern. Liquid surface effects could be the main reason, for example, that a reported separation of a multicomponent mixture with a 5% column loading cannot be successfully carried out at 10%.

A numerical example would illustrate this point nicely. From Pecsok's (3) data on TDPN at 25°C, retention times relative to n-pentane were calculated for a number of typical compounds at three different liquid weight per cents. The large variations and the changes in elution order with liquid loading can be observed in Table IV. The Kováts retention indices are not foolproof either. Using n-pentane and n-heptane as the standards, the retention indices were calculated from the same experimental data (3), using the expression first proposed by Kováts (18). Again, as seen in Table IV, a very significant variation with liquid phase percentage takes place.

TABLE IV[a]

Relative Retention Times (n-Pentane $= 1.00$) and Kováts Retention Indices (n-Pentane $= 500.0$, n-Heptane $= 700.0$) for Various Compounds in TDPN at $25°C$

Solute	Relative retention times liquid weight %			Kováts retention indices liquid weight %		
	1.00	6.00	12.00	1.00	6.00	12.00
n-Pentane	1.00	1.00	1.00	500.0	500.0	500.0
n-Hexane	2.89	2.76	2.46	600.4	598.4	592.6
n-Heptane	8.28	7.90	6.99	700.0	700.0	700.0
Cyclopentane	1.10	1.80	2.41	508.8	557.0	590.8
3-Methylpentane	2.36	2.37	2.15	581.3	583.5	578.7
Diethyl ether	2.72	3.99	4.70	594.8	633.9	659.4
1-Hexene	3.46	3.72	3.68	617.4	627.3	634.1
Cyclohexene	4.38	8.98	12.53	639.7	712.4	760.3

[a] Based on experimental data in Table II of ref. 3.

These examples emphasize the importance of reporting the percentage and surface area of liquid phase with all GLC retention data. However, since it is not feasible to measure surface areas for every column employed, one should at least report the type of solid support used and its mesh size, since these two factors and the percentage largely determine the area.

VIII. PREDICTION OF SOLUTION SURFACE TENSIONS

If one can predict the solution surface tension as a function of the bulk solution composition, then one can estimate $(\partial\gamma/\partial x_2)^{\infty}$, and, in turn, K_a from eq. (11) (provided f_2^{∞} is known or can be estimated). Can solution surface tensions be predicted from the pure component bulk and surface properties? In view of the state of bulk solution theory, which is less complex, one would expect an answer of "no." Surprisingly, the answer is a qualified "yes."

There have been several noteworthy attempts at applying statistical mechanics to the calculation of surface tensions of mixtures. Guggenheim (19) used a lattice model for the liquid state which necessitated some arbitrary assumptions with regard to the geometry of the liquid structure. The end result is that it is only valid when applied to mixtures where the components are nearly the same size and shape. Prigogine (20) approached the calculation of surface tensions using his "smoothed potential" model. His technique is applicable only to mixtures which are nearly ideal and requires the arbitrary choice of a reference substance. Recently Eckert and Prausnitz (21) derived the surface properties from the application of the grand partition function to a cell model of the vapor–liquid interface. They obtained the surface tension through a free energy minimization procedure. The solution surface tension and the surface composition were expressed in terms of the bulk liquid activity coefficients and the pure component properties. The results were in excellent agreement with some experimental results for the surface tension of nonpolar liquid mixtures. Their treatment does appear to provide a sound theoretical basis for the prediction of surface properties of other types of liquid systems.

Finally, there is the parachor approach, a less elegant, empirical, but useful method that is often overlooked. The parachor is essentially a molecular volume, modified to eliminate some of the influences of cohesive forces, which vary from liquid to liquid. The parachor of a molecule can be easily estimated by adding terms for each of its atoms plus terms for the types of bond (double, single, etc.) that are present (22). It is related to the surface tension (γ) by

$$(\gamma)^{1/4} = P\zeta/M = P/V \qquad (13)$$

where P is the parachor, ζ is the liquid density, M is the molecular weight, and V is the liquid molar volume.

If we assume that parachors and volumes are additive, then for a binary system the solution surface tension becomes:

$$\gamma = [(P_1 x_1 + P_2 x_2)/(V_1 x_1 + V_2 x_2)]^4 \qquad (14)$$

where x_1 and x_2 are the solvent and solute bulk liquid mole fractions, respectively.

If we then determine $(\partial \gamma/\partial x_2)$ and let $x_2 \rightarrow 0$, we obtain

$$\left(\frac{\partial \gamma}{\partial x_2}\right)^{\infty} = 4\gamma_1 \left[\frac{P_2}{P_1} - \frac{V_2}{V_1}\right] \qquad (15)$$

Note that γ_1, V_1, and V_2 are functions of temperature only. The values of V_1 and V_2 can be computed from their respective molecular weights and densities. The value of γ_1 can be computed from eq. (13) or, if available, taken from published data. Also, P_1 and P_2 can be calculated from the molecular structure of the compounds with the aid of published tables (22). Hence $(\partial\gamma/\partial x_2)^\infty$ can be estimated rapidly and easily. Equation (15) is valid for solutions of nonpolar or slightly polar molecules which are not too dissimilar in size and shape.

In short, the present state of affairs is that one can make accurate quantitative predictions about mixtures of nonpolar or slightly polar molecules only. Unfortunately, the types of systems which exhibit large liquid surface effects in GLC are not quite that simple. Furthermore, the maximum $(\partial\gamma/\partial x_2)^\infty$ values predictable by the above methods are at least an order of magnitude smaller than those encountered in GLC systems.

The general effect of dissolved substances on the surface tension of the solvent (liquid phase) can be discussed in terms of three types of curves (23). The so-called Type II curves exhibit surface tensions which decrease regularly and more or less gradually with an increase in the bulk solute concentration. On the other hand, Type III curves exhibit a very dramatic lowering of the surface tension in very dilute solution, with the surface tension remaining approximately constant thereafter. Systems which exhibit the large solute adsorption effects observed in GLC fall into category III, while the systems which can be handled by the available theoretical or empirical approaches fall into category II. That is the whole story and explains the meaning of the qualified answer.

IX. A THERMODYNAMIC STUDY OF LIQUID SURFACES BY GLC

It has been suggested (1,8) that GLC offers a new approach to the fundamental physicochemical study of adsorption of vapors on liquids, particularly for volatile solutes on nonvolatile liquids, which are troublesome systems to study by normal static methods. However, before one dares to utilize GLC for these purposes, one must carefully examine the limitations of the technique.

Is the surface zone of a liquid strictly monomolecular with unaltered liquid immediately underneath, or is it a zone in which the outside mono-molecular layer conditions the orientation and properties of the under-lying liquid to a depth of many molecules? Is it not reasonable that the powerful forces involved in the top surface layer, although they are short range, should be capable of influencing neighboring molecules to an impressive depth by means of successive polarization? (The attractive forces exerted by an extended surface have much longer range than those from an isolated molecule. The latter depends on r^{-7} and the former falls off as r^{-4}.)

The experimental evidence that has been cited (24) appears to constitute definite proof of a deep surface layer whose properties differ from those of the bulk liquid. "The surface zone is not merely a monomolecular layer, but is a region in which orientation extends effectively to many molecular lengths. The effective depth of the surface zone is tens or hundreds of angstroms in low molecular weight liquids, thousands of angstroms in long chain molecules" (24).

Now, consider a GLC packing of 5% liquid phase on Chromosorb P; the apparent liquid film thickness is about 300 Å (8). If the surface layer extends hundreds of angstroms, and if the layers nearest to the solid–liquid interface are undergoing partial orientation, then where is the bulk liquid represented here? Without a bulk liquid the Gibbs equation is meaningless and any thermodynamic measurements would be futile. Furthermore, what information could a GLC study, in general, possibly provide that would be pertinent to the surface of a normal bulk liquid? Let us seek some answers.

Guggenheim (25) has pointed out that the Gibbs adsorption formula, although derived for planar interfaces (infinite radius of curvature), may be safely applied to curved interfaces if the thickness of the inhomogeneous layer (i.e., the surface) is negligibly small with respect to the radius of curvature. When this condition is not fulfilled, the formula ceases to be applicable and the very meaning of interfacial (surface) tension becomes ill-defined.

In GLC we have a liquid film of varying thickness spread throughout narrow pores of various contours and diameters. With this situation a direct measurement of the average radius of curvature of the liquid surface is precluded. However, to determine whether GLC falls into the "ill-defined" category, the following simple experiment could be employed.

The vapor pressure (p) of a liquid element with a highly curved surface is related to the vapor pressure of the bulk liquid (p_0) by the expression (26)

$$\ln p/p_0 = 2\gamma M/\zeta rRT \tag{16}$$

where γ is the surface tension, M is the molecular weight, ζ is the liquid density, r is the radius of curvature, and RT has its usual significance. For TDPN at 25°C, $\gamma = 49.9$ dynes/cm (8) and $M/\zeta = 126.2$ cc/mole

(1). Therefore, the radius of curvature for this liquid phase is given by

$$r \, (\text{Å}) = 50.8/\ln \, (p/p_0) \qquad (17)$$

The experiment that is suggested is the direct measurement of p_0 and p (vapor pressure of liquid on the support) for TDPN. The purpose is not to obtain an accurate value of r, but rather an order of magnitude. For example, consider a pressure-measuring device capable of ± 0.001 mm (certainly within the realm of modern instruments). If p_0 is determined to be 0.100 mm, and if there is no discernible difference in the measured values of p and p_0, then it can be ascertained [through eq. (17)] that the lower bound for the radius of curvature is about 2500 Å. For convenience, one can accept this as the minimum value of r which will allow one to neglect the thickness of the surface layer with respect to the radius of curvature. If a more sensitive pressure device and a more volatile liquid phase are employed, perhaps one can strive to attain higher accuracy in the determination of r.

In the last analysis it may turn out that GLC studies of solute adsorption on liquid surfaces will provide thermodynamically meaningful data, pertinent to normal surfaces, as long as a reasonable amount of bulk liquid is present [a 10% liquid phase on Chromosorb W packing, for example, has a film thickness of about 3000 Å (8)]. The fact that some static and GLC values of K_a have been reconciled (8) indicates that the situation certainly is not hopeless.

X. THE GIBBS ADSORPTION EQUATION AND SURFACE COMPOSITION

The addition of a second component to a pure solvent results in a surface layer with a different composition than that of the bulk of the mixture. One component, the solute, is said to be adsorbed at the dividing surface between the two bulk phases. The amount of surface adsorption, or the surface excess concentration, can be obtained from the value of the surface tension of the solution and the Gibbs adsorption equation [eq. (7)].

Strictly speaking, the model of the surface as a separate phase is inherently inconsistent with the rigorous Gibbs equation. This occurs because one assumes a discontinuity of composition between the bulk liquid and the surface phase, whereas, in fact, none exists. However, the discrepancy is minor. Guggenheim (19) discusses this point in terms of his strictly regular solution theory and concludes that the error or in-consistency is small. Accordingly, it is helpful to visualize the surface as a physically distinct phase.

The assignment of a definite numerical value to a surface excess (Γ, moles/cm^2) requires the definition of the position of a dividing surface parallel with and located close to or within the inhomogeneous boundary between the two bulk phases. The way in which the numerical value of any Γ depends upon the positioning of the dividing surface, and the interrelationship of the various Γ resulting, has been thoroughly ex-plored by Guggenheim and Adam (27). They have shown that, irrespec-tive of the location of the dividing surface for a two-component mixture, the quantity ($x_1\Gamma_2 - x_2\Gamma_1$) is invariant; x represents the mole fraction in the bulk liquid phase.

The equation commonly known as the Gibbs Adsorption Equation places the dividing surface such that the surface excess of the solvent component vanishes, i.e., $\Gamma_1^{(1)} = 0$. Then, for a solution at constant temperature and pressure, the surface excess concentration of the solute component becomes (5)

$$\Gamma_2^{(1)} = -\frac{1}{RT}\left(\frac{\partial \gamma}{\partial \ln a_2}\right)_{T,P} \tag{18}$$

Employing the usual convention that $a_2 = x_2 f_2$ and $a_2 \to 1$ as $x_2 \to 1$, one obtains

$$\Gamma_2^{(1)} = -\frac{x_2}{RT}\left(\frac{\partial \gamma}{\partial x_2}\right)_{T,P}\left[1 + x_2\left(\frac{\partial \ln f_2}{\partial x_2}\right)_{T,P}\right]^{-1} \tag{19}$$

Also, since the experimental solute activity coefficient data can be fitted to a polynomial of the form

$$\ln f_2 = \sum_{n=0}^{n=r} a_n x_2^n \tag{20}$$

it follows from eq. (19) that

$$\Gamma_2^{(1)} = -\frac{x_2}{RT}\left(\frac{\partial \gamma}{\partial x_2}\right)_{T,P}\left[1 + \sum_{n=0}^{n=r} n a_n x_2^n\right]^{-1} \tag{21}$$

Finally, since all the n's must be *positive* integers (Henry's law must be obeyed at infinite dilution, therefore, $\ln f_2$ must approach a constant as x_2 approaches zero), it follows that, as $x_2 \to 0$, the summation term in eq. (21) must approach zero. Hence, for dilute solutions we have

$$\Gamma_2^{(1)} \to \frac{x_2}{RT}\left(\frac{\partial \gamma}{\partial x_2}\right)_{T,P} \qquad \text{as } x_2 \to 0 \tag{22}$$

The particular convention, relating to the position of the dividing surface as originally used by Gibbs, suffers from the disadvantages that it is not easily visualized in terms of the physical structure of surfaces and that it is unsymmetrical with respect to the components of the mixture.

A more realistic and useful convention (27) is that in which a portion of the liquid having unit surface area contains $\Gamma^{(N)}$ moles of each species more than a similar portion in the bulk containing exactly the same total number of moles of all species. Thus, in this convention,

$$\sum \Gamma^{(N)} = 0 \tag{23a}$$

and a general relationship in terms of any convention (designated by superscript R)

$$\Gamma_2^{(N)} = -\Gamma_1^{(N)} = x_1\Gamma_2^{(R)} - x_2\Gamma_1^{(R)} \tag{23b}$$

can be deduced (27). It then follows, since $\Gamma_1^{(1)} = 0$, that

$$\Gamma_2^{(N)} = x_1\Gamma_2^{(1)} \tag{23c}$$

The simplest approach to discussion of surface structure and composition is to assume that the inhomogeneous region constitutes a monolayer. This is an admittedly crude approximation (24), but, nevertheless provides results for comparative purposes (27). In this convention (identified by superscript U), $\Gamma_1^{(U)}$ and $\Gamma_2^{(U)}$ represent the actual number of moles of solvent and solute, respectively, in the monolayer. If the area per mole of each is designated $\overline{A}_1$ and $\overline{A}_2$ then

$$\overline{A}_1\Gamma_1^{(U)} + \overline{A}_2\Gamma_2^{(U)} = 1 \tag{24}$$

and this, with eq. (23), yields

$$\Gamma_2^{(U)} = \frac{\overline{A}_1\Gamma_2^{(N)} + x_2}{x_1\overline{A}_1 + x_2\overline{A}_2}$$

and

$$\Gamma_1^{(U)} = \frac{\overline{A}_2\Gamma_1^{(N)} + x_1}{x_1\overline{A}_1 + x_2\overline{A}_2} \tag{25}$$

From these expressions and eq. (24), one can derive the general equation for the monolayer mole fraction, θ_2, of solute.

$$\theta_2 = \frac{\Gamma_2^{(U)}}{\Gamma_1^{(U)} + \Gamma_2^{(U)}} = \frac{\overline{A}_1x_1\Gamma_2^{(1)} + x_2}{x_1\Gamma_2^{(1)}(\overline{A}_1 - \overline{A}_2) + 1} \tag{26}$$

Thus θ_2 may be determined from the experimentally evaluated quantity $\Gamma_2^{(1)}$, provided that values for $\overline{A}_1$ and $\overline{A}_2$ can be obtained.

Martire, Pecsok, and Purnell (8) estimated the surface composition of their systems through eq. (26). They found that, in the first approximation, the molar areas of their solutes (benzene and cyclohexane) and their solvent (TDPN) were equal $(\overline{A}_1 \doteq \overline{A}_2 \doteq 2 \times 10^9 \text{ cm}^2/\text{mole})$. Under these circumstances, eq. (26) reduces to

$$\theta_2 = \overline{A}_1 x_1 \Gamma_2^{(1)} + x_2 \qquad (27)$$

and $\overline{A}_1 x_1 \Gamma_2^{(1)}$ represents an "excess" surface mole fraction. Values of θ_2 for both binary mixtures were then computed from the surface tension and activity coefficient data via eqs. (19) and (27). The plots that were constructed (8) showed that θ_2 rose rapidly and smoothly with x_2; for benzene it reached $\theta_2 = 0.50$ at $x_2 = 0.112$, while for cyclohexane it reached $\theta_2 = 0.50$ at $x_2 = 0.011$. It is apparent from these results that when solute adsorption is present, the surface concentration of the solute exceeds the point of infinite dilution well in advance of the bulk concentration of the solute. The implication of these findings, with respect to GLC systems, will be considered in the next section.

XI. DEVIATION OF THE SOLUTE SURFACE CONCENTRATION FROM THE HENRY'S LAW REGION

When one reports GLC retention data or thermodynamic properties of solutions determined by elution GLC, it is implied that infinite solute dilution has been attained. In GLC systems where liquid surface effects are imperceptible, sample size effects are often noticeable with samples as small as 10 μg. We shall see that, when surface adsorption contributes significantly to retention, the condition of infinite dilution, i.e., sample size independence of retention volume, becomes more difficult to achieve.

The molecular basis of infinite dilution can be best understood by first considering the relationship between Henry's law and the partition coefficients. If we assume ideal behavior for the vapor phase, but do not assume infinite dilution for the solute in the bulk liquid phase, then eq. (6) becomes

$$K_s = RTn_L/f_2 p_2^0 \qquad (28)$$

and from eqs. (4), (6), and (8) we obtain

$$K_a = -\frac{1}{f_2 p_2{}^0}\left(\frac{\partial \gamma}{\partial x_2}\right)\left[1 + x_2\left(\frac{\partial \ln f_2}{\partial x_2}\right)\right]^{-1} \qquad (29)$$

where f_2 refers to the solute activity coefficient at mole fraction x_2.

Now, the general expression which relates the partial pressure (p_2) of the solute component to its mole fraction is

$$p_2 = f_2 p_2{}^0 x_2 \qquad (30)$$

while Henry's law, which applies only at infinite dilution, takes the form

$$p_2 = c' x_2 \qquad (31)$$

Accordingly, as infinite dilution is approached, consistency demands that

$$f_2 p_2{}^0 \rightarrow f_2{}^\infty p_2{}^0 = c' \qquad (32)$$

where c' is the Henry's law constant and is a measure of the solute molecule's "escaping tendency" from a dilute solution.

Equation (32) implies that a concentration region is eventually reached where the solute–solute interactions become negligible and the solute's escaping tendency from the bulk liquid becomes a function of the solute–solvent interactions only. Under these conditions the solute molecule is effectively surrounded by solvent, i.e., it is at infinite dilution.

When infinite dilution has been reached in the bulk liquid, eq. (28) becomes identical to eq. (6), and the bulk partition coefficient becomes independent of concentration. Furthermore, eq. (29) reduces to

$$K_a = -\frac{1}{f_2{}^\infty p_2{}^0}\frac{\partial \gamma}{\partial x_2} \qquad (33)$$

Henry's law behavior for the surface, i.e., concentration independence of K_a, can then be attained when $(\partial \gamma / \partial x_2)$ becomes independent of concentration. This will take place when the surface concentration is dilute enough that solute–solute interactions are unimportant. However, the results (8) discussed in the previous section indicate that, with appreciable solute adsorption at the gas–liquid interface, the surface mole fraction rises much faster than does the bulk mole fraction (e.g., for cyclohexane in TDPN at 25°C, when $x_2 = 0.002$, and $\theta_2 = 0.10$). In general, therefore, one would expect Henry's law for the surface to fail at much lower bulk concentrations.

Let us examine what this means in terms of the maximum allowable sample size in GLC for the cyclohexane–TDPN system at 25°C. If we assume that the maximum surface concentration which permits Henry's law behavior is $\theta_2 = 0.005$, then this corresponds to a maximum bulk liquid concentration of $x_2 \doteq 0.0001$ (8). Let us choose the following characteristics for our column: 5-ft length, $\frac{1}{4}$ in. o.d., 5% by weight TDPN on Chromosorb P, and linear packing density of 3 g/ft.; also, $V_L = 0.045$ (cc TDPN/g packing) at 5% loading (1), and the molar volume of TDPN is 126.2 cc/mole. Hence, for this column, the total number of moles of TDPN is about 5.3×10^{-3}.

Experience tells us that, for the purpose of estimating the maximum liquid-phase concentration, it is reasonable to assume that the solute is injected as a uniform plug over the initial 5% of the liquid phase in the column. Under these conditions the maximum allowable solute concentration will be reached if the cyclohexane sample size is as small as 2 μg or 0.003 μl. Of course, the situation gets worse for solutes with higher values of K_a/K_s, and for lower loaded columns. Furthermore, the assumptions employed were on the conservative side (e.g., the implicit assumption that the surface layer thickness is negligible with respect to that of the bulk liquid).

Accordingly, one should appreciate the sample size limitation on the validity of eq. (1). Considerable caution is necessary in the determination of retention data for systems with large liquid surface effects. One should always use the smallest detectable sample size. In fact, the use of differing sample sizes could explain, in part, the discrepancy between the K_a values of the various workers (1,3,8) (Martin, for example, used approximately 0.02 μl).

Another serious problem dealing with sample size limitations will not be discussed here. Systems with very high activity coefficients (highly insoluble materials) are known to give rise to phase separation at very low solute mole fraction. This one aspect of column overloading has not been studied completely as yet. Preliminary calculations indicate that with analytical scale columns, phase separation should not occur with samples of conventional size, even when f_2^∞ is as large as 150. However, with preparative scale columns, where large solute samples and highly polar (selective) liquid phases are encountered, phase separation becomes an important consideration. Work is now progressing on this problem.

Acknowledgments

The author gratefully acknowledges many helpful discussions with Professors Robert L. Pecsok and J. Howard Purnell.

References

1. R. L. Martin, *Anal. Chem.*, **33**, 347 (1961).
2. F. M. Nelsen and F. T. Eggertsen, *Anal. Chem.*, **30**, 1387 (1958).
3. R. L. Pecsok, A. de Yllana, and A. Abdul-Karim, *Anal. Chem.*, **36**, 452 (1964).
4. R. L. Martin, *Anal. Chem.*, **35**, 116 (1963).
5. W. J. Moore, *Physical Chemistry*, 3rd ed., Prentice-Hall, New Jersey, 1962, pp. 736–738.
6. W. D. Harkins and H. F. Jordan, *J. Am. Chem. Soc.*, **52**, 1751 (1930).
7. D. E. Martire, R. L. Pecsok, and J. H. Purnell, *Nature*, **203**, 1279 (1964).
8. D. E. Martire, R. L. Pecsok, and J. H. Purnell, *Trans. Faraday Soc.*, **61**, 2496 (1965).
9. J. W. McBain and A. M. Bakr, *J. Am. Chem. Soc.*, **48**, 690 (1926).
10. D. E. Martire, *Anal. Chem.*, **38**, 244 (1966).
11. P. Urone and J. F. Parcher, *Anal. Chem.*, **38**, 270 (1966).
12. R. L. Pecsok and B. H. Gump, *J. Phys. Chem.*, **71**, 2202 (1967).
13. M. Rogozinski and I. Kaufman, *J. Gas Chromatog.*, **4**, 413 (1966).
14. S. Brunauer, P. H. Emmett, and E. Teller, *J. Am. Chem. Soc.*, **60**, 309 (1938).
15. R. H. Perrett and J. H. Purnell, *J. Chromatog.*, **7**, 455 (1962).
16. J. H. Purnell, *Endeavour*, **23**, 142 (1964).
17. D. E. Martire, *Anal. Chem.*, **33**, 1143 (1961).
18. E. Kováts, *Helv. Chim. Acta*, **41**, 1915 (1958).
19. E. A. Guggenheim, *Mixtures*, Oxford University Press, London, 1952, ch. 9.
20. A. Englert-Chwoles and I. Prigogine, *J. Chim. Phys.*, **55**, 16 (1958).
21. C. A. Eckert and J. M. Prausnitz, *Am. Inst. Chem. Engrs. J.*, **10**, 677 (1964).
22. O. R. Quayle, *Chem. Rev.*, **53**, 439 (1953).
23. S. H. Maron and C. F. Prutton, *Principles of Physical Chemistry*, 4th ed., Macmillan, New York, 1965, p. 807.
24. J. C. Henniker, *Rev. Mod. Phys.*, **21**, 322 (1949).
25. E. A. Guggenheim, *Trans. Faraday Soc.*, **36**, 397 (1940).
26. G. M. Barrow, *Physical Chemistry*, 2nd ed., McGraw-Hill, New York, 1966, p. 549.
27. E. A. Guggenheim and N. K. Adam, *Proc. Roy. Soc.* (*London*), **A139**, 218 (1933).

Modified Solids for Gas–Solid Chromatography

C. S. G. PHILLIPS, *Inorganic Chemistry Laboratory, Oxford University, Oxford, England,* and C. G. SCOTT, *Hoffmann-La Roche Inc., Nutley, N.J.*

I. INTRODUCTION

The principles of gas–liquid chromatography (GLC) were first clearly enunciated in 1941 (1), but only received experimental verification with the publication in 1952 of the now-classic paper of James and Martin (2). At that time gas–solid chromatography (GSC) was already well established (3–5), but it was apparent that the greatest readily available potential lay with GLC. There then followed a period of development and application of the latter technique so intense that GSC was largely neglected. In the last few years, however, there has been a considerable renewal of interest in GSC, and it has become clear that there are many applications in which it is in fact superior to GLC, while again there are many applications in which the two techniques are complementary so that the best results are obtained by a suitable combination of both. Some of the general features of GSC and its relation to GLC will be demonstrated in this article in which attention is focused on a particular range of solid adsorbents, namely those obtained by modification of activated alumina, silica, or silica–alumina.

The neglect of GSC arose from a number of causes, the most important of which was the nonlinear nature of the adsorption isotherms for the gas–solid interactions examined by the technique. These nonlinear isotherms were reflected in elution chromatograms in which the

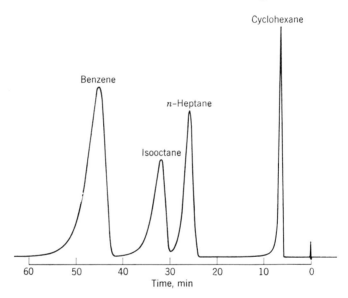

Fig. 1. Elution of hydrocarbons from activated alumina (3.45 g, column length 40 cm) using argon ionization detector (11). (Courtesy of the Institute of Petroleum.)

peaks were markedly asymmetric and consequently broad. Such nonlinearity will always arise at relatively high vapor concentrations when the number of adsorbed molecules is a significant fraction of the adsorbing sites. The development of elution GSC has thus depended upon the development of high sensitivity ionization detectors. Nonlinearity can also arise from heterogeneity of the solid surface if the difference in activity and distribution of different sites is such that there is competition between vapor molecules for the most active sites (6). Thus Figure 1 demonstrates the kind of elution chromatogram obtained from unmodified alumina (7) even with a very small vapor sample and a high-sensitivity detector.

There are a number of ways in which surfaces may be prepared which do not suffer from such heterogeneity. Thus, symmetrical elution peaks have been obtained with graphitized carbon black [Kiselev et al. (8), Halász et al. (9)] or with porous polymer beads [Hollis (10)]. A very general class of suitable surfaces may however be prepared by modification of alumina, silica, or silica–alumina surfaces. Suitable modifiers include a very wide range of inorganic salts, metal complexes, and organic molecules. Figure 2 shows a chromatogram with NaI/alumina,

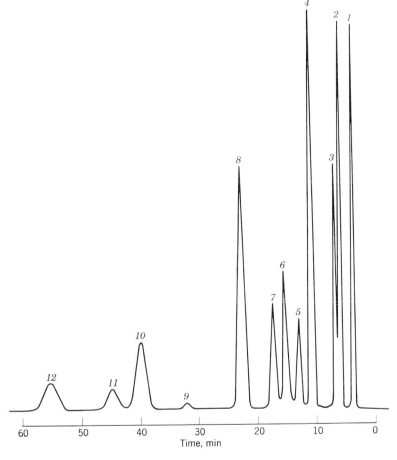

Fig. 2. Elution of miscellaneous adsorbates from NaI/alumina at 175° (11). Column 90 cm × 3 mm i.d. (*1*) *trans*-4-methyl-3-pentene; (*2*) 1,5-hexadiene; (*3*) 2,2,4-trimethyl pentane; (*4*) benzene; (*5*) *trans*-2-octene; (*6*) *cis*-2-octene; (*7*) *n*-nonane; (*8*) toluene; (*9*) *n*-decane; (*10*) ethyl benzene; (*11*) *o*-chlorotoluene; and (*12*) *m*-chlorotoluene. (Courtesy of the Institute of Petroleum.)

and demonstrates the typical symmetry and sharpness of the elution peaks.

The exact nature of these modified surfaces is not yet established, but a plausible model would be that in which the original surface has been completely covered by one or more layers of the modifier so that an adsorbent surface is formed with an area somewhat less than that of the supporting surface and of activity considerably altered by the modifier. The resultant activity is characteristic of the combination of support and modifier because the support affects the activity of the modifier and may do so either by altering the proportions of different crystal faces at the surface or by altering the exact crystal structure adopted by the modifier. Thus it is possible for one modifier to exhibit quite different activities depending on the active solid used to support it.

Such gas–solid columns have a number of advantages over gas–liquid columns.

1. The surfaces are generally stable over a very wide temperature range and are often insensitive to attack by oxygen. Gas–liquid columns bleed-off the column liquid continuously during operation and thus have limited lives, low practical upper limits of temperature operation, and characteristics which change with time. The small amounts of oxygen which almost inevitably occur in the carrier gas slowly oxidize the column liquid, again changing its characteristics (12). The particular suitability of GSC for temperature-programmed operation is illustrated in Figure 3, where attention is drawn to the return of the base line at the end of the chromatogram.

2. The selectivity of gas–solid columns is in general much superior to that available with gas–liquid columns. An example of the change in selectivity obtained with a mere change from NaCl to NaI modification is shown in Figure 4 and more extreme cases are described in detail later in the article. In some cases there is distinction between the type of selectivity available with the two kinds of column. Thus cycloparaffins are retarded on gas–liquid columns but are accelerated on gas–solid columns, paraffin hydrocarbons are well separated on gas–liquid columns if they have the same carbon number but are well separated on gas–solid columns if they have similar boiling points, and *cis*- and *trans*-olefins are usually little separated on gas–liquid columns but are well separated on many gas–solid columns. In such cases a combination of GLC and GSC can often be superior to either alone.

3. Gas–liquid columns are commonly only suited to the operation of elution chromatography: gas–solid columns may also be used for

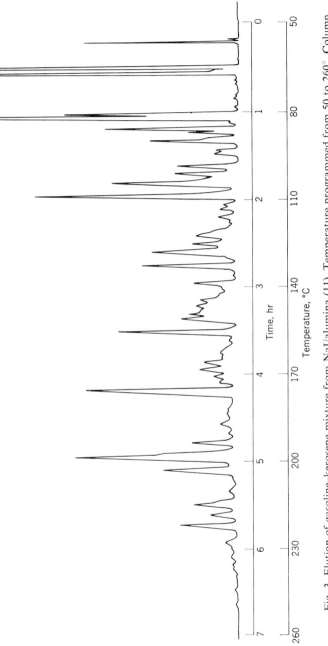

Fig. 3. Elution of gasoline–kerosene mixture from NaI/alumina (11). Temperature programmed from 50 to 260°. Column 150 cm × 3 mm i.d. (Courtesy of the Institute of Petroleum.)

displacement. Now, while the displacement technique is generally inferior to the elution technique for direct analysis and has thus been largely neglected, it does have very distinct advantages in preparative work and in trace concentration. The first arises because high vapor

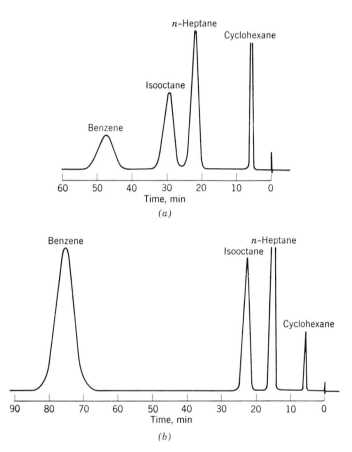

Fig. 4. Elution of hydrocarbons from (a) NaCl/alumina and (b) NaI/alumina at 100° (11). Columns 45 cm × 3 mm i.d. and 80 cm × 3 mm i.d., respectively. (Courtesy of the Institute of Petroleum.)

concentrations favor the displacement technique and the second because displacement chromatography tends to concentrate material in the column, while elution chromatography merely disperses it. Moreover, the inherent separating inferiority of displacement chromatography may be largely overcome when the column is sufficiently selective, as is often the case with gas–solid columns.

On the other hand GSC has a number of disadvantages.

1. The combination of comparatively high surface area and interaction energy results in an increase in operating temperature in comparison with GLC columns with similar elution times. For most of the columns described in this article, a convenient operating temperature would be about 50–75° above that of the comparable gas–liquid column (GSC is thus particularly suited for the analysis of permanent gases). Exceptions are NaOH/alumina (13) and porous polymers (10) which have operating temperatures similar to those of gas–liquid columns.

2. The higher temperature requirement can bring the operating temperature up to a level unsuitable for the chromatography of a thermally unstable substance. The solid surface may also act as a catalyst and enable a reaction to proceed which would not do so even at the same temperature with a gas–liquid column. It should be noted in this connection that with many of the highly selective columns the strongly retarded species (e.g., olefins on $AgNO_3$/alumina, alcohols on any modified alumina) cannot, in practice, be eluted satisfactorily. Most gas–solid columns have a more restricted range of application than do normal gas–liquid columns.

3. Small sample sizes are required for elution chromatography with most gas–solid columns. One microgram would be a suitable sample for a normal (4 mm i.d.) analytical packed column, although 1 mg may be used in the case of hydrocarbons eluted from a column such as NaOH/alumina where the adsorbent–adsorbate interaction is comparatively weak. Vapor sampling rather than liquid sampling or the use of a stream splitter are to be recommended.

The peak shape at high sample sizes will depend upon the curvature of the adsorption isotherm. In most cases the isotherm is concave with respect to the pressure axis corresponding generally to a higher numerical heat of adsorption than heat of vaporization, and a sharp-fronted peak results as in Figure 5. If the isotherm is convex with respect to the pressure axis, a sharp-tailed peak is produced as in Figure 6; the corresponding adsorption isotherm is shown in Figure 7 (14). It is to be noted that benzene will give a sharp-fronted peak on the same column as cyclohexane gives a sharp-backed peak.

When the adsorption isotherm is concave with respect to the pressure axis, vapor molecules compete with one another for sites on the surface. Under these circumstances it is possible for one kind of

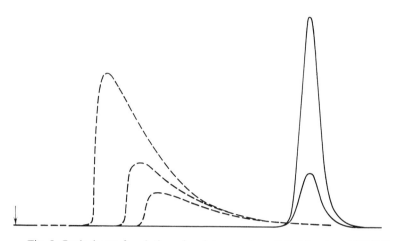

Fig. 5. Peak shapes for elution of cyclohexane from CdI_2/alumina at 18° (14). Continuous lines correspond to small samples (argon ionization detector); broken lines correspond to large samples (katharometer detector). (Courtesy of Butterworths.)

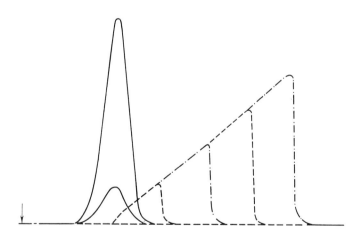

Fig. 6. Peak shapes for elution of cyclohexane from NaOH/alumina at 18° (14). Continuous lines correspond to small samples (argon ionization detector); broken lines correspond to large sample (katharometer detector). (Courtesy of Butterworths.)

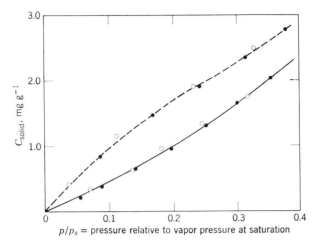

Fig. 7. Adsorption isotherms on 40% NaOH/alumina at 30° determined by McBain quartz spring balance (14). (————) cyclohexane, (------) benzene. (○) adsorption, (●) desorption. (Courtesy of Butterworths.)

molecule (the more strongly adsorbed) to displace another kind (the less strongly adsorbed) from the surface and for the latter molecules to move ahead as a concentrated band.

II. ELUTION CHROMATOGRAPHY

A. Column Materials

Chromatograms with symmetrical elution peaks corresponding to high column efficiencies (low HETP) have been obtained with a very large number of materials prepared by modification of alumina, silica gel, and silica–alumina. A list of those investigated so far is given in Table I. Chromatograms with marked asymmetry even at low sample sizes have been obtained with alumina modified with LiOH, $Al_2(SO_4)_3$, $ZnCl_2$, $CdCl_2$, $CdBr_2$, or with transition metal sulfates, and of course with unmodified alumina, silica gel, or silica alumina.

The modifiers may be classified approximately into four classes:

1. Chemically inactive salts, e.g., the alkali halides. These presumably interact with all adsorbed molecules via London and Debye (dipole–induced dipole) forces and in addition via Keesom (dipole–dipole) forces with polar molecules such as alcohols, ketones, and amines.

TABLE I
List of Modified Adsorbents Which Have Been Found to Give Elution
Chromatograms with Symmetrical Peaks

A Alumina modified with:
  H_2O, I_2, LiOH, LiCl, LiBr, NaOH, NaCl, NaBr, NaI, Na_2CrO_4, Na_2MoO_4,
  Na_2WO_4, KOH, KF, KCl, KBr, KI, KNO_3, K_2CO_3, K_2SO_4, K_2CrO_4,
  $MgSO_4$, CuCl, AgCl, AgI, $AgNO_3$, Ag_2SO_4, CdI_2, Na salts of fatty acids,
  urea
B Silica–alumina modified with:
  LiOH, LiCl, LiBr, LiI, NaOH, NaF, NaCl, NaBr, NaI, KOH, KCl, KBr,
  KI, CsCl
C Silica modified with:
  LiCl, LiBr, LiI, NaCl, NaBr, NaI, KCl, KBr, KI, CuCl, CuBr, Cu(II)alanine,
  $Cu(II)(en)_xSO_4$, Cu(II)tartrate, Cu(II)phenylalanine

2. Salts capable of forming a chemical bond with some adsorbed molecules. Examples include $AgNO_3$ and CuCl which form π complexes with olefins, acetylenes, and aromatics, and many salts which form complexes with amines.

3. Metal complexes. Examples include copper alanine, $AgNO_3$-dodecene, and perhaps metal stearates. Interaction of the adsorbed molecules with the metal is reduced by the presence of the complexing species in the modifier, but there is an additional retardation due to solubility in the rest of the complex. This latter may be markedly affected by the ordered nature of the organic part of the modifier.

4. Organic modifiers. Here particular interest attaches to those modifiers which are known to exert some shape selectivity, e.g., urea, tri-*ortho*-thymotide, and desoxycholic acid.

The general technique for the preparation of the adsorbents is illustrated by the following details for a salt-modified alumina. 100–150 BSS (0.015–0.0104 cm aperture) alumina, having a surface area within the range 110–120 m^2g^{-1} was sieved from 100–200 mesh chromatographic grade material (Peter Spence and Sons Ltd., Widnes, Lancs, England) manufactured by dehydration of gibbsite (γ-$Al_2O_3 \cdot 3H_2O$) at about 400° to give a predominantly crystalline γ-Al_2O_3. The required weight of salt (e.g., about 20% of the weight of the alumina) was dissolved in a predetermined weight of water sufficient to completely wet the alumina when the solution was added and mixed. The water was then slowly removed from the mixture by heating in an oven at 200° and finally drying for 16 hr in a muffle furnace at 250° (400° for alkali metal hydroxides). When cold the material was again sieved. When amounts of modifier are quoted in this article they refer to the weight percentage added to the dry alumina, not to the percentage of the final mixture.

Any contaminant in the carrier gas will tend to be adsorbed onto the column material and this may alter its characteristics. Advantage may sometimes be taken of this effect to produce a particular set of column characteristics. Thus Figure 8 illustrates the symmetrical peaks which may be obtained with alumina modified by the presence of water in the carrier gas stream (15). Insofar as water and sample molecules are

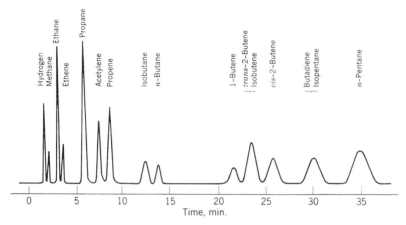

Fig. 8. Separation of hydrogen and hydrocarbons on alumina modified with water (15). Column 200 cm × 6 mm i.d. at 15°. (Courtesy of *Journal of the Institute of Petroleum.*)

merely competing for the same adsorbent sites, a general reduction of retention volumes is to be expected by a factor $(1 + bp_{\text{H}_2\text{O}})$, where b is the Langmuir adsorption coefficient for water, although in practice sample molecules will presumably be adsorbed on more complex sites including those presented by the hydrated salt. In fact, in the presence of water the change in absolute retention volumes is very much greater than that in relative retention volumes, while the effect on Kovats indices is even smaller. This is illustrated by the results quoted in Table II (16). $MgSO_4$/alumina is an example of a system which is very sensitive to the presence of water.

In certain cases, e.g., alumina modified with LiCl or LiBr, considerable hydrolysis can take place, so that the final column has

132   C. S. G. PHILLIPS AND C. G. SCOTT

Effects of Moisture (Drying Conditions) on Retention Volumes and Kovats
Indices at 100°[a]

	Retention volume, ml		Kovats index	
Substance eluted	A^a	C^c	A	C
1. MgSO₄/alumina				
n-Hexane	17.0	73.3	—	—
Hexene-1	36.8	353.3	679.0	721.8
Cyclohexene	39.5	370.2	685.9	729.6
Hexa-1,5-diene	65.3	2691	733.9	790.5
Octane	131.6	908.0	—	—
Benzene	249.6	2689	862.8	885.3
	B^b	C	B	C
2. KBr/alumina				
n-Hexane	21.4	27.7	—	—
Hexene-1	49.2	72.5	662.6	664.6
Cyclohexane	47.8	69.3	659.4	660.8
Hexa-1,5-diene	80.0	125.0	708.3	712.5
Octane	208.6	342.2	—	—
Benzene	172.6	275.1	780.5	781.7

[a] A: Adsorbent oven-dried at 200°; B: Adsorbent oven-dried at 250°; C: Adsorbent oven-dried and then dried *in situ* by passage of slow stream of nitrogen at 250° for 12 hr.

properties expected from a mixed salt-hydroxide modifier. Hydroxide-modified columns tend to be extremely hygroscopic and should be stored with their ends closed off. An NaOH/alumina column left with open ends for more than a month will have formed a hard cake of material at the column ends so that it is impermeable to carrier gas.

If NaI/alumina is prepared in the presence of oxygen, a copious evolution of iodine takes place and some iodate is formed. The resulting column is still entirely satisfactory and its characteristics differ only slightly from those of NaI/alumina prepared in the absence of oxygen, when no iodine is evolved and the final column material has some yellow coloration. (With material prepared in the latter way there is, however, always the risk of oxygen being introduced with the sample or as a contaminant in the carrier gas so that iodine may bleed off into the detector. The former more spectacular preparation is therefore to be preferred for practical columns.)

In addition to acting as catalysts, many columns are themselves changed by interaction with organic vapors. Thus AgNO₃/alumina is reduced to Ag/alumina by olefins and amines at temperatures which vary with the exact mode of preparation but are generally above 100°. CuCl$_2$/alumina and CuCl$_2$/silica gel are highly reactive and produce chlorination, aromatization, and cracking of hydrocarbons from 100° upwards. The reaction with paraffinic hydrocarbons may be used to produce CuCl/alumina and CuCl/silica gel (17).

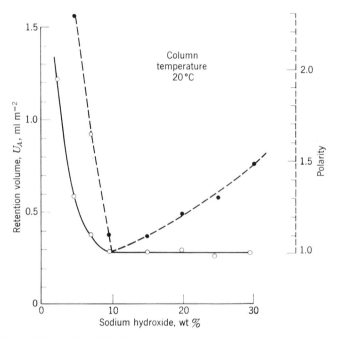

Fig. 9. Effect of NaOH/alumina ratio on retention volume for *n*-pentane (———) and on polarity of surface as measured by ratio of retentions for butadiene and *n*-pentane (------). (Courtesy of Butterworths.)

The thermogravimetric balance is a very useful tool in the investigation of the way in which the nature of the column material may be altered by the temperature at which it is prepared.

Symmetrical elution peaks are only obtained when the weight of modifier used is sufficient to give at least a monolayer coverage. The effect of the percentage weight of modifier on the retention volume and on the selectivity of the column (e.g., retention volume of butadiene/ retention volume of *n*-pentane) is shown in Figure 9 while Figure 10 illustrates changes in the BET surface area (7).

Relatively little work has been done on the factors affecting the efficiency of packed adsorbent columns, and it is probable that quite marked improvements might be obtained by a careful investigation of the effects of particle size, packing techniques, etc. However some modified adsorbent columns have HETP's as small as 0.4 mm, many have values of 0.6 mm, and most are below 1.2 mm at the optimum flow rate. This is as good as is generally achieved with packed GLC columns. In the region of low flow rates, as in GLC, the longitudinal diffusion (B)

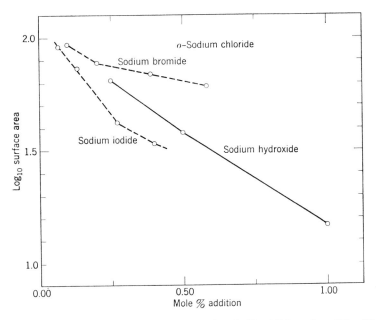

Fig. 10. Relation between surface area and mole % addition of modifier (7).

and the multipath (A) terms will be expected to dominate the van Deemter equation. At high flow rates, where the mass-transfer (C) terms become dominant, some difference will be expected between GSC and GLC because of the absence of any liquid diffusion (C_l) term and the possible presence (18) of an activated adsorption term similar to that discussed by Khan (19) for adsorption at the liquid–gas interface in GLC. The existence of such a term may be surmised from the considerable differences in the high flow rate pattern between, say, Na chromate/alumina and KCl/alumina, where there is a considerable increase of

HETP with flow rate in the first case and a very small increase in the second.

The reproducibility of modified-adsorbent columns also requires more investigation. Such columns have, in general, a very long life and retention volumes are normally constant to within 1 or 2% with the same column either before and after continued use or before and after storage of the column. Comparison between different columns prepared in the same way shows that retention volumes are generally reproducible to within about 5% in terms of the activity of the surface (i.e., for retention volumes per unit area), but to this must be added the variability of surface area resulting from modification which, even under apparently similar conditions, can be $\pm 10\%$. It should be possible to improve on these latter figures with careful attention to the details of preparation.

B. Retention Data and Selectivity

The pattern of retention times is found to vary (a) with the nature of the modifier, (b) the nature of the support, (c) the percentage of modifier, (d) the presence of contaminants (e.g., H_2O), and (e) the temperature of operation of the column.

The most marked effects are achieved by (a), although very significant changes may be brought about by (b). (c) and (d) have been discussed above and (d) will be considered further below, especially in relation to the further modification of e.g., $AgNO_3$ columns with olefin. Increase of temperature, as in GLC, decreases retention times and selectivity within an homologous series, although there are cases where a specific separation factor between two compounds of different types (either structurally or chemically distinguished) may increase with rise of temperature. The various effects are best discussed in terms of the classes of vapor sample. Most of the emphasis will be on hydrocarbon vapors for which modified aluminas, silica gels, and silica-aluminas are most suitable and for which the most data are available.

1. n-Paraffins

At a given temperature the free energy of adsorption of even a paraffin hydrocarbon is much greater on these modified adsorbents than is the free energy of solution in the liquid of a GLC column. As a result comparable retention times are only obtained at temperatures markedly higher than those found in GLC.

Table III (20) gives a number of elution times for n-nonane from a 4 mm i.d. column of length 120 cm operated at 150° and with a carrier gas flow rate of 20 ml min^{-1}. For comparison the same column packed with 20% squalane on Celite gives a retention time of 65 min at 65° and 15 min at 100°. The free energy of adsorption is found to increase linearly with chain length, so that just as in GLC a linear relation is

TABLE III

Column material	%	Elution time	Slope of alkane plot	Surface area for Ar, m^2g^{-1}
$LiOH/SiO_2,Al_2O_3$	9.6	5.94	0.285	83
$LiCl/SiO_2,Al_2O_3$	15.9	58.4	0.318	156
$LiBr/SiO_2,Al_2O_3$	27.9	47.6	0.315	143.5
$LiI/SiO_2,Al_2O_3$	37.2	25.1	0.292	86.5
$NaOH/SiO_2,Al_2O_3$	15.1	16.0	0.289	35.5
$NaF/SiO_2,Al_2O_3$	15.7	20.2	0.284	55.5
$NaCl/SiO_2,Al_2O_3$	20.7	236.0	0.376	223
$NaBr/SiO_2,Al_2O_3$	31.4	183.5	0.367	198
$NaI/SiO_2,Al_2O_3$	40.0	142.8	0.371	178
$KOH/SiO_2,Al_2O_3$	20.0	54.5	0.326	82.5
$KCl/SiO_2,Al_2O_3$	25.0	153.0	0.380	178
$KBr/SiO_2,Al_2O_3$	34.6	142.3	0.367	148
$KI/SiO_2,Al_2O_3$	42.5	197.4	0.395	161
$CsCl/SiO_2,Al_2O_3$	43.0	78.0	0.343	83
$LiCl/SiO_2$	15.9	66.6	0.330	157
$LiBr/SiO_2$	27.9	1.68	0.204	10.0
LiI/SiO_2	37.2	20.3	0.284	86
$NaCl/SiO_2$	20.7	340.0	0.387	293
$NaBr/SiO_2$	31.4	392.0	0.400	279
NaI/SiO_2	40.0	23.5	0.290	95.5
KCl/SiO_2	25.0	198.0	0.368	192.5
KBr/SiO_2	34.6	273.0	0.398	247
KI/SiO_2	42.5	3.0	0.194	11.1
NaI/Al_2O_3	40.0	30.2	0.330	56

found between log (retention time) and the number of carbon atoms. Values for the slope of such an alkane plot (i.e., the log of the ratio of retention times of two adjacent members of the homologous series) are also given in Table III. The corresponding values for squalane columns are 0.390 at 65° and 0.325 at 100°. It will be seen that there is a general relation between retention time and slope. This is to be expected, for a high free energy of adsorption of nonane should be related to a high *difference* in the free energy of adsorption between two *n*-paraffins. A plot of log (retention time) against alkane slope gives a line of slope 10.5 (a slope of 9 would be expected on the simple picture of *n*-nonane as merely 9 CH_2 units) with a scatter of points, the most marked of which is LiOH/silica–alumina. There is also a general relation with surface area, values of which are given in the third column of Table III, and have been determined for argon adsorption at liquid oxygen temperature using the method of Nelsen and Eggertson (21).

2. *Isoparaffins*

On a nonpolar GLC column, retention times of isomeric paraffin hydrocarbons are fairly closely related to boiling points (22). Certain liquids, e.g., benzyl diphenyl, show some selective retardation of straight-chain molecules and this can become quite considerable in the specialized column liquids such as those described by Maczek (23) containing tri-*ortho*-thymotide, or desoxycholic acid. In such cases the branched hydrocarbons have even lower retention times in relation to their boiling points. On the other hand, the gas–solid columns described in this article retard the branched hydrocarbons relative to their position in the boiling point sequence. Just as in GLC there are useful differences in pattern between one adsorbent column and another, but the most marked differences are between gas–solid and gas–liquid columns, so that for many purposes some combination of GSC and GLC will prove considerably more powerful and flexible than either alone.

Extreme retardation of straight-chain paraffins can, of course, be obtained by use of molecular-sieve adsorbents. The use of this effect to determine molecular shape has also been extended to the silanes, germanes, and the mixed hydrides of silicon and germanium (24).

3. *Cycloparaffins*

Even larger differences between the behavior of GLC and GSC columns are observed with respect to cycloparaffins. On GLC columns cycloparaffins are considerably retarded in relation to their boiling point, but with GSC columns they are just as considerably accelerated. This is illustrated by the ratios of the retention times of cyclo- and *n*-paraffins given in Table IV.

4. *Olefins and Aromatics*

Hydrocarbons containing π electrons and π orbitals are able to exhibit additional strong interactions with solid surfaces, whether

TABLE IV
Ratios of Retention Times for Cyclo- and *n*-Paraffins on Three Columns

Hydrocarbons whose retention time ratios are given	Silicone 702, GLC on Celite at 50°	Cu alanine, GSC on Al_2O_3 at 100°	KCl, GSC on Al_2O_3 at 170°
Cyclopentane/*n*-pentane	1.55	1.05	1.08
Cyclohexane/*n*-hexane	2.04	0.98	0.94
Cycloheptane/*n*-heptane	2.66	1.05	0.94
Cyclooctane/*n*-octane	2.55	1.07	0.84

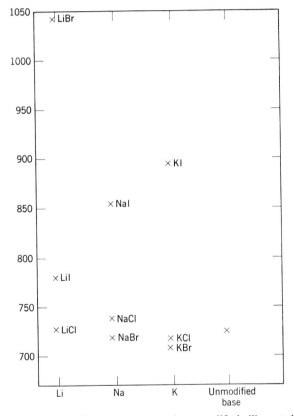

Fig. 11. Kovats indices for benzene on various modified silicas at 150° (20).

through polarization of these electrons by the surface dipoles or by formation of chemical bonds of the Ag^+-olefin type, in which the π electrons of the hydrocarbon are thought to act as donors and the unfilled π orbitals as π acceptors. Very large retardations on these molecules may thus be brought about. It is convenient to relate these retardations to the retention times of the *n*-paraffins, and this may be done by quoting them as Kovats retention indices (25), [where, e.g., a Kovats index of 750 corresponds to a log (retention time) exactly half-way between those of *n*-heptane (700) and *n*-octane (800)].

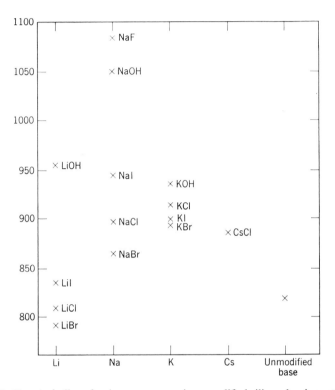

Fig. 12. Kovats indices for benzene on various modified silica–aluminas at 150° (20).

Figures 11 and 12 give a series of Kovats indices (11) for benzene from which it can be seen that, e.g., benzene will emerge just before *n*-undecane from the NaF/silica–alumina column. By appropriate choice of column, olefins or aromatics may be brought, more or less at will, anywhere in the elution sequence. There are also very significant distinctions between different aromatic molecules. Thus on NaI/alumina Kovats indices for ethylbenzene, *m*- and *p*-xylene, *o*-xylene, and *n*-propyl benzene are 1030, 1060, 1080, and 1090, but on LiBr/silica gel the corresponding indices are 1390, 1520, 1570, and 1480. Thus, as well as an increase in the retention times of the aromatics relative to alkanes, there is a particular marked increase for the xylenes.

The effect of the support is brought out by a comparison of Figures 11 and 12. It will be seen that the effect of a salt on one support cannot be predicted with any certainty from its effect on another.

Some values illustrating the change in Kovats index of hexene-1 and of hexa-1,5-diene are given in Table V. It will be seen that the increase in Kovats index is approximately twice as much with the diene as with

TABLE V

Kovats Indices on Modified Aluminas at 100° [a]

Modifier	Hexene-1	Hexa-1,-5-diene	Modifier	Hexene-1	Hexa-1,-5-diene
CdI_2	57.0	111.9	KF	86.5	193.2
KNO_3	60.5	136.9	KCH	90.9	195.0
K_2SO_4	67.9	150.1	LiCl, 200°	108.2	204.4
KCl	70.4	149.8	LiCl, 310°	126.0	225.6
KBr	71.4	150.1	LiBr, 200°	142.6	256.8
KI	73.8	153.1	LiBr, 320°	166.5	280.2
Un-modified					
Al_2O_3	74.6	164.1	LiBr, 410°	188.1	321.2
NaBr	75.0	155.2	LiCl, 410°	200.8	351.8
$CdBr_2$	84.0	144.6	$CdCl_2$	218.2	285.3

[a] Each value tabulated is the increase in Kovats index over the value obtained with a squalane (GLC) column (593.2 for hexene-1 and 562.4 for hexa-1,5-diene). Adsorbents have been dried at 150° unless another temperature is recorded.

the monoolefin in keeping with a free energy of adsorption of two olefin groups. The pattern of retention times for a series of isomeric olefins changes quite distinctly from one solid column to another and also between GSC and GLC columns in general. Particular separations which may be difficult on any one column may often become quite simple by a suitable choice of composite column. Gas–solid columns are especially useful for the separation of *cis–trans* isomers, for interaction of the double bond with the surface can be very sensitive to the particular molecular geometry at that double bond. Thus the *cis-* and *trans-* isomers of heptene-3 have a difference of boiling point of only 0.08° and emerge as one peak from nearly all GLC columns. They are, however, well separated on very many GSC columns as is shown by the separation factors (retention time of *cis*-isomer/retention time of *trans*-isomer) given in Table VI.

TABLE VI

Ratios of Retention Time for *cis*-Heptene-3 and Retention Time for
trans-Heptene-3 (Less Retarded) at 100° on Modified Aluminas (16)[a]

Modifier	Ratio	Modifier	Ratio
KCl	1.26	LiCl, 400°	1.57
CdI$_2$	1.32	LiBr, 400°	1.63
NaCl	1.34	CdBr$_2$	1.78
NaBr	1.35		

[a] All adsorbents have been dried at 250° unless another temperature is recorded.

With the chemically interacting columns, olefins and aromatics are usually so strongly retarded that elution chromatograms cannot be obtained at temperatures below those at which chemical reactions take place on or with the column. The order of interaction strength may, however, be deduced from displacement chromatography. Thus on AgNO$_3$/alumina the following order of decreasing interaction is found (20): octene-1, hexa-1,5-diene, *cis*-heptene-1 with *cis*-heptene-3, heptene-1, diisobutylene, *trans*-heptene-3, toluene, hexene-1, cyclo-hexene, penta-1,3-diene with 4-methyl-*cis*-pentene-2, chlorobenzene with benzene, 4-methyl-*trans*-pentene-2.

It is of some interest that while AgNO$_3$- and Ag$_2$SO$_4$-modified supports have very strong retardations of olefins and aromatics, AgCl and AgI are very similar to alkali halides as modifiers. Presumably the ability of the Ag cation to complex with double bonds is very largely quenched by complexing with the Cl and I anions. AgI/alumina shows anomalous behavior particularly with olefins in the immediate neighbor-hood of the transition temperature of crystalline AgI (145.8°). This suggests that the column contains at least some free (i.e., unadsorbed on the alumina) AgI. The behavior is affected by time and by the presence of moisture.

The use of most of these modified adsorbents for the elution chromatography of other compounds is generally limited by the very strong interactions between polar molecules and the polar surfaces. Chemical reaction often takes place before a satisfactory elution tem-perature is reached. Thus alkyl halides lose hydrogen halide, alcohols lose water, amines lose ammonia, and aldehydes (and to a lesser extent ketones) polymerize. Reaction rate at any temperature is of course very much a function of both vapor molecule and surface.

Halogenated aromatics are satisfactorily separated on modified aluminas at temperatures as high as 175° (Table VII), but cyclohexyl

TABLE VII

Kovats Retention Indices for Some Halogenated Aromatics

	20% NaBr on alumina at 175°	50% CdI$_2$ on alumina at 175°
Fluorobenzene	695	765
Chlorobenzene	835	890
Bromobenzene	905	980
o-Dichlorobenzene	970	985
m-Dichlorobenzene	920	975
p-Dichlorobenzene	940	990
o-Chlorotoluene	915	1000
m-Chlorotoluene	945	1015
p-Chlorotoluene	970	1035

chloride decomposes on KCl/alumina at 90° (first-order velocity constant is 2×10^{-4} sec^{-1}) and tert-butyl chloride starts to decompose even on Celite at about 20°.

Such columns can nevertheless act as useful subtractors, and may be used for concentrating trace quantities subtracted, by use of displacement development.

C. Some Comments on Analytical Applications

The previous section will have made it clear that there is an enormous range of selectivity available with gas–solid columns. With gas–liquid columns the range is very much less; in fact a number of workers (26,27) have commented on the fact that the major distinctions between different gas–liquid columns can be simulated by an appropriate mixture of a nonpolar with a highly polar liquid column. Many analytical problems may thus be relatively easy with a gas–solid column when they are difficult with a gas–liquid column. In many cases the best results will be obtained by a proper combination of gas–solid and gas–liquid columns. The performance of such mixed columns may be easily predicted from the known properties of each with a simple nomographic approach. In general it will be necessary to run the gas–

liquid part of the column at a lower temperature than the gas–solid, although the same kind of result may be achieved by temperature programming: it may be noticed that bleed-off from the gas–liquid column can be effectively removed by the subsequent gas–solid.

The very marked distinctions between gas–solid columns and gas–liquid columns makes the identification of compounds from retention data much more certain when they are chromatographed on two or more columns of very different characteristics. Classes of compounds may often be distinguished in a plot of log (retention time in GSC) against log (retention time in GLC) when compounds of a similar class commonly fall on or near the same straight line.

Analysis by class may also be achieved by using a short length of a suitable gas–solid column as a subtractor and comparing the chromatogram (elution GLC or GSC) with and without this. Thus NaBr/alumina (among many others) removes organic compounds with functional groups (ketones, alcohols, etc.) while $AgNO_3$/alumina or CuCl/alumina is very convenient for the additional removal of olefins, acetylenes, and aromatics. Some of the superior selectivity which is often provided by GSC can, where necessary, be traded in part exchange for some other desirable characteristics. One example is the concentrating characteristics of displacement development as we shall illustrate below. Another is analysis time. Fast analysis with gas–solid columns has been relatively little investigated, but its potentialities have been amply demonstrated by Halász and his co-workers (28). Packed capillary columns may be constructed. Figure 13 illustrates a typical chromatogram obtained. In another example, Halász and Heine (29) obtained an excellent separation of methane, ethane, and ethylene in 2 sec. Aluminum tubing, the inside of which has been oxidized to alumina, may be also used for capillary columns, and the surface of alumina modified with salts (7).

One rather general technique which deserves much more investigation is the further modification of solid surfaces by adsorption of vapor molecules. Thus if $AgNO_3$/alumina is treated with an olefin a column material is produced which gives excellent elution chromatograms. Figure 14 illustrates the elution of cyclohexane from 1-dodecene/$AgNO_3$/alumina at 18° (7). The original activity of the salt surface is reduced, in principle, by a calculable amount, and to this is added the retention provided by the highly oriented and thin film of the adsorbed vapor. The possibility of constructing efficient columns with selectivities

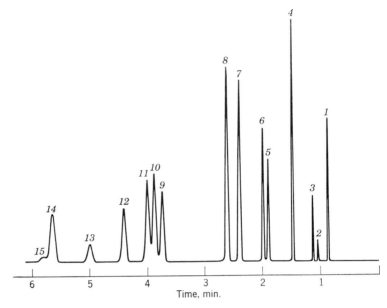

Fig. 13. Separation of low-boiling hydrocarbons using a capillary column (10 m) at 80° packed with alumina and modified by using a carrier gas (hydrogen) moistened with crystalline sodium sulfate. (*1*) methane; (*2*) ethane; (*3*) ethylene; (*4*) propane; (*5*) propylene; (*6*) acetylene; (*7*) isobutane; (*8*) *n*-butane; (*9*) butene-1; (*10*) *trans*-butene-2; (*11*) isobutene; (*12*) *cis*-butene-2; (*13*) isopentane; (*14*) *n*-pentane; (*15*) butadiene. Reproduced from Halász and Heine (28) by courtesy of the authors and *Nature*.

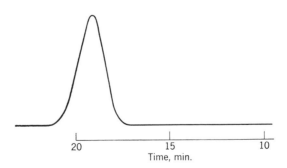

Fig. 14. Elution of cyclohexane from AgNO$_3$/alumina further modified with dodecene-1 (7). Column length 40 cm, temperature 18°.

which may be varied *in situ* is thus considerable. We happen to have investigated $AgNO_3$-modified columns in most detail, but for general practical application other surfaces are more suitable because of the relative ease with which $AgNO_3$-modified columns are decomposed. A

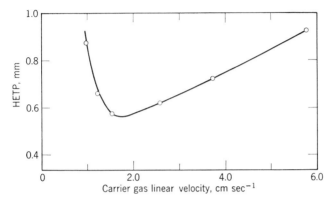

Fig. 15. HETP/flow rate plot for column described in legend to Figure 14 (7).

study of such columns will also be of interest in connection with the theory of the efficiency of gas chromatography, particularly as the liquid film is spread out as part of a monolayer rather than as globules. Figure 15 shows a typical HETP/flow rate curve.

III. DISPLACEMENT CHROMATOGRAPHY

In displacement chromatography each component of the sample is displaced from the column by the vapor of a more strongly adsorbed substance. The more strongly adsorbed substance may be a component of the sample, or it may be an added substance used to further separate two components of the sample in the chromatogram. The most strongly adsorbed component is finally displaced either by a moving heater (30), or by a carrier gas containing a constant concentration of a vapor even more strongly adsorbed and commonly referred to as the displacer. The latter may be achieved by saturating the carrier gas with pure displacer at some suitable temperature below that of the column (5,11). The chromatogram consists of a series of steps each consisting ideally of one component, the nature of which is characterized by the step height or detector signal while its amount is proportional to the step length or

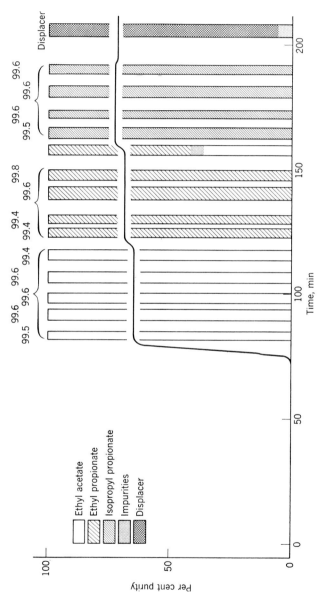

Fig. 16. Displacement of 5 g of ethyl acetate, ethyl propionate, and isopropyl propionate mixture from activated carbon at 75°. Displacer, *m*-xylene vapor from liquid at 45° (11). (Courtesy of the Institute of Petroleum.)

time during which the component emerges. It may be noted that the detector signal and time axes thus exchange roles from those found in elution chromatography. Molecules of one component which move ahead of their step are slowed down because they are only competing with less adsorbed molecules for adsorbent sites, while those which stray into the following step are correspondingly accelerated.

The chief merits of displacement chromatography are (*a*) its ability to concentrate substances, (*b*) its efficient function at high vapor concentrations, e.g., 1 part in 10 of carrier gas, and (*c*) the relatively low temperature, by comparison with elution chromatography, at which it operates. (*a*) leads to its use in trace analysis, (*b*) to its use for preparative work, and (*c*) makes it possible to make use of adsorbent/vapor systems which are unsuitable for elution chromatography because of chemical reactions taking place in the column.

A. Preparative Applications

Figure 16 illustrates the displacement chromatogram of a 5-g sample of esters from a relatively small column containing only 48 g of activated carbon (Type 207C, Sutcliffe Speakman, Leigh, Lancs, England) (11). The purities of the steps were investigated by taking samples and analyzing these by elution (GLC) chromatography. With 350 g of carbon, which can still be packed into a fairly compact (3 ft long) laboratory column, similar separations were achieved with a sample of 50 g. There is no reason why this sample size should not be extended upward very considerably so that a large laboratory apparatus could be made to produce several kilograms per hour.

The degree of separation achieved is not, however, as great as that in elution chromatography from the same column material, and closely similar substances give rise to mixed steps. Mixed steps can also occur when the sample contains species of different chemical type. The choice of column for a particular preparative separation is thus commonly a more complex matter than the choice of a column for an analytical separation by elution chromatography. Advantage may, however, be taken of the range of selectivities available with gas–solid columns. Thus Figure 17 shows the successful preparative separation of the *cis–trans* isomers of heptene-3 using 25 g of AgNO$_3$/alumina for 1 g of heptene-3 (11). Again the purity of the steps was investigated by elution chromatography, although in this case the column was a gas–solid one.

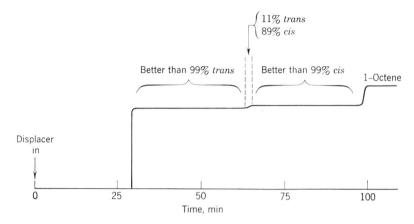

Fig. 17. Displacement of 1 g of a mixture of *cis*- and *trans*-heptene-3 at 75° from AgNO₃/alumina. Displacer octene-1 vapor from liquid at 45° (11). (Courtesy of the Institute of Petroleum.)

B. Trace Concentration and Analysis

The concentration of trace impurities in a displacement chromatogram is illustrated in Figure 16, and in Figure 18 which shows the elution chromatograms obtained in the analysis of rising step between toluene and *meta*-xylene during the displacement of a 50-g mixture of benzene, toluene, and *meta*-xylene (from a carbon column at 100°) (11) with bromobenzene displacer.

Again the most interesting applications of the technique involve the use of highly selective columns. We illustrate the method by considering the analysis of traces of olefins in paraffinic hydrocarbons (31). It may be noted that we are essentially combining chromatography with the selective formation of chemical compounds.

n-Heptane was first freed from olefins by passing the liquid through a column of AgNO₃/alumina (about 10 g of adsorbent for 100 g of heptane.) Small quantities of hexene and heptene were then added to 100-g samples of the purified heptane. These samples were then forced under slight nitrogen pressure and at room temperature through an AgNO₃/alumina column (3 mm i.d. and 1 g of packing). When the column was free of liquid, its temperature was raised to 75° and the last traces of heptane eluted with nitrogen. The hexene and heptene were then displaced from the column by a stream of nitrogen which had been saturated with purified octene at 45°. When the olefin samples were in

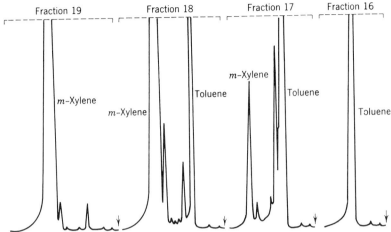

Fig. 18. Elution chromatograms for fractions taken at changeover from toluene to *m*-xylene step in displacement from activated carbon at 100°. Displacer bromobenzene vapor from liquid at 80° (11). (Courtesy of the Institute of Petroleum.)

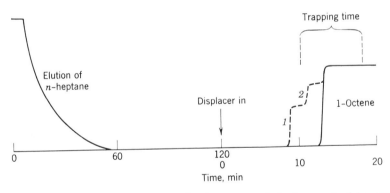

Fig. 19. Elution of last traces of *n*-heptane, and displacement of hexene (step 1) and heptene (step 2) from a AgNO₃/alumina column (31). (Courtesy of *Nature*.)

the range 1–10 mg, distinct hexene and heptene steps were produced (Fig. 19), the lengths of which were found to be proportional to the quantities of olefins added originally, so that this direct method is suitable for quantitative analysis down to 1 part in 10^5. The limit could be lowered considerably by use of a correspondingly lower concentration of octene displacer with some reduction in column temperature. An alternative and more satisfactory method is to trap out the front of the octene step and analyze this with elution chromatography. Figure 20 illustrates the type of chromatogram thus obtained when only 1 μg of each olefin was added.

The peak areas were found to be independent of the amount of packing in the column, indicating that there was no significant irreversible adsorption. The method can thus be used for the quantitative

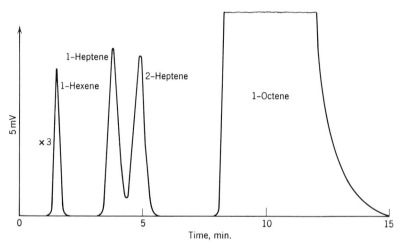

Fig. 20. Elution analysis of octene front (see Fig. 19) on gas–liquid (squalane) column with flame-ionization detector. 1 μg each of hexene-1, heptene-1, and heptene-2 from 100 g of n-heptane (31). (Courtesy of Nature.)

analysis of olefins in paraffins at the 1 in 10^8 level. There would appear to be no inherent difficulty in extending the method to even lower levels.

Blank runs on unadulterated 100-g samples of n-heptane which had been purified by passage through $AgNO_3$/alumina produced no detectable elution peaks before octene, showing that the lower (and presumably any higher) olefins had been effectively removed down to a level of 1 part in 10^{10}. Selective adsorbent columns should thus have a useful application in the preparation of solvents substantially free from traces of a particular kind of impurity. The octene used as displacer was itself purified by a pseudo-displacement technique. Twenty-five grams of $AgNO_3$/alumina was first saturated with commercial octene at room temperature and purged with nitrogen. The column temperature was then raised to 120° to release about 1.5 g of purified octene which was trapped out at low temperature. Less stringent purification was sufficient when milligram quantities of olefins were concerned.

Acknowledgments

We wish to thank Messrs. W. G. Pye and Co. Ltd. for the loan of an argon chromatograph and the Hydrocarbon Research Group of the Institute of Petroleum for financial assistance.

References

1. A. J. P. Martin and R. L. M. Synge, *Biochem. J.*, **35**, 1358 (1941).
2. A. T. James and A. J. P. Martin, *Biochem. J.*, **52**, 242 (1952).
3. G. Hesse, *Ann. Chem.*, **546**, 251 (1941).
4. S. Claesson, *Arkiv Kemi*, **A23**, No. 1 (1946).
5. C. S. G. Phillips, *Discussions Faraday Soc.*, No. 7, 241 (1949).
6. D. H. Everett, in *Gas Chromatography 1964*, A. Goldup, Ed., Institute of Petroleum, London, 1965, p. 223.
7. C. G. Scott, Ph.D. thesis, Oxford (1964).
8. A. V. Kiselev, in *Gas Chromatography 1964*, A. Goldup, Ed., Institute of Petroleum, London, 1965, p. 238.
9. I. Halász and C. Horvath, *Anal. Chem.*, **36**, 1178 (1964).
10. O. L. Hollis, *Anal. Chem.*, **38**, 309 (1966).
11. C. G. Scott and C. S. G. Phillips, in *Gas Chromatography 1964*, A. Goldup Ed., Institute of Petroleum, London, 1965, p. 266.
12. G. R. Primavesi, in *Gas Chromatography 1964*, A. Goldup, Ed., Institute of Petroleum, London, 1965, p. 356.
13. C. G. Scott, *Nature*, **187**, 143 (1960).
14. C. G. Scott, in *Gas Chromatography 1962*, M. van Swaay, Ed., Butterworths 1962, p. 36.
15. C. G. Scott, *J. Inst. Petrol.*, **45**, 118 (1959).
16. G. C. Clayfield, Ph.D. thesis, Oxford, 1964.
17. A. Hart-Davis, thesis, part II, Oxford, 1966.
18. S. Blume, unpublished results.
19. M. A. Khan, *Nature*, **186**, 800 (1960).
20. T. P. O'Brien, B.S. thesis, Oxford, 1964.
21. F. M. Nelsen and F. T. Eggertson, *Anal. Chem.*, **30**, 1387 (1958).
22. T. W. Godden, thesis, part II, Oxford, 1966.
23. A. O. S. Maczek and C. S. G. Phillips, in *Gas Chromatography 1960*, R. P. W. Scott, Ed., Butterworths, 1960, p. 284.
24. P. L. Timms, C. C. Simpson, and C. S. G. Phillips, *J. Chem. Soc.*, **1964**, 1467.
25. Recommendations for the publication of retention data, in *Gas Chromatography 1964*, A. Goldup, Ed., Institute of Petroleum, London, 1965, p. 350.
26. A. B. Littlewood, *J. Gas. Chromatog.*, **1**, 16 (1963).

27. L. Rohrschneider, *J. Chromatog.*, **17**, 1 (1965).
28. I. Halász and E. Heine, *Nature*, **194**, 971 (1962).
29. I. Halász and E. Heine, *Chem. Ingr.-Tech.*, **37**, 61 (1965).
30. N. C. Turner, *Oil Gas J.*, **48** (April 1943).
31. C. G. Scott and C. S. G. Phillips, *Nature*, **199**, 66 (1963).

Optimum Conditions in Gas Chromatographic Analysis

István Halász and Erwin Heine, *Institut für Physikalische Chemie der Universität Frankfurt/Main, Germany*

I. INTRODUCTION

That compounds not resolved in a chromatographic column cannot then be separated by devices (such as a detector or an integrator) behind the column is an often-forgotten truism. In special cases, of course, such as when specific detectors are used, separation may appear to be achieved, but it also follows that in this case the chromatographic column may be unnecessary. Despite this, however, much more effort has been expended recently in the development of auxiliary devices for gas chromatographic equipment, and in the coupling of this method with other analytical tools, than in attempts to find the best column types and the best conditions for the gas chromatographic separation itself.

This paper is aimed at focusing attention on the column performance and discusses optimum conditions for nonprogrammed, analytical gas chromatography. All considerations are based on the assumptions that every mixture has one pair of compounds which are hardest to resolve and that the whole separation problem can be reduced to that of resolution of this pair. Optimal parameters for this separation may then be calculated and, as will be seen, consideration of these leads to a classification of column types and a basis for determining the best choice of column type for a given analytical problem. The conditions of analysis throughout this discussion are calculated for one pair of compounds but, of course, the conclusions can be extended to separation problems involving any number of components, within reasonable retention time limits, as long as these have a generally similar chemical nature. The calculations implied above are based, in practice, on the results of simplified experiments which may be extended to produce a solution to difficult problems with confidence.

The theory of gas chromatography appears highly sophisticated to the analyst, and therefore is often neglected by him. This is, in fact, an erroneous attitude. In order to overcome this attitude, and to provide a self-contained basis for discussion, we will start by outlining the essential theory. In our opinion, this amount of theory is necessary and sufficient to the successful prosecution of practical analytical work. Only those parameters which can be taken directly from the chromatogram itself or from the experimental conditions appear in the equations developed. To this extent, therefore, it is a very practical theory.

II. NOMENCLATURE

In Figure 1 a chromatogram is shown as an illustration of the usual definitions of practical quantities. t_o is the gas holdup (retention time for an inert gas), t_R is the retention time, t_R' the net retention time, and w is the peak width (the baseline intercept of the tangents to the inflection points). The *capacity ratio*, k', is defined as the ratio of the net retention time to the gas holdup ($k' = t_R'/t_o$). We then have the well-known equations:

$$t_R = t_o + t_R' = t_o[1 + k(V_s/V_m)]$$

$$t_R = t_o\left(1 + \frac{k}{a}\right) = t_o(1 + k') = \frac{L}{\bar{u}}(1 + k') \qquad (1)$$

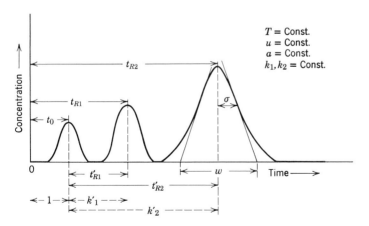

Fig. 1. Chromatogram illustrating chromatographic parameters.

where k is the thermodynamic partition coefficient of the sample between the stationary and mobile phases, and a is the *phase ratio* defined as the ratio of the volume of the mobile phase V_m to the volume of the stationary phase V_s. From eq. (1) it is seen that $k' = k/a = kV_s/V_m$, if equilibrium between mobile and stationary phase is achieved. At high carrier-gas velocities it may sometimes be observed that k' is decreasing with increasing carrier-gas velocity; this is a clear indication that equilibrium is not being attained (1). In such a situation, chromatographic theory is inapplicable; in addition, the practical problems of achieving separation are increased.

III. COMPRESSIBILITY OF THE CARRIER GAS AND COLUMN PERMEABILITY

The time-averaged mean carrier-gas velocity $\bar{u}$ is easily calculable from the chromatogram since, as implied in eq. (1), $\bar{u} = L/t_o$, where L is the column length. $\bar{u}$ is an important parameter, because it is inversely proportional to the retention time. The outlet velocity of the carrier gas u_o is calculable from $\bar{u}$ via the James-Martin (2) pressure-correction factor j; thus $u_o = \bar{u}/j$. The sample size s is defined in this paper as the sample entering the column, i.e., the injected sample size times any relevant splitting ratio, the latter being < 1.

It can be shown (3) that

$$\bar{u} = (Kj'/\eta L)\Delta p \tag{2}$$

where η is the viscosity of the carrier gas, $\Delta p = p_i - p_o$ (i.e., the pressure drop across the column) and j' is a further pressure-correcting factor (3) derived on the same premises as those leading to j. As a definition:

$$j' = \frac{3}{4} \left\{ \frac{4 + 4(\Delta p/p_o) + (\Delta p/p_o)^2}{3 + 3(\Delta p/p_o) + (\Delta p/p_o)^2} \right\} = \left\{ \frac{(p_i/p_o) + 1}{2} \right\} j \tag{3}$$

We see that $0.75 < j' < 1$ and so, for gases, $\bar{u}$ deviates from the corresponding value for liquids (where $j' = 1$) by no more than 25% because of its compressibility. Some j' values are given in Table I as a function of the dimensionless quantity $\Delta p/p_o$. This table will prove to be frequently useful.

The specific permeability coefficient (4), briefly called the per-

TABLE I

Values of the Pressure Correction Factor j'
for Selected Values of $\Delta p/p_o$

$\Delta p/p_o$	j'
0	1.000
0.5	0.987
1.0	0.964
1.5	0.943
2.0	0.923
2.5	0.907
3.0	0.892
4.0	0.871
5.0	0.855
6.0	0.842
7.0	0.832
8.0	0.824
9.0	0.818
10.0	0.812
∞	0.750

meability K, is independent of carrier gas, temperature, and column length. For ideal open tubes

$$K = d^2/32 \qquad (4)$$

where d is the inner diameter of the column. According to the Kozeny–Carman equation (5,6), in regularly random-packed columns:

$$K = (d_p^2/180)[\epsilon^3/(1 - \epsilon)^2] \qquad (5)$$

where d_p is the average particle diameter and ϵ is the interparticle porosity, i.e., the fraction of column cross section available to moving gases. To a good approximation, $\epsilon = 0.4$ for conventional packed columns as used in gas chromatography and is more or less independent of the particle size of the support. For such columns $K = d_p^2/1000$ is a good empirical approximation.

IV. RELATIVE PEAK WIDTH, EFFICIENCY, AND RESOLUTION

The measurement of zone spreading in chromatography is most conveniently made in terms of peak width relative to retention, these being measured in the same units. Either of the following functions may be used:

$$h = (L/16)(w/t_R)^2 \qquad (6)$$

or

$$H = (L/16)(w/t_R')^2 = [(1 + k')/k']^2 h \qquad (7)$$

Both h (15,16) and H (7,17) are empirical constants which are more or less independent of the column length (8). They may, of course, be given a theoretical basis and, contrary to belief, the physical definition of H is as well founded as that of h (9). The former has the small, mainly theoretical disadvantage that it is zero for an inert gas peak, but it has the considerable advantage of being closely related to the most important practical quantity, the resolution R. Furthermore, the maximum number of peaks which can be separated between the inert gas peak and the peak which is characterized by H is approximately inversely proportional to $H^{1/2}$; this is especially applicable to capillary columns (10). h and H are described in the literature as "height equivalent to a theoretical plate" HETP, and as "height equivalent to an effective theoretical plate" HEETP (7), respectively. Practical considerations will determine whether h or H is to be preferred.

The efficiency of a column is usually described in terms of n or N, which are defined as follows:

$$n = 16(t_R/w)^2 = L/h \qquad (8)$$

and

$$N = 16(t_R'/w)^2 = L/H = [k'/(1+k')]^2 n \qquad (9)$$

As can be seen from eqs. (6)–(9), relative peak broadening and, hence, column efficiency is always defined for one component of a mixture only. Consequently, these values alone can never entirely characterize the separation of two compounds. To avoid misunderstanding caused by analogy with the common nomenclature of distillation, the use of the terms "number of theoretical plates" for n and "number of effective plates" for N, in chromatography, should really be avoided. However, the practice is very strongly established.

To calculate H or N, the gas holdup has to be known. The determination of t_0 which is thus required can sometimes be difficult, especially with flame-ionization detection (11). If t_0 is required only in a rough approximation, the gas holdup is calculable from flow data via eq. (4) for open tubes, if the inner diameter and column length are known, and via eq. (5) for conventional packed columns if a porosity $\epsilon \approx 0.40$–0.45 is assumed.

It should be pointed out that, for a given column at constant flow rate and constant temperature, the efficiency is a function of the retention time (or k' value) of the components. In the present discussion the peak width and retentions have been quoted in time units. The relative peak widths, the efficiencies, and the resolution are calculable on this basis only if the outlet velocity of the carrier gas p_o is constant from situation to situation. If this is not the case in practice, these values, i.e., w, t_R, and R, have to be given their correct dimensions of volume. This point is particularly important to note in the context of programmed chromatographic techniques.

A. The van Deemter Equation

The relative peak broadening (h or H), as a function of the carrier gas velocity, may be described by the virtually complete form of the van Deemter equation. This equation is usually given with h as parameter. In this paper it shall be given for H because this quantity is more important for practical analytical purposes:

$$H = A + (B/u_o) + C_m u_o + C_s \bar{u} \tag{10}$$

or,

$$H = A + B(j/\bar{u}) + C_m(\bar{u}/j) + C_s \bar{u} \tag{11}$$

where A, B, C_m, and C_s are coefficients independent of pressure. It should be clearly noted here that these coefficients are related to those of the more usual form of van Deemter equation through eq. (7).

The second term on the right-hand side of the equations accounts for peak broadening due to longitudinal gas phase diffusion. The third and fourth terms account for peak broadening due to mass transfer in the mobile and stationary phases, respectively. The pressure dependence of the diffusion coefficient in the gas phase ($D_{g_o} p_o = D_{g_i} p_i = \bar{D}_g \bar{p}$) is taken into account in these equations (6,7). For columns with very great phase ratio, for example conventional open tubes, the C_s term can usually be neglected, whereas for those with a small phase ratio, for example, conventional packed columns, the C_m term is sometimes negligible.

As pointed out, when the van Deemter equation is expressed in terms of h, the constants on the right-hand side of eqs. (10) and (11) have to be multiplied by the factor $[k'/(1 + k')]^2$. This, however, does not lead to any difference in the shape of the h vs. $\bar{u}$ and H vs. $\bar{u}$ plots.

The characteristic quantities at the minimum of the h (or H) vs. $\bar{u}$ curve are designated h_{min} or H_{min}; $\bar{u}_{min}$ is clearly the same for both.

B. Effect of the Length and the Pneumatic Resistance of the Column on h vs. $\bar{u}$ Curves

Let us suppose that the constants of the van Deemter equation are independent of the column length. With elongation of a column, other parameters remaining constant, the hydrodynamic resistance of the

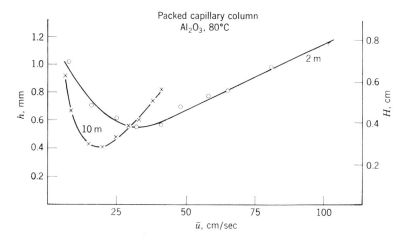

Fig. 2. Effect of column elongation (GSC). Sample: propane. Column type: packed capillary. $K = 8 \times 10^{-7}$ cm²; $t_c = 80°C$; i.d. = 0.32 mm; $d_p =$ 0.10–0.15 mm; 26 mg alumina per meter column length; $k' = 0.62$. Carrier gas, hydrogen moistened over $Na_2SO_4 \cdot 10H_2O$ at 20°C. $s = 10^{-6}$ g; FID detection.

column rises. So, to achieve the same mean carrier-gas velocity $\bar{u}$, a higher pressure drop Δp across the column is needed. Correspondingly, at constant outlet pressure, the pressure-correction factor j becomes smaller. If C_s can be neglected in comparison with C_m, the minimum of the H vs. $\bar{u}$ curve will be found at $\bar{u}_{min} = j(B/C_m)^{1/2}$. Thus, with elongation of a column, $\bar{u}_{min}$ shifts in the direction of smaller velocities, when $C_m \gg C_s$. Furthermore, it is calculable that the descending and ascending branches for the longer column shall be steeper (8,12). This effect of column elongation on the H vs. $\bar{u}$ curve of a packed capillary column (where generally $C_m \gg C_s$) is well demonstrated by the experimental data shown in Figure 2.

The same situation may be expected for two column types having the same $H_{\min}$ for a given compound but of different permeability to flow. If $C_m \gg C_s$, the minimum of the H vs. $\bar{u}$ curve for the column with higher (better) permeability should appear at higher $\bar{u}_{\min}$. This is obviously very convenient for high-speed analysis. Open tube columns have, by definition, great phase ratios and their behavior is typical of the effect discussed.

It might be expected from eqs. (10) and (11) that the elongation of conventional packed columns (where $C_s \gg C_m$) has no influence on the H vs. $\bar{u}$ curve at high velocities. On the contrary, the shape and location of the H vs. $\bar{u}$ curve are found experimentally (1) to be a function of the column length. In particular, the ascending branch of the H vs. $\bar{u}$ curve is much steeper for long than for shorter columns. This arises because the pneumatic resistance is of great importance.

The usual simplifying assumption made in gas chromatography, that h is independent of the column length, is thus seen to be valid only at relatively low carrier gas velocities. It is unfortunate that it is not valid in the conditions of high-speed analysis. Nevertheless, this simplification will be generally adopted in the further discussion since discussion to the contrary becomes unnecessarily complicated.

C. The "Column Constants" of the van Deemter Equation

Much work has been done in attempts to theoretically evaluate the constants of the van Deemter equation. For this purpose, the equation is almost always discussed in h vs. $\bar{u}$ form. The velocity-independent first term (the so-called *eddy diffusion* term) should be independent of the identity of the solute, the pressure, the carrier, and the temperature. It has been found experimentally (13,14) that A is dependent upon all these variables. The constant of the second (longitudinal diffusion) term should be dependent only on the gaseous diffusion coefficient of the solute in the carrier gas. In many cases it has been found experimentally that it also depends on other variables. For the third and fourth (mass transfer) terms, it can also be said, in general, that the theoretical predictions cannot be verified experimentally (13,14).

This gap between experiment and theory is filled by the introduction by theorists of arbitrarily adjustable constants (λ, γ, and d_f). Recent theory has attempted to give physical meaning to these quantities. Even so, it seems best to regard the van Deemter equation as no more than a short McLaurin series which adequately describes the experimental results in terms of a number of empirical constants. For the practical analyst, if no other, this seems the only rational course.

D. Resolution

For constant outlet velocity of the carrier gas, the resolution (R) is defined by:

$$R = 2\{[(t'_{R2} - t'_{R1})/(w_2 + w_1)]\} = 2\{[(t_{R2} - t_{R1})/(w_2 + w_1)]\} \quad (12)$$

The relative retention r_{12} is a thermodynamic function and is independent of the column type for given solvent, solutes, and temperature. This can be written:

$$r_{12} = k_2/k_1 = k_2'/k_1' = t'_{R2}/t'_{R1} \neq t_{R2}/t_{R1} \quad (13)$$

For two peaks with small relative retention ($r_{12} < 1.1$), the column efficiency (n or N) is effectively the same for both; hence,

$$R = \frac{(r_{12} - 1)}{r_{12}} \sqrt{\frac{N_2}{16}} = \frac{(r_{12} - 1)}{r_{12}} \sqrt{\frac{L}{16H_2}} = \left(\frac{r_{12} - 1}{r_{12}}\right) \frac{t_R'}{w} \quad (14)$$

or, to an excellent approximation,

$$R = \frac{(r_{12} - 1)}{r_{12}} \frac{k'}{(1 + k')} \sqrt{\frac{n_2}{16}} = \frac{(r_{12} - 1)}{r_{12}} \frac{k'}{(1 + k')} \sqrt{\frac{L}{16h_2}} \quad (15)$$

Equation (14) shows that the resolution of any number of pairs of substances of the same r_{12} is proportional only to the square root of N. The right-hand side of eq. (14) shows, furthermore, that from the point of view of the resolution, only the net retention time t_R' (and not the retention time t_R) is of interest. This finding most strongly reinforces the view expressed earlier that, for practical purposes, one should use H instead of h and, as first pointed out by Purnell (17), N should be used rather than n.

1. Resolution at Different Temperatures

As is seen from eq. (15), the resolution R is a function of (a) the relative retention r_{12}, (b) the capacity ratio k', and (c) the relative peak broadening h. These all vary with temperature. In most cases r_{12} and k' decrease, and $(h)^{-1/2}$ increases, with increasing temperature. Thus, these factors can compensate or, more commonly, overcompensate each other. Consequently, the resolution vs. temperature curve usually passes through a maximum (10). This maximum is the optimum temperature for the analysis of the given pair of substances with a given column. However, this temperature is often technically inconvenient; for example, it frequently is found to be subambient. In such situations a column type with a lower phase ratio has to be used as a compromise.

Using H, instead of h, the discussion of the R vs. temperature curve is simpler [cf. eq. (14)], because the temperature dependence of k' is included in that of H.

The resolution of a mixture of n-hexane/n-heptane for unit length of column (R/L) as a function of temperature is shown in Figure 3.

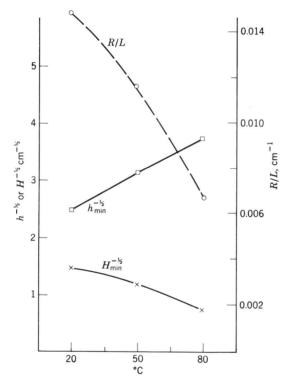

Fig. 3. Relative peak broadening of n-heptane and resolution of n-hexane/n-heptane at various temperatures (GLC). Packed capillary column: stationary phase; 2.1% by weight squalane (0.34 mg squalane and 16 mg Chromosorb W per meter column length). $L = 10$ m; i.d. $= 0.35$ mm; $d_p = 0.10$–0.12 mm (120–140 mesh). Carrier gas: nitrogen. $K = 18.5 \times 10^{-7}$ cm^2; $s = 0.5 \times 10^{-6}$ g; FID detection.

The maximum of this curve is not shown, because no measurements were made at subambient temperatures. The temperature dependence of the inverse of the square root of minimal relative peak broadening is also demonstrated in Figure 3. The increase of $h_{min}^{-1/2}$ with increasing temperature is, in this particular example, overcompensated by the decrease of the partition coefficient [which determines k' in eq. (7) at constant phase ratio], hence $H_{min}^{-1/2}$ decreases at higher temperatures as well as R/L. Since the relative retention becomes smaller at higher temperatures, R/L drops with increasing temperature more rapidly than does $H_{min}^{-1/2}$.

The curves in Figure 3 demonstrate very clearly that, as predicted by eqs. (14) and (15), the resolving power of a column is defined only by r_{12} and N together (or, alternatively, by r_{12}, k', and n).

V. OPTIMUM ANALYTICAL CONDITIONS

In gas chromatography it is important that: (1) separation should be as complete as possible; (2) analysis time should be short; and (3) technical difficulties should be minimized; for example, temperatures below 30°C and pressures above 5 at clearly introduce extra experimental difficulty.

In this paper only isothermal and isobaric conditions of analysis are discussed. Consequently, the problem of separating a mixture is reduced to that of the resolution of the two compounds with the smallest relative retention. In practice, sufficient and quick separation is obtained for symmetrical peaks with $R = 1.5$. If the relative retentions within a mixture differ grossly, programmed temperature and/or programmed pressure is probably to be recommended.

A. Separation Factor

As first derived by Purnell (17), and according to eq. (14), the minimum necessary N value [or separation factor S (17)] for resolution is:

$$S = N_{ne} = [4Rr_{12}/(r_{12} - 1)]^2 \qquad (16)$$

where S is a function only of the nature of the pair of substances to be resolved, of the stationary phase, and of the temperature. It is noteworthy that it is independent of the column type used.

B. Necessary Time of Analysis

It can be shown (18) that at every point of the H vs. $\bar{u}$ curve the necessary time of analysis t_{ne} (corresponding to N_{ne}) for the given carrier gas velocity is:

$$t_{ne} = (H/\bar{u})(1 + k_2')S \qquad (17)$$

or

$$t_{ne} = (1 + k_2')(HL/K)(\eta/\Delta pj')S \qquad (18)$$

The necessary time of analysis depends on (a) the identity and speed of the carrier gas ($\bar{u}$, η); (b) the column properties, H, L, Δp, and k'; and (c) the temperature, which is implicitly involved in determining S, k', H, η, and Δp.

C. Necessary Column Length and Pressure Drop

Corresponding to t_{ne} there is a necessary column length (L_{ne}) and necessary pressure drop (Δp_{ne}) for every point of the H vs. $\bar{u}$ curve. These are given (3) by:

$$L_{ne} = HS \qquad (19)$$

$$\Delta p_{ne} = (\eta/Kj')H\bar{u}S \qquad (20)$$

From a H vs. $\bar{u}$ curve a t_{ne} vs. Δp_{ne} curve is calculable via eqs. (17)–(20) for any given temperature. To every point of the latter curve there corresponds the column length (L_{ne}) defined by eq. (19). In Figure 4 the H vs. $\bar{u}$ curve of n-heptane on a packed capillary column is shown for different temperatures. The $H/\bar{u}$ vs. $H\bar{u}$ curve, calculated from Figure 4, is shown in Figure 5. This latter curve is of great importance because the time of analysis is proportional to $H/\bar{u}$ and the price of the speed, i.e., the pressure drop, is proportional to $H\bar{u}$. The t_{ne} vs. Δp_{ne} curve, calculated from Figures 4 and 5, is given in Figure 6. The necessary column lengths for every point on Figures 5 and 6 are not shown on the diagrams since this would lead only to confusion.

D. Optimum Parameters

If the permeability of a column is poor, relatively short columns have to be used. The maximum pressure drop is frequently limited by the pressure-regulating and injection equipment of the gas chromatographic system and this determines the shortest feasible time of analysis

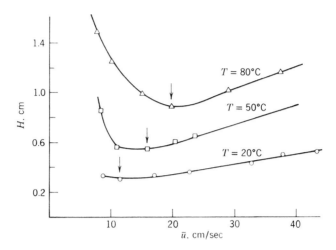

Fig. 4. H vs. $\bar{u}$ curve of n-heptane with a packed capillary column (GLC) (100). $K = 11 \times 10^{-7}$ cm^2; $L = 10$ m; i.d. $= 0.32$ mm; $d_p = 0.10$–0.12 mm (120–140 mesh). Stationary phase: 0.28 mg squalane per meter column length on Chromosorb W. $a = 242$; $k' = 5.2$ (20°C); 1.63 (50°C); 0.66 (80°C). Carrier gas: hydrogen. $s = 10^{-6}$ g; PI $= 18$ poise (50°C). FID detection.

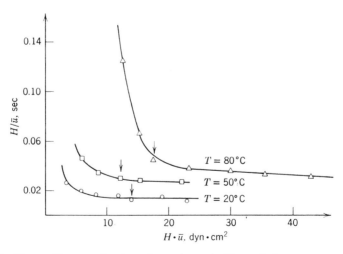

Fig. 5. $H/\bar{u}$ vs. $H\bar{u}$ curve for the column shown in Figure 3. Parameters are the same as in Figure 4.

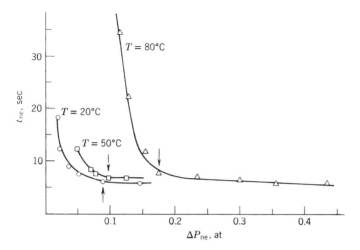

Fig. 6. Necessary pressure drop vs. necessary time of analysis at a resolution $R = 1.5$ for n-hexane/n-heptane (100). Parameters are the same as in Figure 4.

on the t_{ne} vs. Δp_{ne} curve. In such cases the best operating parameters are those corresponding to the minimum of the H vs. $\bar{u}$ curve, i.e., those calculated from H_{min} and $\bar{u}_{min}$. It is clearly preferable to have a column system at a temperature where the minimum of this curve is flat and broad with a small H_{min} value.

If the permeability, the column length, and the pressure-regulating system of the equipment allow it, short times of analysis are available using much higher carrier gas velocities than $\bar{u}_{min}$. The optimum (minimum) time of analysis corresponds to conditions at the minimum of the t_{ne} vs. Δp_{ne} curve (Fig. 6) or at the minimum of the $H/\bar{u}$ vs. $H\bar{u}$ curve (Fig. 5); both curves have the same shape, as is clear from eqs. (18) and (20). Since the diffusion coefficient in the gas phase is a function of $\bar{p}$ (or $\bar{u}$), both curves pass through a minimum (19–21). The descending branch of these curves is very steep; the minimum is flat and broad (the ascending branches are not shown in Figs. 5 and 6). To save carrier gas, and to have the smallest possible pressure drop across the column, it is advisable to work at the beginning of this minimum, i.e., to use the smallest $\bar{u}$ on the flat minimum. This point is designated by $(H/\bar{u})_{opt}$, $(H\bar{u})_{opt}$, H_{opt}, and $\bar{u}_{opt}$, respectively. Because $H_{opt} > H_{min}$, longer columns have to be used at this higher velocity.

It may be shown from eq. (2) that the pressure drop at constant t_o (or $\bar{u}$) increases with the square of the column length. Increasing $\bar{u}$

(because $\bar{u}_{opt} > \bar{u}_{min}$) means increasing the pressure drop even further. For this reason and because of probable limitations imposed by the inlet pressure, high permeability (large K value) of the column and low H_{opt} are the crucial conditions for high performance and short time of analysis.

The optimum parameters of analysis are given the symbols t_{opt}, Δp_{opt}, and L_{opt}. Calculation of these is made with the help of a H vs. $\bar{u}$ curve determined for any column length since we assume H to be independent of L. As pointed out earlier this is not always true, but in most practical cases this Calculation is a good enough approximation (22). In doubtful cases it is advisable to repeat the measurements on a column of length not far away from L_{opt}.

In Table II, parameters calculated from the separation of n-hexane/n-heptane mixtures are listed. These were calculated from the data of Figures 4–6. Parameters with the subscript "min" were calculated from the H_{min} and $\bar{u}_{min}$ points shown with arrows in Figure 4. Arrows in Figures 5 and 6 show the "optimum" values for all the three temperatures calculated in Table II.

The relative retention of n-hexane/n-heptane is unusually high, so the separation problem is simple and a quite short column could be used with a correspondingly short time of analysis. Pressure drop offers no limitation in the separation of such mixtures as n-hexane/n-heptane.

TABLE II

Calculated Operating Parameters (from Figs. 3–5) for a
Packed Capillary Column

	Good solvent			Poor solvent
	20°C	50°C	80°C	20°C
r_{nC_6/nC_7}	3.19	2.76	2.35	1.05
S	76.4	88.5	108	15,900
t_{opt}, sec	6.14	7.02	7.88	1,270
t_{min}, sec	12.57	7.34	7.88	2,664
Δp_{opt}, at	0.088	0.098	0.18	18.3
Δp_{min}, at	0.022	0.069	0.18	4.57
L_{opt}, cm	33	53	96	6,860
L_{min}, cm	24	48	96	5,000
u_{opt}, cm/sec	32.8	20.4	19.9	32.8
u_{min}, cm/sec	11.4	15.9	19.9	11.4
H_{opt}, cm	0.43	0.60	0.89	0.43
H_{min}, cm	0.31	0.54	0.89	0.31

With the help of eqs. (16)–(20) further optimum parameters can be calculated from Table II data for the resolution of n-heptane and any other compound, if the retention of n-heptane relative to this compound is known. The data in the last column of Table II relate to a hypothetical, difficult separation problem involving n-heptane ($r_{12} = 1.05$). In this case the pressure limitation of normal equipment forces us to work in conditions determined by the minimum of the H vs. $\bar{u}$ curve, because $\Delta p_{opt} = 18.3$ at. In this case, working with the "min" parameters, a separation with $\Delta p = 4.57$ at can be obtained.

In order to take complete advantage of the optimum conditions, care has to be taken in the choice and construction of equipment. Thus, the volume of the injection system and that of the connections to the column, and between the column and detector, should be small in comparison with the free gas volume of the column itself. Minimum volume, as well as quick response, of the detector is also very necessary. These practical points may well be a worthwhile investment since the "minimum" time of analysis can be greater by more than a factor of two than the "optimum" time.

1. Speed of Analysis

The speed of an analysis is logically to be expressed in units of time, but can often be described profitably by the quantity N per unit time (7). From eqs. (16) and (17) it follows that $N/t = \bar{u}/H(1 + k')$. The N/t factor may be immediately calculated from a H vs. $\bar{u}$ curve or, even more conveniently, from the chromatogram itself. For simple calculation it can be assumed that the analysis is finished at t_R, i.e., at the final peak maximum.

2. Carrier Gas Viscosity

As the carrier gas viscosity decreases, longer columns must be used [eq. (20)], all other conditions being constant. The viscosities of the carrier gases used generally are similar, with the exception of hydrogen. Its viscosity is roughly a factor of two smaller than that of the others. The apparent advantage ensuing in the use of longer columns from the use of hydrogen as carrier gas is unfortunately reduced to some extent by the higher H values resulting from the high interdiffusion coefficients of the samples in hydrogen. In effect, a change from nitrogen to hydrogen carrier gas influences the shape of the H vs. $\bar{u}$ curve in the same way as does shortening of the column.

VI. STATIONARY PHASES

The most frequently used stationary phases in gas chromatography
are liquids (GLC) and uncoated active solids (GSC). Impregnation of
an active solid, for example alumina, silica, ferric oxide, or graphitized
carbon black, with a common partitioning liquid, leads to production of
a new stationary phase for which the partition coefficients k and the
relative retentions r_{12} of the sample correspond neither to the values
obtained on an active solid nor to those obtained with the partitioning
liquid. Perhaps the most characteristic feature of such stationary
phases is that the relative retentions (r_{12}) of many substances vary with
the variation of the solid-to-liquid ratio (23–25). Purnell (40) has described this form of chromatography as gas–solid–liquid (GSLC). The
dependence of retention volume on composition is considerable if the
percentage of the liquid is small ($< 2\%$ by weight of the solid). Since,
in the highly dispersed state, the vapor pressure of the partitioning
liquid may be reduced by several orders of magnitude (26), the active
solid–liquid combination ought to be considered a uniform stationary
phase. It seems, therefore, reasonable to speak not of GSLC but of gas
adsorption-layer chromatography (GAC).

It bears mentioning that most of the "inactive" supports used in
GLC have turned out to be more or less active (27–29), especially with
respect to polar substances. This effect becomes still more evident when
the "inactive" support is introduced, highly pulverized, as a porous
layer in the column.

A. Comparison of Stationary Phase Types

In columns of low phase ratio (for example conventional packed
columns), the speed of analysis is determined mainly by the C_s term in
the van Deemter equation [eq. (10)]. This term, in GSC columns, is
probably a factor of 5–100 smaller than in GLC columns. This offers
an obvious advantage, but in addition the sublimation pressure of solids
is several orders of magnitude smaller than the vapor pressure of liquid
stationary phases. The "bleeding" of the column is thus usually negligible in GSC. This is of great importance in quantitative work, and, in
particular, in temperature and/or pressure-programmed gas chromatography.

The above advantages are balanced out to some extent by undesirable properties of the solid stationary phase, viz.,

(*a*) Only solids with suitable mechanical resistance and surface properties can be used in GSC.

(*b*) The number of such active solids is limited, most of them being "polar" and of poor reproducibility.

(*c*) The heat of adsorption is usually higher than are heats of solution. The temperatures of analyses must thus, in GSC, usually be from 100 to 200°C higher than in GLC.

(*d*) Much smaller sample sizes are permissible in GSC than in GLC on account of sample size effect on H (or h).

In GAC all the advantageous properties of both GSC and GLC appear, thus mass transfer in the stationary phase is fast, "bleeding" of the column is minimal, analysis temperatures are relatively low, and finally the variety of the stationary phases available is extremely high since relative retentions are continuously manipulatable by varying the concentration of the partitioning liquid. While it must be admitted the preparation of such columns is not always simple, it is never impossible. GAC thus has much to recommend it.

B. Optimum Stationary Phase

The first step in finding the optimum column for the resolution of a given pair of substances is the choice of the best stationary phase. As is seen from eq. (14), a small N value is sufficient for a given separation, i.e., a short column can be used and quick analysis is obtainable if r_{12} is great. The relative retentions of a great number of compounds on different stationary phases at several temperatures are tabulated in the literature (e.g., ref. 30). The chosen stationary phase and/or the temperature stability of the sample, in the first instance, determine the temperature of analysis. The N value, however, is not independent of the stationary phase since rapid mass transfer yields small N values. Thus, in a few instances, this may modify the initial choice of temperature. In general, however, only if r_{12} values are similar on several stationary phases does the mass transfer problem arise. A final, but sometimes important factor is the "loadability" of the stationary phase at a given phase ratio. This is clearly associated with solution phenomena and the concentration limits within which k is constant. Finally, the solvent

I. HALÁSZ AND E. HEINE

vapor pressure ("bleeding") may be a decisive factor. All these features are contributory, but in broad terms it is the solution (adsorption) properties of the stationary phase which are determining.

VII. PRINCIPLES OF COLUMN COMPARISON

According to eq. (14) it seems possible to characterize the different column types by N values for a given relative retention. Unfortunately this is not practical, because N is not an exclusive function of the column type, but depends very strongly on the capacity ratio k', the phase ratio, the carrier gas velocity, the temperature, etc. Furthermore, N alone does not give any indication of the speed of analysis. Thus, the particular separation problem always determines the best column type to be used and no generalization is possible.

Two facts emerging from practical experience are important in assisting in the choice of column type for the resolution of some two compounds: (a) in well-prepared analytical columns, h_{min} is more or less independent of the column type and usually lies between 0.5 and 1 mm and (b) best results are achieved (18) if $k' = 1–5$ (less commonly, $k' = 0.5–10$).

Any separation problem can be defined in respect to two compounds as the problem of choice of a suitable stationary phase and operating temperature. These together then determine the partition coefficient k and, with the k' limits given above, the phase ratio is also determined ($a = k/k'$). The phase ratio is characteristic of the column type; consequently, following the above line of argument, the analytical problem itself determines the best column type. With h_{min} and k' determined, it then follows that $\bar{u}_{min}$ and H_{min} are also determined ($H_{min} = 0.7–4$ mm) and, hence, so are the "minimum" parameters via eqs. (17)–(20).

The shape of the H vs. $\bar{u}$ curve (i.e., the position and degree of flatness of the minimum and the subsequent slope of the ascending branch) determines the relationship between "minimum" and "optimum" parameters, and is characteristic of a given column type. It is influenced by the permeability (k) of the column. Furthermore the permeability determines the maximum column length usable in routine analysis.

It is possible to compare column types with the help of t_{ne}/S vs. $\Delta p_{ne}/S$ or t_{ne} vs. Δp_{ne} curves at constant temperature. The former seem to be more general because the variables are independent of the relative retentions. The t_{ne} and Δp_{ne} values, however, are functions of H and $\bar{u}$ and the superiority of one column type over the others depends upon these. Thus, briefly, the column with the phase ratio yielding optimum k', for a given partition coefficient, represents the probable best choice. The comparison of different column types is better done with constant capacity ratios at different temperatures.

A. Performance Index

A measure of column performance has been defined by Golay (31,32), termed the performance index (PI) and defined by:

$$PI = 30.7 h_{min}^2 \frac{\eta}{K} \left[\frac{1 + k'}{k' + \frac{1}{16}} \right] \tag{21}$$

or

$$PI = 30.7 H_{min}^2 \frac{\eta}{K} \left[\frac{k'^4}{(1 + k')^3(k' + \frac{1}{16})} \right] \tag{22}$$

In the cgs system, PI is measured in poise (dyne cm^{-2} sec). To facilitate comparison, the PI is not determined for hydrogen, but for all other usual carrier gases having about the same viscosity. The PI is clearly a function of k' and, in fact, passes through a minimum at about $k' = 3$, all other parameters being constant. As may be shown by experiment (3), the PI of an open tube, for example, varies by less than a factor of 10 (normally smaller than 3) for k' values between 0.05 and 3. Furthermore, relative retention (or separation factor) does not appear in the definition equation of the PI. Thus the PI is independent of the separation problem and is characteristic only of the column.

1. Some Comments on the Performance Index

As pointed out earlier h_{min} and optimum k' are independent of the column type. Supposing the validity of this and that "best" values of $h_{min} = 10^{-1}$ cm, $k' = 3$, and $\eta = 2 \times 10^{-4}$ poise, eq. (21) yields:

$$PI = (8 \times 10^{-5})/K \text{ (poise)} \tag{23}$$

As seen, the PI is inversely proportional to the permeability. Describing column performance by PI, open tubes (with high permeability) always appear some orders of magnitude superior to conventional packed columns no matter what separation problem is considered [see eqs. (4) and (5)] at equal achievement. The characterization of column types through PI alone can thus lead to confusion.

B. Performance Parameter

For difficult separation problems where reduction of analysis time has to be paid for with inconveniently high inlet pressures, it follows that any means of minimizing pressure drop is helpful. From eqs. (17) and (20) it is seen that analysis time and pressure drop are proportional to $1/\bar{u}$ and $\bar{u}$, respectively. The product of special interest, termed performance parameter, is independent of $\bar{u}$ (3) and is defined by:

$$PP = \Delta p_{ne} t_{ne} = H_{opt}^2 (1 + k')(\eta/Kj')S^2 \qquad (24)$$

The PP in the cgs system is again given in units of poise. For practical use it is better to express pressure in kg/cm^2 (1 at = 9.81×10^5 dyne/cm^2) when PP values are given in units of at sec. The separation factor S in eq. (24) shows that the PP, in contrast to PI, depends on the particular separation problem. However, PP is only of interest, if Δp_{opt} is greater than the maximum pressure drop allowed by the inlet system of the equipment. Simple separation problems on several column types are characterized by t_{opt} values.

C. Parameters Determinable from the Chromatogram

The chromatogram provides information on: (a) the relative peak width (h, H); (b) the relative position of peaks (a, k', r_{12}); and (c) the gas permeability of the column (K). As has been shown, only the phase ratio a and the permeability K of these parameters is significant in the choosing of column type (3). It follows that we may characterize column types on this basis. It should be pointed out, however, that the third criterion of column types, the shape and position of the H vs. $\bar{u}$ curves, required for calculation of the best column type and optimum parameters cannot at present be calculated or estimated, the views of theorists notwithstanding, but has to be determined experimentally. The correlations given in this paper facilitate indeed the rough determination of optimum conditions, but the final touches of finesse result, unquestionably, from trial and error, i.e., via the empirical measurement of the H vs. $\bar{u}$ curve at several temperatures and on different stationary phases. This cannot be too strongly emphasized.

VIII. COMPARISON OF COLUMNS

Following from the discussion above, analytical columns may be type classified as in Table III. Familiar column types (conventional-

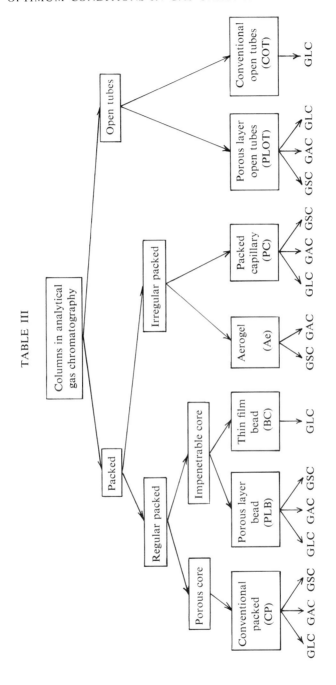

TABLE III

packed, open-tube, and bead columns) are discussed here only briefly, with most attention being given to the less-familiar ones.

A. Packed Columns and Open Tubes

Packed columns are distinguished from open tube columns by the fact that, in the former, the solid support may itself be a stationary phase or coated with a liquid stationary phase. The carrier gas thus cannot pass through the column axially in a direct line for more than a short distance. Thus the gas space is irregular. Only the wall of open tubes is coated with a solid or a liquid stationary phase and so the shape of the free gas cross section is (more or less) unchanged over the length of the column. A major consequence of the above is that a packed column can have over a hundred times more surface area per unit gas volume than can an open tube column. Over the whole likely range of "film thicknesses" the packed column has almost always a considerably lower phase ratio and greater loadability than does the open tube. Therefore, almost by definition, an open tube is bound to be more suitable for separating substances with high partition coefficients (i.e., high-boiling compounds) while substances with low partition coefficients (i.e., low-boiling compounds) are certain to be better separated with packed columns.

Because of the high loadability, the concentration of the sample in the carrier gas at peak maximum may rise even as high as a few percent in packed columns. In open tubes, however, this concentration is smaller by at least a factor of 10. Consequently, much more sensitive detectors are necessary behind open tubes than behind packed columns and, for the same reason, an injection splitting device must, at this time, be used with open tubes. To build a splitting system for quantitative analysis is not simple (34–37).

The minimum of the H vs. $\bar{u}$ curve is shifted to higher carrier gas velocities on moving from conventional packed columns to open tubes. The permeability of a typical packed column ($d_p = 0.1$ mm) is about 2×10^{-7} cm^2 and that of an open tube (i.d. $= 0.25$ mm) is about 200×10^{-7} cm^2. Due to the different hydrodynamic properties implicit in eqs. (4) and (5) the onset of turbulence in packed columns occurs at Reynold numbers between 2 and 500 in contrast to the situation with open tubes where it occurs at Re > 2000 (38). In the normal mode of GC operation this constitutes some advantage for open tubes.

1. *The Support*

The porous supports commonly used in GLC and GSC have specific surface areas in the ranges 0.5–5 and 10–800 m^2/g, respectively.

2. *The Support in* GLC *and* GAC

Ideally, the support in GLC should be inactive. Most of the usual siliceous type "inactive" supports (Chromosorb, firebrick, Celite, kieselguhr, Sterchamol, etc.) are, however, more or less active. This property is more apparent if the amount of the stationary liquid is small and/or if polar compounds have to be separated (39–43). Hence the boundary between GLC and GAC is often only poorly defined. Several methods of deactivation of the support by surface modification have been proposed (39–41). Other inorganic supports which have, from time to time been suggested are fibrilar Boehmite (44), metal oxides (25,45–47), inorganic salts (48–50) and the most "apolar" solid support, graphite or graphitized carbon black (11,51,52). As well as the nature, the pore size and structure of the solid may have effect on its properties (53–55) while those of the column material (56) may sometimes be of importance.

The plastic supports used up to now are usually more inactive. These include Teflon and other fluorine-containing polymers (57) such as Fluoropak, polyethylene (58), organic ion exchangers (59), and polyaromatics (60). The specific surface area of porous organic supports is smaller than that of the siliceous type. Occasionally these organic supports are used in GSC, too. In general, their low surface area demands small amounts of liquid stationary phase and, in turn, lower temperatures of analysis.

3. *Support in* GSC

The reproducible preparation of adsorptively active supports (charcoal, silica gel, activated alumina, molecular sieves, etc.) is difficult. Newer solid stationary phases such as porous glass (61,62), graphite (63,64) organic compounds (65) and polystyrene polymers (66) may attain importance for special problems. Solid-coated solids, e.g., alumina coated with inorganic salts (67) or with ferric oxide (68,69), firebrick with inorganic eutectics (70) or with resins (71), and other mixtures (65), appear to have a promising future.

B. Regular and Irregular Packed Columns

In contrast to irregular packed columns, in regular packed columns the inner diameter of the column is larger by a factor 10 or more than the particle size of the support. Thus, close-sphere packing may be attained. The interparticle porosity of regular (random) packed columns is about 0.4–0.45 (72,73). Because of the constancy of porosity, the permeability of these columns depends, in practice, only on the particle size of the support. The dependence of the packing density and permeability on various other column properties has been thoroughly investigated (73).

C. Conventional Packed Columns (CP)

The support in a regular packed column may either be porous or have a core impenetrable to the carrier gas (for example, glass beads). The former, the conventional packed column, was first used in gas chromatography by James and Martin (2). As pointed out earlier, this column type has the smallest phase ratio and permeability. The $\bar{u}_{min}$ of these columns is thus the smallest ($\bar{u}_{min} = 4$–7 cm/sec). It is easy to build CP columns and insensitive detectors can be used because of the high loadability. Thus, CP columns can be used in the simplest gas chromatographic equipment. For these reasons, most routine analyses are made on conventional packed columns. According to the nature of the stationary phase, CP columns can be used in GSC, GAC, or GLC. Excellent resolutions can be achieved, especially for compounds with small partition coefficients (74).

The usual inner diameter of CP columns is between 2 and 4 mm. Very occasionally, the diameter may be 1 mm. Almost invariably the particle size lies between 0.1 and 0.2 mm, with narrow sieve fractions. The relative peak broadening is proportional to the particle size of the support (75,76), whereas the permeability of the column decreases with the square of d_p [eq. (5)]. The above-mentioned particle size thus represents the practical compromise. With extremely high pressure drops, supports with d_p as small as 0.003 mm may be used (77). The speed of analysis of CP columns, if characterized by N/t, is poorer than that of most other column types (14,78).

A fast GSC separation of C_1–C_4 hydrocarbons on alumina (22) may be seen in Figure 7; here $N/t = 23$/sec for n-butane. In order to

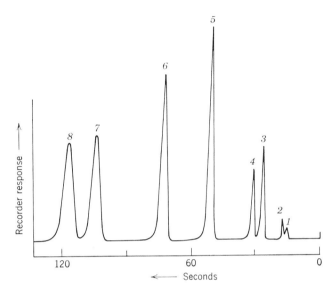

Fig. 7. Optimum separation of C_1–C_4 hydrocarbons on a conventional packed column (22). (*1*) air; (*2*) methane ($k' = 0.29$); (*3*) ethane (1.00); (*4*) ethylene (1.31); (*5*) propane (2.78); (*6*) propylene (4.33); (*7*) isobutane (6.63); (*8*) *n*-butane (7.54). $K = 10^{-7}$ cm^2; $t_c = 80°$C; $L = 2$ m; i.d. $= 4$ mm; $d_p = 0.10$–0.15 mm. Support: 13.4 g of alumina per meter of column length; carrier gas: hydrogen moistened over Na$_2$SO$_4$·10H$_2$O at 20°C. $\Delta p = 3.1$ at; $\bar{u} = 16.3$ cm/sec; $s = 0.2$ ml gas. Catharometer detection. Performance index (for propane, N_2) = 400 poise.

carry out this separation, optimum parameters were calculated from the h vs. $\bar{u}$ curve shown in Figure 8 as described earlier.

With liquid stationary phases in conventionally loaded packed columns, a value for N/t of only 6–10/sec is obtained, although Purnell and Quinn's equations (18) show that a value around 20 should be readily attainable at low k'.

1. *Micropacked Columns*

A number of publications (79–84) deal with micropacked columns, i.e., conventional packed columns having an inner diameter smaller than 1 mm but where the particle-to-column diameter ratio is identical with that of CP (d_c/d_p greater than about 5) (37). Figure 9 shows a chromatogram obtained with a micropacked column (85). The relative peak broadening is remarkably low and the speed of analysis appears far better than that attainable on CP columns. It is, however, worse than

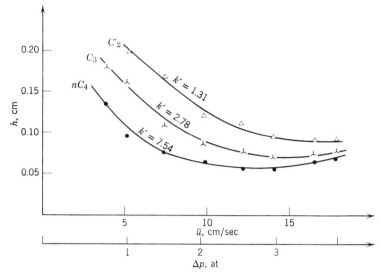

Fig. 8. h vs. $\bar{u}$ curves for a conventional packed column (22). Parameters are the same as in Figure 7.

with packed capillary columns. Unfortunately, the class of columns designated here as micropacked columns are commonly described in the literature as packed capillary columns. This is unfortunate since the true packed capillary has different characteristics.

D. Regular Packed Columns with Impenetrable Core

The advantage of these columns is the quick mass transfer in the stationary phase and the slightly better permeability than is found with conventional packed columns of the same particle size. A serious disadvantage in GLC is that this support has a minute surface area; consequently, at a given "film thickness" the amount of the liquid stationary phase is small and only very limited sample sizes are allowable.

A recently developed variant of these columns is one in which the packing comprises springs of metal wire (86); the permeability is excellent, the loadability poor, and the relative peak broadening normal. Stainless steel spirals (65) and gauze helices (87,88) have also been proposed.

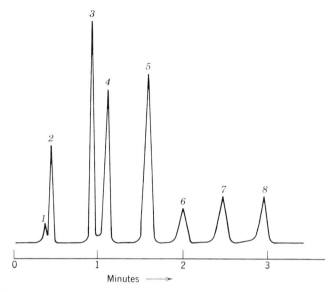

Fig. 9. Separation of C_5–C_7 hydrocarbons on a micropacked column (85). (1) isopentane; (2) n-pentane; (3) 1-hexene; (4) n-hexane; (5) benzene; (6) cyclohexane; (7) 1-heptene; (8) n-heptane. $t_c = 50°C$; $L = 1$ m; i.d. = 0.9 mm; $d_p = 0.10$–0.12 or 0.14–0.20 mm. Chromosorb W coated with 15% by weight squalane. k' for n-heptane: ca. 8. Carrier gas: nitrogen. $\Delta p = 2$ at; H for n-heptane: 0.31 mm. N/t for n-heptane: 18/sec.

1. Thin-Film Bead Columns (BC)

Callear and Cvetanovic (89) first used microglass bead supports in gas chromatography in 1955 to reduce the activity of the support and, hence, the tailing effect. Systematic research by Littlewood (90) has done much to make this support as popular as it is. The preparation of BC-type columns is simple. For example, by the technique of dynamic deposition of the liquid stationary phase in a dry packed bead column (91), glass or metal beads of diameter between 0.5 and 1 may be uniformly impregnated with 0.05–3% partitioning liquid. The lower percentage of the liquid characterizing BC-type columns is partially compensated for by the greater packing density of the beads (39). If the amount of liquid is larger, a large part of the liquid forms pools around the contact points of the beads (92) and tailing effects appear (93). Glass powder with higher specific surface area has also been used (94), but its irregular form and higher catalytic activity are disadvantageous.

The specific surface area of glass beads is small, being only about
0.03 m²/g at a diameter of 0.1 mm. This allied with the thin-film requirement, allows only the use of samples of about 0.1 mg (90,95). Because of
the uniform spherical form of the beads, the permeability of these
columns is slightly better than that of conventional packed columns
(6,39,90,96,97). This allows higher carrier gas velocities and so the
sample concentration in the carrier gas (i.e., detector signal) becomes
higher than in all other column types except CP and PLB columns.

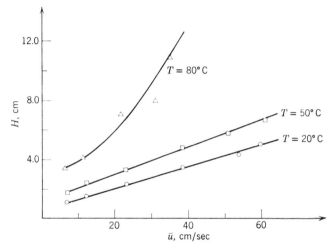

Fig. 10. H vs. $\bar{u}$ for a bead column at different temperatures (100). Sample:
n-heptane. $K = 4.4 \times 10^{-7}$ cm²; $L = 2$ m; i.d. $= 4$ mm; $d_p = 0.10$–0.12 mm.
Support: squalane (32.6 mg/m column length) on glass beads. $k' = 2.7$ (20°C),
1.0 (50°C), and 0.45 (80°C). Carrier gas: nitrogen. $s = 1$ µg; FID detection;
PI $= 4780$.

This can be of interest when combining gas chromatography with mass
spectroscopy.

    Optimum capacity ratios for substances of high partition coeffi-
cients can be obtained with BC columns at lower column temperatures
than with CP columns (95,97–99).

    In Figure 10, H vs. $\bar{u}$ curves for a thin-film bead column are shown
at three temperatures. The minimum of the curves was not achieved
since it occurred at such low velocity. The most remarkable feature is
the very high temperature dependence of the data, especially at high
flow rates. Better results than these have been reported (90); a value of
$H_{\min} \approx 1$ mm at $\bar{u} = 2$ cm/sec was achieved.

2. Porous-Layer Bead Columns (PLB)

Golay (101) and other authors (6,17,102,103) pointed out the theoretical advantages of a packed column with a porous layer surrounding a hard, impenetrable core of high specific surface area. Horvath (25,65,104) first proposed a general method to achieve this result. He deposited various materials, in the particle range of 1 μ or less, from solvents onto the surface of the nonporous glass or metal beads. The coating procedures are simple and the powdered particles are apparently held to the surface by van der Waals forces. PLB columns can obviously be used in GLC, GAC, and GSC, and even solid supports with inconvenient mechanical properties (e.g., graphite) can be employed. Special methods for preparing glass beads coated with diatomaceous earth (105–107), with a fibrilar Boehmite (Baymal, a colloidal alumina) (107) and with metallic mirrors (108) have been described. Porous layers on glass beads may also be produced by etching (109,110). Good results are also obtained with PLB if organic supports such as polyethylene beads are coated with carbon black (111) or sponge spicules with tristetrahydrofurfuryl-phosphate (112). The range of possibilities is thus seen to be almost unlimited.

The advantage of PLB columns is their small phase ratio, and hence, the prospect of lower temperature of analysis as in CP.

In Figure 11 a separation of polar substances on a PLB column may be seen. Glass beads were coated with zirconium dioxide and then with triethylene glycol. The analysis is fast and, interestingly, the stationary phase has an "apolar" character although both components of the adsorption layer are "polar." The h vs. $\bar{u}$ curves of two hydrocarbons on this same column are shown in Figure 12. Although the capacity ratios are different (0.53 and 2.9) the shapes and positions of both curves are similar, resulting in different positions if H vs. $\bar{u}$ is plotted.

E. Irregular Packed Columns

The name "irregular packed column" is used (1) when the interparticle porosity ϵ is extremely high (> 0.9) and the support is irregularly dispersed in the column (e.g., aerogel columns) or (2) if the inner diameter of the column d_c is relatively small ($d_c/d_p \leq 5$), resulting in an irregular packing. The latter class are truly packed capillary columns if their inner diameter is smaller than 1–2 mm.

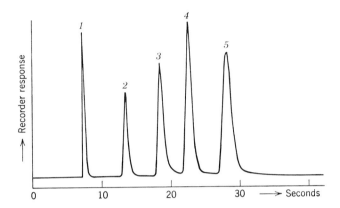

Fig. 11. Separation on porous-layer bead column (25). (*1*) methane; (*2*) diethyl ether ($k' = 0.81$); (*3*) acetone (1.46); (*4*) benzene (2.03); (*5*) ethyl acetate (2.6). $K = 1.6 \times 10^{-7}$ cm²; $t_c = 100°C$; $L = 2$ m; i.d. $= 2$ mm. Particle size of glass beads: 0.90–0.1 mm; 7.31 g of PLB per meter column length, 6.24% ZrO₂, 0.156% triethyleneglycol (2.44% measured on ZrO₂) and 93.604% glass beads. Carrier gas: hydrogen. $\Delta p = 4$ at; $\bar{u} = 26.4$ cm/sec; flowrate: 90 ml/min (at 20°C); $s = 1.5$ μg. FID, full scale deflection 1×10^{-9} A. N/t for ethylacetate: 149/sec.

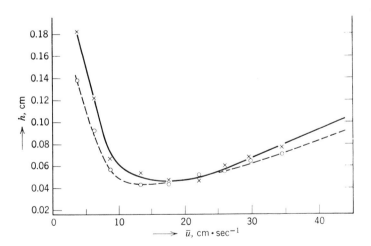

Fig. 12. H vs. $\bar{u}$ for PLB column (25). (———) n-heptane, $k' = 2.9$: (-----) n-pentane, $k' = 0.53$. Column and conditions the same as in Figure 9.

1. *Aerogel Columns* (Ae)

This column type was first described by Gerlach (78). Although the particles appear to be closely packed, the packing is in fact highly dispersed and only 2–4% of the total column volume is occupied by the stationary phase. Extremely small particle size (1 μ), high porosity ($\epsilon > 0.9$), not too low a permeability ($K = 0.3$ to 5×10^{-7} cm^2), and small inner diameter (0.3–0.5 mm) are the characteristics of these columns.

Aerogel columns are prepared by dispersing light silica in a glass tube and drawing it out to a capillary of 0.4 mm i.d. (22,113,114). The highly dispersed silica used (e.g., Aerosil 2491/380) has a bulk density of 60 g/liter and a specific surface area of 380 $\pm$ 40 m^2/g. The primary particles (diameter 30–150 Å) are spherical and free of pores and agglomerate to straight and branched secondary chains, which form a tertiary structure consisting of irregular three-dimensional networks with a particle size in the order of magnitude of 1 μ. The preparation of such columns is not easy. Up to now only silica supports have been used and these can be coated with a liquid or mixed with a highly dispersed solid (ferric oxide, carbon black, etc.) as stationary phase. No one has yet succeeded in constructing aerogel columns with an inner diameter larger than 1 mm.

The weight of the support per unit column length is small, but, because of the high specific surface area of the dispersed silica, the total surface area is high. The column used to provide the data in Figure 13 was filled with 7.5 mg of Aerosil per meter of column length. This corresponds to 2.85 m^2 of surface of the poreless SiO$_2$. This value is closely comparable with the 3.48 m^2 per meter length (26 mg) of porous alumina in a packed capillary column of 0.32 mm i.d. (22) and with the reputed 22.5 m^2 per meter (4.5 g) of porous Chromosorb P in a conventional packed column of 4 mm i.d. (41).

The relative peak broadening as a function of the carrier gas velocity is shown in Figure 13. The H value is obviously very small over a wide range of capacity ratios ($k' = 0.5$–8). The permeability of aerogel columns is between one-third and one-thirtieth of that of an open tube [note that small d_p is compensated by high porosity, eq. (5)]. Thus, these columns lie between packed open tubes, and so H values at high linear carrier-gas velocity are considerably lower than those for packed capillary columns operating in the high-speed region. Even more favorable is a comparison between aerogel and CP columns. Since analysis time is proportional to $H/\bar{u}$ [eq. (17)], very short analysis times can be achieved with aerogel columns. The pressure drop necessary for the analysis is proportional to $H\bar{u}/K$ [eq. (20)] and the low permeability of these columns is more than compensated by the low H values. Hence very short columns can be employed. Accordingly, and this is perhaps the most important conclusion, the inlet pressures necessary for analysis

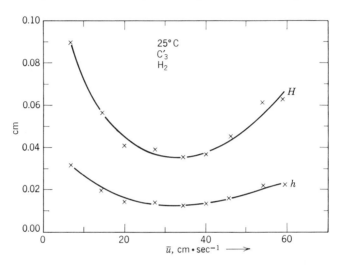

Fig. 13. Relative peak broadenings on an aerogel column (78). Sample: propylene. $t_c = 25°C$; $K = 0.26 \times 10^{-7}$ cm²; $L = 0.2$ m; i.d. $= 0.4$ mm; $d_p = $ about 1 μ. Support: dispersed silica, 340 m²/g, 7.5 mg/m of column length. $a = 38.5$; $k' = 1.46$; $s = 1$ μg; FID detection; PI for propylene ($k' = 1.46$) and N₂: 51 poise.

within seconds can be obtained with commercial gas chromatographic equipment. From Figure 13, for propylene elution, we find $N/t = 430$ sec⁻¹, a remarkably high figure.

A quick separation on an aerogel column of only 20 cm in length is shown in Figure 14. A true analysis time of 1 sec for the baseline separation of propane–propylene is obtained, if nonoperative time (dead time) is subtracted. The nonoperative time is determined by gas flow through tubes leading to the column and can be reduced by proper construction. The peak widths of about 0.2 sec are, in fact, comparable with the injection time.

A further device which has proved of value with Ae columns is that of using moist carrier gas with a dispersed silica support. Figure 15

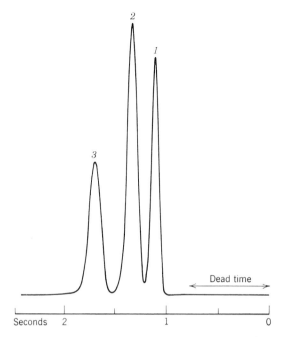

Fig. 14. C_1–C_3 separation on an aerogel column at 25°C (78). Parameters same as in Figure 13, except: (*1*) methane; (*2*) propane; (*3*) propylene. $\Delta p = 4$ at. $\bar{u} = 55$ cm/sec; $s = 5 \times 10^{-8}$ g. 0.2 m; 0.4 mm; 25°C; H_2; $K = 0.27 \times 10^{-7}$ cm^2; $s = 0.05$ μg. FID detection.

shows the separation of saturated and unsaturated hydrocarbons at ambient temperature. The peaks of "polar" compounds remain symmetrical even at large capacity ratios. The speed of analysis is still high at high k' values ($N/t = 127$ sec^{-1} for component *13* in Fig. 15 at $k' = 7.2$). The permeability of the aerogel column corresponds to that of a conventional packed column with particle size of 0.09–0.1 mm (i.e., approximately 30 mesh).

2. *Packed Capillary* (PC) *Columns*

This column type was first proposed by Halász and Heine in 1962 (3,12,22,114,115). As the name indicates, they are *packed* columns, usually with inner diameter comparable to open capillary tubes (i.e. 0.25–0.50 mm), where the particle diameter of the support is larger than one-third to one-fifth of the inner column diameter. PC columns are packed loosely and irregularly and the volume of the support comprises

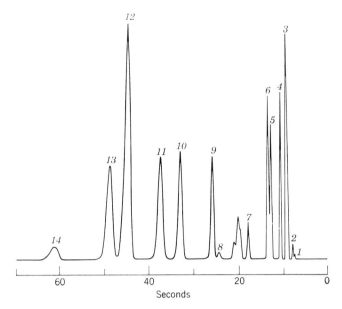

Fig. 15. Separation of C_1–C_6 hydrocarbons on an aerogel column with moist carrier gas (78). (1) methane; (2) ethane; (3) propane; (4) propylene; (5) isobutane; (6) n-butane; (7) 1-butene; (8) isopentane; (9) n-pentane; (10) n-1-pentene; (11) 3-methyl-1-butene; (12) 2-methyl-1-butene; (13) 2-methyl-2-butene ($k' = 7.2$); (14) n-hexane. $K = 0.864 \times 10^{-7}$ cm²; $L = 1.6$ m; $\Delta p = 4$ at; $\bar{u} = 22$ cm/sec. Carrier gas: hydrogen moistened over $Na_2SO_4 \cdot 10H_2O$ at 20°C. FID detection. N/t for compound (13) = 127/sec. $s = 0.15$ µg; 27°C; 0.4 m.

less than two thirds of the internal volume of the column. PC columns have only 25–35%, sometimes 50% of the packing density of CP columns (116). Some particles stick into small depressions in the glass wall; this helps to stabilize the packing. Only a few channels exist for the carrier gas because of the high $d_p:d_c$ ratio and the continuous change of cross section prevents a parallel flow pattern. The gas cross section can change, from one place to another within a column, by a factor of 100 or more. Consequently a mechanical mixing takes place in the gas phase.

Packed capillary columns are produced simply by drawing out glass tubes (113) which are initially loosely filled with a *granular* solid of narrow mesh range (12,22,116). Supports with poor mechanical properties, as for example pelleted graphitized carbon black (117), can be employed. It is even possible to build PC columns of porous layer beads.

The advantages of columns with high particle-to-column diameter ratio, particularly for wide columns, are discussed in detail in the literature (73,82,118–120), and seem to have considerable potential in the preparative area.

One can extend the Kozeny–Carman equation [eq. (5)], which is defined for regular packed columns, formally to irregular packed columns by introducing a suitable apparent particle diameter. At ϵ values close to 1, small changes will influence the permeability enormously; hence, there is need for great care in column construction. The permeability of regularly packed columns is independent of inner

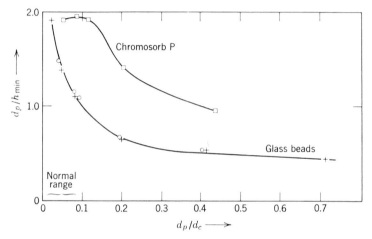

Fig. 16. Dependence of relative peak broadening (h) on the particle-to-column diameter (d_p/d_c) ratio (73). Sample: methane ($k' = 0$). Courtesy of *Analytical Chemistry*.

diameter of the column. When the particles are nearly as big as the column, however, single particles may clog up the gas passage and the permeability is much reduced. The apparent porosity of PC columns is usually about $\epsilon = 0.6$ and the permeability is in the order of 10^{-6} cm^2, i.e., it is better by a factor 10 than that of CP columns of the same particle size. In consequence, PC columns of great length may be used and these are stable to at least $\bar{u} = 150$ cm/sec, which corresponds in many cases to an outlet velocity of 450 cm/sec.

It is often assumed that h can never be smaller than the particle diameter d_p. In Figure 16 results due to Sternberg and Poulson (73) are shown. These workers investigated relative peak broadening as a function of d_p/d_c for CP columns with Chromosorb P and glass beads as supports. The coordinates in Figure 16 are dimensionless, the h values being given in units of the particle size d_p of the support. The sharp descent of the curves near $d_p/d_c = 0.2$ is evident, and it is apparent that $h/d_p > 1$ is not the magic limit it is sometimes assumed to be. It must be pointed out that this small value was obtained for an unretained compound and certain corrections were applied to the results.

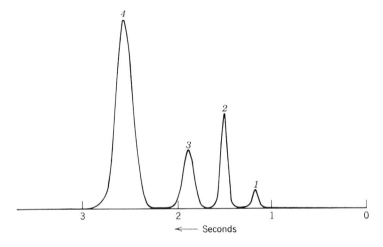

Fig. 17. Quantitative separation in 3 sec on a packed capillary column (115). (*1*) methane; (*2*) ethane; (*3*) ethylene; (*4*) propane. $K = 2.3 \times 10^{-7}$ cm²; $t_c = 70°C$; $L = 1$ m; i.d. $= 0.3$ mm; $d_p = 0.1$–0.15 mm. Alumina activated at 500°C, heated by 140°C; 130 m²/g; 25 mg alumina/meter of column length. Carrier gas: hydrogen; Flow rate: 13 ml/min at 20°C and 1 at. $\Delta p = 4$ at; $\bar{u} = 80$ cm/sec; $s = 10^{-7}$ g. FID, full scale deflection: 2×10^{-8} A. N/t for propane: 250/sec.

The pressure-independent van Deemter coefficients A, B, and C_m are not very different for PC and CP columns, if the other parameters are constant (22). The minima for the h vs. $\bar{u}$ curves of the PC column lie at higher $\bar{u}$ values; the ascending branch of the curves is flatter than that for the CP column, as is seen in a comparison with Figures 2, 4, and 8. This is a consequence of the better permeability of PC columns but, as might be expected, $h_{\min}$ values are very similar for both column types.

The high permeability, combined with the attainability of H values comparable to those of other column types, allows fast analyses as shown by the example in Figure 17. That PC columns are realistic analytical weapons is shown by the fact that quantitative analyses of the four compounds shown was reproducibly possible with an absolute error of 0.1% (115). Further evidence on this matter may be derived from the literature (121,122).

Analytical applications involving PC columns containing graphitized carbon black (117), solid-coated alumina (123), liquid-coated alumina (22,114), chromosorb with squalane (22), and firebrick with tri-2,4-xylenylphosphate (116) have been successfully developed. The combination of PC and other column types is also possible (124).

F. Open Tubes

Golay was the first to work with open-tube columns (31,125). Excellent permeability, great phase ratio, and low loadability are the characteristics of these columns, as was pointed out earlier (Sec. VIII-1). The wall of the tube may be coated with liquid stationary phase (conventional open tubes) or with a porous layer of solid (porous layer open tubes).

1. *Conventional Open Tubes* (COT)

This column type can be used only in GLC, and the preparation of such columns is not always simple (31,126–128), especially if the liquid phase is polar. The tubes can be made of metal (31), of plastic (129), or of glass (113). The properties of COT columns have been summed up in excellent fashion elsewhere (33,128,130) and require no further elaboration. With decreasing inner diameter of the tube, H decreases but the permeability and the stability of the column diminish concomitantly. A good compromise seems to be an i.d. of 0.25 mm, but it should be mentioned that excellent results have once been obtained with a 35-μ column (7). The h value of COT columns is similar to that achieved in other column types, but, because of the excellent permeability, very long columns (131) up to at least 1000 ft (7) can be built with corresponding performance. The highest speed of analysis yet attained, $N/t = 2500/\text{sec}$ (7) was achieved via COT.

Because of their high phase ratios, high partition coefficients are, in fact, essential to the realization of the best aspects of COT columns. Practical advantage then arises because they can be operated at temperatures 50–200°C lower than CP columns whose low-load operation can be restricted by solid activity. For the same reason, the mass transfer term in the mobile phase C_m can become comparable or sometimes greater than C_s. In consequence, a linear ascending branch appears if h (or H) is plotted vs. u_o (and not as usual vs. $\bar{u}$). With such columns optimum parameters cannot be calculated from eqs. (17)–(20).

Another consequence of the high phase ratio is that in practical analysis the capacity ratios of the compounds are small ($k' = 0.1$–3) and the ratio of H/h (or n/N) is high. As long as the performance of a column is given with the h or n values, the efficiency of the COT columns

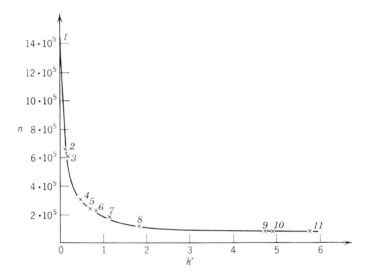

Fig. 18. Dependence of n on the capacity ratio in an open tube (126). (*1*) methane; (*2*) *i*-pentane; (*3*) *n*-pentane; (*4*) *n*-hexane; (*5*) benzene; (*6*) cyclohexane; (*7*) *n*-heptane; (*8*) toluene; (*9*) *p*-xylene; (*10*) *n*-xylene; (*11*) *o*-xylene. $K = 2.5 \times 10^{-5}$ cm²; $t_c = 60°C$; $L = 140$ m; i.d. $= 0.3$ mm. Squalane column; Carrier gas: nitrogen. $\Delta p = 2.7$ at; $\bar{u} = 23.8$ cm/sec or 3.5 ml/min (60°C, 1 at). FID detection.

must be grossly overestimated (17). This danger is clearly illustrated in Figure 18, where the efficiency n is plotted vs. the capacity ratio of an open tube (126). In Figure 19 the relative peak broadening (h or H) vs. velocity of *n*-heptane is shown. This shows the high carrier gas velocities allowable with this column type.

2. Porous Layer Open Tubes (PLOT)

Golay (31,125) and Purnell (17) pointed out, in their theoretical considerations, that excellent capillary columns could, in principle, be produced by replacing the smooth inner wall of a COT by a uniform porous layer of support material.

Such a layer can, in fact, be produced by special chemical reactions *in situ* in the tube. For example, a layer of alumina may be produced on an aluminum wall (132,133) while the inside of glass tubes may be etched to a porous silica layer (134–139). Liquid-modified columns also show properties of great interest (132,135).

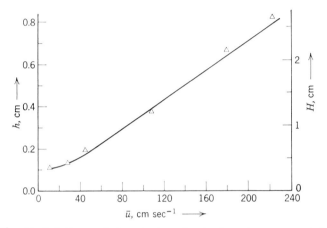

Fig. 19. Relative peak broadening of *n*-heptane in an open tube (140). $K = 2.4 \times 10^{-5}$ cm^2; $t_c = 80°C$; $L = 30$ m; i.d. $= 0.28$ mm. Squalane column; $k' = 1.22$. Carrier gas: hydrogen. $s = 5 \times 10^{-7}$ g. FID detection.

By extension of the technique used to produce porous layer beads (Sec. VIII-D-2), Halász and Horváth devised (64,140) a general method for producing a porous layer of support attached to the inner wall of a COT tube. Several active, solid, stationary phases have been used in PLOT columns, e.g., graphitized carbon black (64), fibrilar Boehmite (44), molecular sieve (141), and colloidal silica (142–143). In GAC, PLOT columns have employed ferric oxide coated with triethylene glycol (140) and diatomaceous earth (144,145) coated with squalane.

The best results are achieved with PLOT if the layer is built from a solid of very small particle size (about 1 μ or less) and the solid has no internal surface area. Thus, there is quick mass transfer in the stationary phase. Because of the porous support, the effective surface area of the inner wall of a PLOT-type column is larger by a factor F than the surface area of a conventional open tube with a smooth inner wall. This factor is called the roughness factor (31) and usually lies between 5 and

7 (137,140), but may be much higher. Therefore, greater amounts of the partitioning liquids may be used than in COT columns, and this results in quicker mass transfer in GLC and in a more useful lower phase ratio. Depending on the thickness of the support and of the liquid phase, and on the inner diameter of the column (0.25–0.5 mm), a great variety of phase ratios a can be produced in PLOT columns.

Ettre et al. (145) have discussed the influence of a on the properties of a PLOT column with a 20–40 μ support thickness (diatomaceous earth) and a 0.5 mm i.d. A PLOT column with a film thickness of only

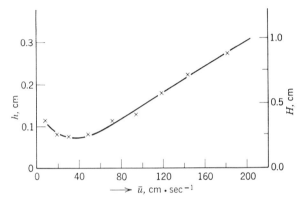

Fig. 20. Relative peak broadening of n-heptane in porous layer open tube (140). $K = 1.5 \times 10^{-5}$ cm²; $t_c = 80°C$; $L = 28.5$ m; i.d. = 0.25 mm. Stationary phase: highly dispersed ferric oxide (5.5 mg/m coated with triethylenglycol (0.55 mg/m). $k' = 1.21$; Carrier gas: hydrogen. $s = 10^{-6}$ g. FID detection.

0.01–0.02 μ (squalane) has a phase ratio $a = 400$–600 which is similar to conventional open-tube columns. Such columns have small h values but, as in COT, the sample size is restricted to about 0.1 to 1 × 10⁻⁶ g. If the film thickness, however, is 0.1–0.2 μ, this results in 3–5 μl of partitioning liquid per meter column length and $a = 55$–85. The relative peak broadening is not quite as good in this case, but the sample size can be increased by a factor of about 10. With a film thickness of 0.4–0.5 μ (a about 30), 0.27-mg sample size can be handled. This is similar to the loadability of CP columns. However, $h \approx 1$ cm, which is useless practically except for quick trace analysis or for operation in combination with a mass spectrometer.

The high permeability of PLOT-type columns of 0.5 mm i.d. ($K = 7 \times 10^{-5}$ cm²) obviously allows the use of very long and, consequently, very efficient columns with small pressure drop. The H and h vs. $\bar{u}$ curves of PLOT columns are shown in Figure 20. The capacity ratio for n-heptane is practically the same as in Figure 19, i.e., for a COT column. Note, however, the lower and broader minimum and the flatter ascending branch in Figure 20. The latter is important in high-speed analysis while the broad minimum is very desirable if the pressure is to be programmed (146). It may be mentioned here, in passing, that temperature programming, with constant inlet pressure, results also in programmed flow. Since constant flow rate in programmed temperature work is difficult to achieve, PLOT columns suggest themselves for use. Finally, the measurement of physical constants via gas chromatography (147) is convenient and speedy with PLOT-type columns (140).

In Figure 21 the separation of some polar compounds with a PLOT column is shown; the time of analysis is less than 1 min. The permeability of the column used is smaller by a factor 11.5 than the value calculated from the nominal inner diameter of the column (before coating with the graphitized carbon black). The reason is, partly, that the thickness of the solid support is not negligible, but mainly that the inner wall of the tube is not smooth.

G. Comparison of Column Types

In Section VII the principles of column comparison were discussed. Summing up briefly, the best type of column for a given problem is that with the highest permeability in which the phase ratio allows $k' = 1-5$ for the compounds of the mixture and where the H vs. $\bar{u}$ curve is low and flat with a small slope of the ascending branch. In trace analysis highly loadable column types are preferred.

When looking at the seven column types as listed in the last row of Table III, one can deduce from earlier discussion that on going from left to right, i.e., from CP to COT, the permeability and the phase ratio of the columns increases. In the same sense, the H vs. $\bar{u}$ curves become generally flatter with a smaller slope of the ascending branch. The $H/\bar{u}$ value given in time units is, as shown earlier, characteristic of the speed of analysis attainable with any column. On the other hand, the time of analysis according to eqs. (16) and (17) is determined solely by the capacity ratio and the relative retention of the compounds to be separated. At a given capacity ratio the data presented show that there is hardly any difference in the relative peak broadening (H) of the different column types. In consequence, attainability of high $\bar{u}$ easily is

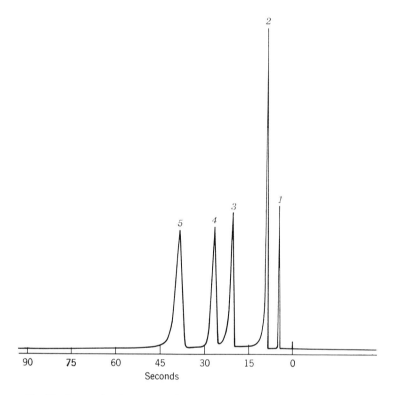

Fig. 21. Separation in a porous-layer open tube (64). (*1*) methane; (*2*) dichlor-methane; (*3*) trichlor-methane; (*4*) CF$_2$Cl—CFCl$_2$; (*5*) tetrachlor-methane K = 6.8 × 10^{-6} cm^2; t_c = 80°C; L = 8 m; i.d. (nominal): 0.5 mm. 12.8 mg graphitized carbon black/meter column length. Carrier gas: hydrogen. Δp = 2.3 at; $\bar{u}$ = 178 cm/sec; flow rate: 35 ml/min (20°C, 1 at). s = 7 × 10^{-7} g. FID, full scale deflection: 5 × 10^{-10} A. N/t = [$\bar{u}/H(1 + k')$]$_{opt}$ = 95 sec.

the main determining factor for speed. Broadly stated, increasing speed is attained by going from left to right across the column types listed in Table III.

In consequence of the increasing phase ratio as we go from left to right, from CP to COT, a price is paid for speed. The maximum allowed sample sizes become progressively smaller and smaller and the injected liquid or gas samples have to be split at the column head. This may introduce quantitative uncertainty; in addition, a high splitting ratio means high flow rate and waste of the carrier gas at the injection port.

Since the time of sample introduction and evaporation is independent of the column type, the higher carrier gas flow at the injection point results in much lower concentration of the sample at both the injection port and the detector. Roughly, the sample concentration in the carrier gas at the end of the column at peak maximum is in the order of 1% of that met with in CP systems (if the concentration of the compound in the *sample* is greater than 20%) and perhaps less by a factor of 10 or more in COT.

IX. EXPERIMENTAL COLUMN DATA

In the previous sections several approaches to column comparison were discussed from a number of viewpoints. In Table IV some experimental results for different column types are shown; these, it is hoped, will at least give some feeling for the orders of magnitude of the parameters involved. One, but not always the best, way is to compare columns for a given separation problem, stationary phase, and temperature in terms of their t_{ne} vs. Δp_{ne} curves. This approach is adopted later.

To avoid any misunderstanding, Table IV cannot exactly establish the order of superiority of the several column types, because temperature, carrier gas, and stationary phase are varied. It is an unfortunate fact that no one has yet made the necessary comparisons in fixed conditions. As a result, the best that can be done is to draw together, as in Table IV, the most nearly comparable data.

The results on BC-type columns quoted here are extremely poor and are not truly characteristic of this column type; this particular column was overloaded with stationary phase. Unfortunately, we have been unable to find better detailed and more representative data. The sample in each case is n-heptane, except for the aerogel column where the sample is propylene. Most of the results for GLC operation relate to Chromosorb W coated with squalane, except in the case of the PLB system where 93.66% (by weight) glass beads were coated with 6.2% ZrO_2 and 0.16% triethylene glycol (GAC) and the aerogel column where Aerosil was the stationary phase. In calculating the stationary phase per unit column length of the PLB column, the weight of ZrO_2 was neglected and, formally, only that of triethylene glycol is given. This is not strictly correct for GAC operation because the active support and the relative amount of liquid *together* determines the properties of the stationary phase.

TABLE IV.

Type		t_c, °C	i.d., mm	K, cm² × 10⁷	a, V_m/V_s	d_1, μm	k', nC_7	Stat. phase, mg/m	h_{min}, mm
CP	GLC	50	4.0	2.1	54	—	7.8	185.4^c	1.25
PLB	GAC	100	2.0	2.2	130	—	2.9	11.7^d	0.47
BC	GLC	50	4.0	4.4	166	—	2.6	32.6^c	1.9
PC	GLC	50	0.3	18.5	267	—	1.6	0.28^c	0.96
Ae	GSC	25	0.4	0.26	39	—	1.46^b	7.5^c	0.12
PLOT	GLC	80	0.5^a	419	37	0.69	4.23	4.3^c	1.3
COT	GLC	50	0.5	700	485	0.26	0.87	0.31^c	4.3
COT	GLC	50	0.5	182	145	0.44	2.9	0.26^c	1.2

^{a} Calculated from t_o. ^{b} For propylene. ^{c} Squalane.

In calculating the average film thickness d_l (given in microns) of the PLOT column, a roughness factor of 5.2 has been assumed (140). The $(H/\bar{u})_{opt}$ values are given in milliseconds. Although nitrogen and hydrogen carrier gases are both used, performance indices calculated are always for nitrogen, to facilitate the comparison. Performance parameters were calculated for a separation factor $S = 92$ (i.e., n-hexane/n-heptane separation on squalane at 50°C). It is assumed that the compound with the capacity ratio given in Table IV has the greater retention time of the pair to be resolved.

The speed of analysis, characterized by N/t, depends on the capacity ratio. The relevant k' of the CP column is a little higher than is normal in routine work. It must be pointed out that much better N/t values are described in the literature than are given in Table IV. However, these latter values seem to be characteristic, except, of course, for the exceptional results quoted for PLB and Ae columns.

Overlapping of the permeability and phase ratio, of the different column types, resulting in the change of order given in the second but last line in Table III, is demonstrated in Table IV. The h_{min} values are very similar indeed, except that of the COT with unusually high inner diameter (i.d. = 0.5 mm). The $\bar{u}_{min}$ given for conventional packed columns is unusually high (instead of 3–6 cm/sec it is about 30 cm/sec) and that of packed capillary columns uncommonly low. Up to now the speed of analysis has been given in terms of the N/t value. Another important characteristic of the speed of analysis is, of course, the value of $(H/\bar{u})_{opt}$, which is more independent of the capacity ratio than is N/t.

Experimental Column Comparison

$\bar{u}_{min}$, cm/sec	$\bar{u}_{opt}$ cm/sec	$(H/\bar{u})_{opt}$, msec	Carrier gas	PI, poise	PP, at × sec	N/t, sec^{-1}	Ref.	Table or figure
10.3	10.3	15.5	H_2	480	1.78	7.3	3	II, IV
20	26	3.7	H_2	44.6	0.133	70	25	7
6.6	60.6	109	H_2	13,120	648	2.5	3	III, IV
6.5	26.8	16.9	N_2	44.6	0.521	23	3	III, IV
34.5	40	0.93	H_2	50.8	0.156	430	78	1
20	20	10.0	H_2	2.6	0.008	19	140	I, II, 2
33.7	150	30.8	H_2	30.8	0.938	17	3	III, IV
19.5	52.4	10.3	N_2	5.8	0.108	25	3	III, IV

^{d} 6.2% ZrO_2 + 0.16% TEG. ^{e} Aerosil.

One column in Table IV shows the amount of stationary phase in milligram per meter column length. This, it should be noted, corresponds roughly to the loadability of the column.

In Figure 22 the t_{ne} vs. Δp_{ne} curves for the columns given in Table IV are shown. It should be mentioned again that these curves are calculated from the H vs. $\bar{u}$ curves and that every point on these curves corresponds to a different column length [eq. (19)]. Here again the value $S = 92$ was assumed; this corresponds to a very simple separation with $r_{12} = 2.67$. Hence the times of analysis and pressure drop are very small in Figure 22. Because t_{ne} and Δp_{ne} are linear functions of the separation factor S [eqs. (17) and (20)] the coordinates in Figure 22 have only to be extended by a constant factor to find the time and pressure drop for, for example, the separation of n-heptane from another closely eluted compound, i.e., the example shown in Table II. Comparing these curves with the h_{min}, PI, PP, and N/t values in Table IV it is to be seen how difficult, or perhaps hopeless, it is to characterize a column with only one parameter. Although the values quoted are specific for the given separation on a given column and temperature, some general rules are illustrated in Figure 22. The optimum pressure drop on open tubes (PLOT, COT) may be a factor of 100 smaller than that with packed columns. Consequently, with the same pressures, much longer capillary columns can be used with an experimentally limited pressure drop and the efficiency (N or n) must increase by the same factor. This allows much increased resolution in difficult separations. The *pressure drop* is not the only price which must be paid for the speed of analysis; contingent upon it is a *limit to the maximum efficiency of the column.*

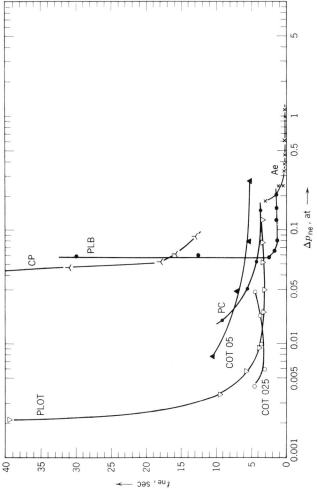

Fig. 22. Time of analysis and pressure drop on different column types. Parameters as in Table IV.

Thus capillaries are doubly favored for speed. Of course open tubes can only be employed if their phase ratio is adequate to the separation problem. As an example of the significance of this, we see that in Figure 22 the optimum times of analysis in packed columns (CP, PLB, PC, and Ae) are shorter than those in open tubes. The assumption that high-speed analysis is achieved *only* in open tubes is thus not correct. If the relative retention is not too small, pressure drop does not introduce any limitation and then high speeds of analysis are obtainable with packed columns.

X. SUMMARY

The most important characteristics of different column types are: (*a*) the permeability K, (*b*) the phase ratio a, (*c*) the position and shape of the H vs. $\bar{u}$ curve, and (*d*) the maximum sample size corresponding to the condition that the H vs. $\bar{u}$ curve remain unchanged with further reduction of sample. The given separation problem determines the choice of stationary phase and temperature and these together, the phase ratio. If optimum capacity ratios ($k' = 1$–5) are wanted, the last determines the primary choice of column type. Temperature and pressure drop *limits* also influence the choice of the column type. Bearing these criteria in mind it is an open question whether the optimum column for any specific purpose is likely to be commercially available.

A general practical rule is: *choose the column with the highest possible permeability in which the desired phase ratio is attainable.* The higher the desired separation factor, the more important is the matter of permeability. If, on the other hand, the speed of analysis is of major interest, then $(H/\bar{u})_{\mathrm{opt}}$ is the important parameter.

In contrast to distillation, for example, the optimum parameters for a gas chromatographic separation are not calculable. The reason for this is that the H vs. $\bar{u}$ curve is not calculable on an *ad hoc* basis. The "constants" of the van Deemter equation are empirical ones and are a function of the column length, capacity ratio, temperature, etc. Fortunately there are some general rules deducible from practice. h_{min} values are typically 0.07–0.4 cm, while typical H values as seen in the diagrams are in the region of 0.1–2.5 cm. The orders of magnitude of permeability and $(H/\bar{u})_{\mathrm{opt}}$ are illustrated in Table IV. Consequently, a rough approximation of optimum parameters is always possible via eqs. (16)–(20).

If the ratio of the net retention times (t_R') of the compounds is high (for example greater than 5–10) optimum conditions cannot be found in isothermal and isobaric conditions. Thus, programming one of the parameters is indicated. In this situation combination of different stationary phases or column types can help (124) but the simplest possibility is to program the temperature and/or the inlet pressure. Programmed gas chromatography always leads to shorter times of analysis but to *worse* resolution than is achievable with optimized constant temperature or pressure operation.

It has been shown that optimum conditions for gas chromatography can be only extremely roughly assessed. A minimum knowledge of practical theory, however, is shown to markedly reduce the time and effort spent in trial and error. Gas chromatographic analysis is today partly a science but, to a greater degree, an art.

XI. List of Symbols

A	Constant in the van Deemter equation, eddy diffusion
Ae	Aerogel column
a	V_m/V_s = phase ratio of the column
at	1 kg weight (kilopond) per cm^2
B	Pressure-independent constant in the van Deemter equation, longitudinal diffusion
BC	Conventional column packed with liquid-coated beads
C_m	Pressure independent constant in the van Deemter equation, mass transfer in the gas phase
C_s	Constant in the van Deemter equation, mass transfer in the stationary phase
COT	Conventional open tube column
CP	Conventional packed column
D_g	Diffusion coefficient of the solute in the gas phase
d_c	Inner diameter of the column
d_p	Particle diameter of the support
H	$Lw^2/16(t_R')^2 = L/N$
H_{min}	Minimum H value in the H vs. $\bar{u}$ curve
H_{opt}	H at the beginning of the minimum of the $H/\bar{u}$ vs. $H\bar{u}$ curve
h	$Lw^2/16t_R^2 = L/n$
h_{min}	Minimum h value in the h vs. $\bar{u}$ curve
i.d.	Inner diameter
j	$p_o/\bar{p}$ = James-Martin pressure-correcting factor
j'	Pressure-correcting factor in the equation: $\bar{u} = (K\Delta p/\eta L)j'$

K	$-\eta u\,dp/dx$ = specific gas permeability
k	Partition coefficient
k'	kV_s/V_m = capacity ratio of the column
L	Column length
L_{ne}	HS = necessary column length
L_{opt}	L calculated from H_{opt} with eq. (19)
N	$16(t_R')^2/w^2$
n	$16t_R^2/w^2$
PC	Packed capillary column
PI	Performance index defined in eqs. (21) and (22)
PLB	Conventional column packed with porous-layer beads
PLOT	Porous layer open-tube column
PP	Performance parameter defined in eq. (24)
p	Pressure
p_i	Inlet pressure
p_o	Outlet pressure
$\bar{p}$	$p_o j$ = column length averaged pressure
Δp	Pressure drop on the column
Δp_{ne}	$H\bar{u}S/Kj'$ = necessary pressure drop across the column
R	$[2(t_{R2} - t_{R1})]/(w_1 + w_2)$ = resolution
r_{12}	$k_2/k_1 = k_2'/k_1' = t_{R2}'/t_{R1}'$
S	$[4Rr_{12}/(r_{12} - 1)]^2$ = separation factor = N_{ne}
s	Sample size entering the column
$t \simeq t_R$	Time of analysis
t_c	Column temperature
t_{ne}	$H(1 + k')S/\bar{u}$ = necessary time of analysis
t_o	Gas holdup time
t_R	Retention time of peak measured from the start
t_R'	$t_R - t_o$ = net retention time
$\bar{u}$	Time-averaged mean carrier gas velocity
u_o	Outlet velocity of carrier gas
u_{min}	$\bar{u}$ value at the minimum of the h (or H) vs. $\bar{u}$ curve
u_{opt}	$\bar{u}$ at the beginning of the minimum of the $H/\bar{u}$ vs. $H\bar{u}$ curve
V_m	Volume of the gas phase in the column
V_s	Volume of the partitioning stationary phase in the column
w	Peak width at base line, segment of peak base intercepted by tangents to the inflection points
x	Distance from inlet end of column
η	Carrier gas viscosity
ϵ	Interparticle porosity [eq. (5)]

Acknowledgment

We express our gratitude to the Bundesminister für Wissenschaftliche Forschung, to the Deutsche Forschungsgemeinschaft and Max-Buchner Forschungsstiftung for financial furtherance of the works referred to in this paper. The authors are very much obliged to Prof. J. H. Purnell for his comments and for rewriting the English manuscript.

References

1. G. Deininger, Ph.D. thesis, University of Frankfurt/Main, Germany, 1966.
2. A. T. James and A. J. P. Martin, *Biochem. J.*, **50**, 679 (1952).
3. I. Halász, K. Hartmann, and E. Heine, in *Gas Chromatography 1964*, A. Goldup, Ed., The Institute of Petroleum, London, 1965, p. 38.
4. J. H. Purnell, *Gas Chromatography*, Wiley, New York, 1962, p. 60.
5. P. C. Carman, *Flow of Gases through Porous Media*, Butterworths, London, 1956, p. 8.
6. J. Bohemen and J. H. Purnell, *J. Chem. Soc.*, **1961**, 360.
7. D. H. Desty, A. Goldup, and W. T. Swanton, in *Gas Chromatography*, N. Brenner, J. E. Callen, and M. D. Weiss, Eds., Academic Press, New York, 1962, p. 105.
8. I. Halász, *J. Gas Chromatog.*, **5**, 51, (1967).
9. I. Halász, *J. Gas Chromatog.*, **4**, 8 (1966).
10. I. Halász and G. Schreyer, *Z. Anal. Chem.*, **188**, 367 (1961).
11. W. Schneider, H. Bruderreck, and I. Halász, *Anal. Chem.*, **36**, 1533 (1964).
12. I. Halász and E. Heine, in *Advances in Chromatography IV*, J. C. Giddings and R. A. Keller, Eds., Dekker, New York, 1967, p. 207.
13. H. D. Papendick, Ph.D. thesis, University of Frankfurt/Main, Germany, 1966.
14. I. Halász, paper presented at the 3rd International Symposium on Gas Chromatography, Houston, Texas, 1965.
15. E. Glueckauf, *Trans. Faraday Soc.*, **51**, 34 (1955).
16. M. J. E. Golay, *Nature*, **182**, 1146 (1958).
17. J. H. Purnell, *Nature*, **184**, 2009 (1959); *J. Chem. Soc.*, **1960**, 1268.
18. J. H. Purnell and C. P. Quinn, in *Gas Chromatography 1960*, R. P. W. Scott, Ed., Butterworths, 1960, p. 184.
19. R. Loyd, B. O. Ayers, and F. W. Karasek, *Anal. Chem.*, **32**, 698 (1960).
20. R. Kieselbach, *Anal. Chem.*, **32**, 880 (1960).
21. R. Kieselbach, *Anal. Chem.*, **33**, 23 (1961).
22. I. Halász and E. Heine, *Anal. Chem.*, **37**, 495 (1965).
23. C. G. Scott and D. A. Rowell, *Nature*, **187**, 143 (1960).
24. I. Halász and E. E. Wegner, *Nature*, **189**, 570 (1961).
25. I. Halász and C. Horvath, *Anal. Chem.*, **36**, 2226 (1964).
26. G. Kabaker, Ph.D. thesis, University of Frankfurt/Main, Germany, 1965.
27. P. Urone and R. L. Pecsok, *Anal. Chem.*, **35**, 837 (1963).
28. E. D. Smith and L. Johnson, Jr., *Anal. Chem.*, **35**, 1204 (1963).
29. A. B. Littlewood, *J. Gas Chromatog.*, **4**, 36 (1966).

30. J. S. Lewis, "Compilation of Gas Chromatographic Data," in *ASTM Spec. Tech. Publ.*, **343** (1963).
31. M. J. E. Golay, in *Gas Chromatography 1958*, D. H. Desty, Ed., Butterworths, London, 1958, p. 36.
32. M. J. E. Golay, in *Gas Chromatography 1961*, N. Brenner, J. E. Callen, and M. Weiss, Eds., Academic Press, New York, 1962, p. 11.
33. L. S. Ettre, in *Open Tubular Columns in Gas Chromatography*, Plenum Press, New York, 1965.
34. I. Halász and W. Schneider, *Anal. Chem.*, **33**, 978 (1961).
35. I. Halász and W. Schneider, in *Gas Chromatography 1961*, N. Brenner, J. E. Callen, and M. D. Weiss, Eds., Academic Press, New York, 1962, p. 287.
36. L. R. Durrett, M. C. Simmons, and I. Dvoretzky, in *Am. Chem. Soc., Div. Petrol, Chem. Symp.*, **6**, No. 2 B, 63 (1962).
37. D. R. Clarke, *Nature*, **198**, 681 (1963).
38. R. Byron, W. E. Stewart, and E. N. Lightfoot, in *Transport Phenomena*, Wiley, New York, 1960, pp. 154, 192.
39. A. B. Littlewood, in *Gas Chromatography*, Academic Press, New York, 1962, p. 209.
40. J. H. Purnell, in *Gas Chromatography*, Wiley, New York, 1962, p. 233.
41. S. Dal Nogare and R. S. Juvet, Jr., in *Gas–Liquid Chromatography*, Interscience, New York, 1962, p. 141.
42. E. D. Smith and L. Johnson, Jr., *Anal. Chem.*, **35**, 1204 (1963).
43. V. Kusy, *Anal. Chem.*, **37**, 1748 (1965).
44. J. J. Kirkland, *Anal. Chem.*, **35**, 1295 (1963).
45. J. King, *J. Phys. Chem.*, **67**, 1397 (1963).
46. H. W. Kohlschüttler and W. Hoppe, *Z. Anal. Chem.*, **197**, 133 (1963).
47. E. Smolkova, O. Grubner, and L. Felt, in *Gas Chromatographie 1965*, H. G. Struppe, Ed., Akademie Verlag, Berlin, 1966, p. D 163.
48. A. G. Altenau and L. B. Rogers, *Anal. Chem.*, **36**, 1432 (1965).
49. J. A. Favre and L. R. Kallenback, *Anal. Chem.*, **36**, 63 (1964).
50. K. Konishi and Y. Kano, *Bunseki Kagaku*, **13**, 299 (1964).
51. G. Blandenet, W. Jequier, and W. Robin, *Compt. Rend.*, **259**, 3523 (1964).
52. T. F. Brodasky, *Anal. Chem.*, **36**, 1604 (1964).
53. P. D. Klein, *Anal. Chem.*, **34**, 773 (1962).
54. A. V. Kiselev, Y. S. Nikitin, R. S. Petrova, K. D. Scherbakova, and Ya. I. Yashin, *Anal. Chem.*, **36**, 1526 (1964).
55. N. C. Saha and J. C. Giddings, *Anal. Chem.*, **37**, 830 (1965).
56. A. G. Kelso and A. B. Lacey, *J. Chromatog.*, **18**, 156 (1965).
57. J. J. Kirkland, *Anal. Chem.*, **35**, 2003 (1963).
58. E. H. Braun, *J. Gas Chromatog.*, **3**, 13 (1963).
59. G. Urbach, *Anal. Chem.*, **36**, 2368 (1964).
60. O. L. Hollis, *Anal. Chem.*, **38**, 309 (1966).
61. S. P. Zhdanov, V. I. Kalmanovskii, A. V. Kiselev, M. M. Fiks, and Ya. I. Yashin, *Zh. Fiz. Khim.*, 1118 (1962); *Russ. J. Phys. Chem.*, **1962**, 595.
62. I. Lysyj and P. R. Newton, *Anal. Chem.*, **36**, 2514 (1964).
63. V. S. Vasileva, A. V. Kiselev, Y. S. Nikitin, R. S. Petrova, and K. D. Scherbakova, *Zh. Fiz. Khim.*, 1889 (1961); or *Russ. J. Phys. Chem.*, **1961**, 930.
64. I. Halász and C. Horvath, *Nature*, **197**, 71 (1963).

65. I. Halász and C. Horvath, *Anal. Chem.*, **36**, 1178 (1964).
66. O. L. Hollis, *Anal. Chem.*, **38**, 309 (1966).
67. C. G. Scott, *J. Gas Chromatog.*, **4**, 4 (1966).
68. G. F. Shipman, *Anal. Chem.*, **34**, 877 (1963).
69. J. King, *J. Phys. Chem.*, **67**, 1397 (1963).
70. W. W. Hanneman, *J. Gas Chromatog.*, **1**, 18 (1963).
71. M. S. Vigdergauz and M. I. Afanasev, *Khim. Tekhnol. Topliv Masel*, **8**, 55 (1965).
72. S. Dal Nogare and R. S. Juvet, Jr., in *Gas–Liquid Chromatography*, Interscience, New York, 1962, p. 135.
73. J. C. Sternberg and R. E. Poulson, *Anal. Chem.*, **36**, 1492 (1964).
74. R. P. W. Scott, in *Gas Chromatography 1958*, D. H. Desty, Ed., Butterworths, London, 1958, p. 189.
75. J. C. Giddings, K. L. Mallik, and M. Eikelberger, *Anal. Chem.*, **34**, 1026 (1962).
76. A. V. Kiselev, Yu. L. Chermenkov, and Ya. I. Yashin, *Neftekhimiya*, **5**, 141 (1965).
77. M. N. Myers and J. C. Giddings, *Anal. Chem.*, **38**, 294 (1966).
78. I. Halász and H. O. Gerlach, *Anal. Chem.*, **38**, 281 (1966).
79. H. V. Carter, *Nature*, **197**, 684 (1963).
80. W. Virus, *J. Chromatog.*, **12**, 406 (1963).
81. M. S. Vigdergauz and L. V. Andrejev, *Khim. Tekhnol. Topliv Masch.*, **9**, 64 (1964).
82. W. C. Berezkin, A. T. Swjatoshenko, and A. T. Klemmentjewskaja, in *Gas Chromatographie 1965*, H. G. Struppe, Ed., Akademie Verlag, Berlin, 1966, p. H 453.
83. M. S. Vigdergauz and L. V. Andrejev, *J. Chromatog.*, **18**, 266 (1965).
84. W. F. Wilhite, *J. Gas Chromatog.*, **4**, 47 (1966).
85. M. S. Vigdergauz and L. V. Andrejev, paper presented at the 5th Symposium on Gas Chromatography, 1964, Brighton.
86. R. Teranishi and T. R. Mon, *Anal. Chem.*, **36**, 1490 (1964).
87. I. Sorensen and P. Soltoft, *Acta Chem. Scand.*, **10**, 1673 (1956).
88. A. Kwantes and G. W. A. Rijnders, in *Gas Chromatography 1958*, D. H. Desty, Ed., Butterworths, London, 1958, p. 125.
89. A. B. Callear and R. J. Cvetanovic, *Can. J. Chem.*, **33**, 1256 (1955).
90. A. B. Littlewood, in *Gas Chromatography 1958*, D. H. Desty, Ed., Butterworths, London, 1958, p. 23.
91. I. Lysyj and P. R. Newton, *Anal. Chem.*, **36**, 949 (1964).
92. J. C. Giddings, *Anal. Chem.*, **35**, 439 (1963).
93. D. T. Sawyer and J. K. Barr, *Anal. Chem.*, **34**, 1052 (1962).
94. A. Liberti, G. P. Cartoni, and U. Palotta, *Ann. Chim. (Rome)*, **48**, 40 (1958).
95. C. Hishta, J. P. Messerly, R. F. Reschke, D. H. Frederick, and W. D. Cooke, *Anal. Chem.*, **32**, 880 (1960).
96. R. J. Cvetanovic, *Can. J. Chem.*, **36**, 623 (1958).
97. J. G. Nikkely, *Anal. Chem.*, **34**, 472 (1962).
98. C. Hishta, J. P. Messerly, and R. F. Reschke, *Anal. Chem.*, **32**, 1730 (1960).
99. D. H. Frederick, B. T. Miranda, and W. D. Cooke in *Gas Chromatography*, N. Brenner, J. E. Callen, and M. D. Weiss, Eds., Academic Press, New York, 1962, p. 27.

100. K. Hartmann, Ph.D. thesis, Universität Frankfurt/Main, Germany, 1965.
101. M. J. E. Golay in *Gas Chromatography 1960*, R. P. W. Scott, Ed., Butterworths, London, 1960, p. 139.
102. J. C. Giddings, *Anal. Chem.*, **34**, 458 (1962).
103. S. D. Norem, *Anal. Chem.*, **34**, 40 (1962).
104. C. Horvath, Ph.D. thesis, Universität Frankfurt/Main, Germany, 1963.
105. R. A. Dewar and C. E. Maier, *J. Chromatog.*, **11**, 296 (1963).
106. D. E. Johnson, C. F. Rodriguez, and W. Schlameus, *J. Gas Chromatog.*, **3**, 345 (1965).
107. J. J. Kirkland, *Anal. Chem.*, **37**, 1458 (1965).
108. W. Graham, *Chem. Ind. (London)*, **1962**, 1533.
109. Ya. I. Yashin, S. P. Zhdanov, and A. V. Kiselev, in *Gas Chromatographie 1963* H. P. Angelee and H. G. Struppe, Eds., Akademie Verlag, Berlin, 1964, p. 125.
110. R. W. Ohline and R. Jojola, *Anal. Chem.*, **36**, 1681 (1964).
111. C. G. Pope, *Anal. Chem.*, **35**, 654 (1963).
112. J. L. Webb, *J. Gas Chromatog.*, **3**, 384 (1965).
113. D. H. Desty, J. N. Haresnape, and B. H. F. Whyman, *Anal. Chem.*, **32**, 302 (1960).
114. I. Halász and E. Heine, *Nature*, **194**, 971 (1962).
115. I. Halász and E. Heine, *Chem. Ingr. Tech.*, **37**, 61 (1965).
116. C. Landault and G. Guiochon, in *Gas Chromatography 1964*, A. Goldup, Ed., Butterworths, London, 1965, p. 121.
117. W. Schneider, H. Bruderreck, and I. Halász, *Anal. Chem.*, **36**, 1533 (1964).
118. J. C. Giddings, *Anal. Chem.*, **34**, 1186 (1962).
119. J. C. Giddings, *Anal. Chem.*, **37**, 609 (1965).
120. P. D. Schettler, C. P. Russel, and J. C. Giddings, *Anal. Chem.*, **37**, 835 (1965).
121. I. Halász, in *Gas Chromatography 1962*, M. van Swaay, Ed., Butterworths, London, 1963, p. 133.
122. I. Halász and W. R. Marx, *Chem. Ingr. Tech.*, **36**, 1115 (1964).
123. H. Bruderreck, *Erdöl Kohle*, **16**, 847 (1963).
124. I. Halász, E. Heine, C. Horvath, and H. G. Sternagel, *Brennstoff-Chem.*, **44**, 387 (1964).
125. M. J. E. Golay, in *Gas Chromatography 1957*, V. J. Coates, H. J. Noebels, and I. S. Fagerson, Eds., Academic Press, New York, 1958, p. 1.
126. I. Halász and G. Schreyer, *Chem. Ingr. Tech.*, **32**, 675 (1960).
127. G. Dijkstra and J. de Goey, in *Gas Chromatography 1958*, D. H. Desty, Ed., Butterworths, London, p. 58.
128. R. Kaiser, *Gas Phase Chromatography*, Vol. 2, *Capillary Chromatography*, Butterworths, London, 1963.
129. R. P. W. Scott and G. S. F. Hazeldean, in *Gas Chromatography 1960*, R. P. W. Scott, Ed., Butterworths, London, 1960, p. 114.
130. D. H. Desty in *Advances in Chromatography*, J. C. Giddings and R. A. Keller, Eds., Dekker, New York, 1965, p. 199.
131. R. Martin and J. C. Winters, *Anal. Chem.*, **35**, 1930 (1963).
132. D. L. Petitjean and C. F. Leftoult, *J. Gas Chromatog.*, **1**, 18, No. 3, (1963).
133. D. H. Desty in *Advances in Chromatography*, J. C. Giddings and R. A. Keller, Eds., Dekker, New York, 1965, p. 224.
134. M. Mohnke and W. Saffert, in *Gas Chromatography 1962*, M. Van Swaay, Ed., Butterworths, London, 1962, p. 216.

208   I. HALÁSZ AND E. HEINE

135. W. Leipnitz and M. Mohnke, *Chem. Tech.*, **14**, 753 (1962).
136. S. P. Zhdanov, V. I. Kalmanovskii, A. V. Kiselev, M. M. Fiks, and Ya. I. Yashin, *Zh. Fiz. Khim.*, **36**, 1118 (1962); or *Russ. J. Phys. Chem.*, **1962**, 595.
137. F. Brunner and G. P. Cartoni, *Anal. Chem.*, **36**, 1522 (1964).
138. F. Brunner and G. P. Cartoni, *J. Chromatog.*, **18**, 390 (1965).
139. F. Brunner, G. P. Cartoni, and A. Liberti, *Anal. Chem.*, **38**, 298 (1966).
140. I. Halász and C. Horvath, *Anal. Chem.*, **35**, 499 (1963).
141. J. E. Purcell, *Nature*, **201**, 1321 (1964).
142. R. D. Schwartz, D. J. Brasseaux, and G. R. Shoemake, *Anal. Chem.*, **35**, 497 (1963).
143. R. D. Schwartz, D. J. Brasseaux, and R. G. Mathews, *Anal. Chem.*, **38**, 303 (1966).
144. L. S. Ettre, J. E. Purcell, and S. D. Norem, *J. Gas Chromatog.*, **3**, 181 (1965).
145. L. S. Ettre, J. E. Purcell, and K. Billeb, paper presented at the 19th Annual Summer Symp. on Anal. Chem., Am. Chem. Soc., Edmonton (Canada), June 23, 142 (1964).
146. A. Zlatkis, D. C. Femimore, L. S. Ettre, and J. E. Purcell, *J. Gas Chromatog.*, **3**, 75 (1965).
147. J. H. Purnell, *Endeavour*, **23**, 142 (1964).

Physical Measurement by Gas Chromatography

JOHN R. CONDER, *Department of Chemistry,*
University College of Swansea, Singleton Park, Swansea, Wales

I. INTRODUCTION

Gas chromatography is one of the most widely used scientific inventions of recent years. Established for a decade as a major analytical technique, it is now being developed rapidly in two other fields: the separation of materials on a preparative or plant scale, and the measurement of physical properties. It is the purpose of this review to show how a variety of physical phenomena can be studied by GC techniques and that this approach is often strongly competitive, in speed, simplicity, and accuracy, with conventional methods.

The operation of a column to separate the components of a mixture depends upon basic thermodynamic phenomena and rate processes. Thus, to optimize the column conditions for analytical separation one requires a knowledge of such quantities as the temperature variation of the partition coefficients of solute components between the two chromatographic phases, and the dependence of rates of mass transport in mobile and stationary phases upon flow rate and liquid distribution. Such information can be obtained by using GC in the first place to investigate the physical processes operating in the column. This possibility has been appreciated since the early days of GC (1–3). Indeed, activity coefficients in solution and gas–solid adsorption isotherms have been measured several times by the technique, but it is only recently that this work has led to an understanding of how the experiments should be designed in order to yield reliable and accurate results. Perhaps the most significant recent development has been the application of GC to study a variety of physical phenomena which have not hitherto been used to effect GC separations for analysis, e.g., adsorption at liquid–gas interfaces, deviations from ideality of gas vapor mixtures, liquid–crystalline behavior and complexing equilibria. The use of some of these phenomena as a basis for separation promises to extend considerably the scope and efficacy of analytical and preparative GC. Gas chromatography not only provides an appropriate means of obtaining the physical data required for effective GC separation, but also offers a route to information of general physicochemical interest.

The subject of physical measurement by GC can be divided into two broad areas of study: (a) equilibrium properties, and (b) rate processes. In general, the equilibrium properties of the system determine the retention volume, whereas rate processes broaden the chromatographic bands and modify solute concentration profiles.

Of the two fields, the study of equilibrium properties has received by far the larger share of attention: rate processes have been studied largely with a view to improving the efficiency of separation. In principle diffusion coefficients in both gas and liquid phases can be calculated from studies of band shape (4) and a few such attempts have been made. However, the nature of the terms in the rate equation is still uncertain and the subject of continuing controversy, and until the issue is resolved no GC determinations of diffusion coefficients can be regarded as reliable. The present review is therefore concerned entirely with the much more comprehensive range of studies which are founded on measurement of the equilibrium properties of the system.

II. THE CHROMATOGRAPHIC PROCESS

A. Modes of Chromatographic Operation

It is expedient to regard the chromatogram obtained at the outlet of a column as the response to a given sample input profile. The terms *sample input profile* and *chromatogram* are used to refer to the traces obtained on recorders connected to detectors at the column inlet and outlet, respectively. Assuming linear detector response, the traces represent the respective solute concentrations as functions of time. Comparison of the chromatogram with the input profile gives information on the processes operating in the column. This viewpoint, which has been advocated by Reilley, Hildebrand, and Ashley (5), is valuable because it emphasizes a fact often forgotten, that the input profile must be known before any information can be derived from the chromatogram.

It is possible to conceive of a large number of different forms of sample input profile. In practice only two basic types need be considered in the present context. These characterize, respectively, *frontal analysis* and *elution* chromatography. (The term frontal development would better parallel elution, but we let merit yield to custom.)

1. *Frontal Analysis*

In this case a continuous stream of mixed carrier gas and solute vapor flowing along the column is instantaneously replaced by a continuous stream of carrier gas containing solute vapor at a different concentration. The concentration profile is therefore step-shaped at the column inlet. As the *boundary* (the region of concentration change; or, more precisely, the solute concentration profile expressed as a function of distance along the column at constant time) progresses along the column, solute condenses, or is removed from, the stationary phase. After a time the whole column reaches equilibrium with the gas stream and the boundary breaks through at the outlet. The boundary profile is recorded at the outlet as the chromatogram. Examples are shown in Figure 1. The boundary is called a *front* boundary when the solute concentration increases with time [(*a*) and (*b*) in Fig. 1], and a *rear* boundary when the concentration decreases [(*e*) in Fig. 1]. To a first approximation, as discussed later, the shaded areas represent the amounts of solute taken up by the stationary phase.

2. *Elution*

In the elution technique, the column is first equilibrated with a continuous stream of pure carrier gas, or of carrier gas containing solute vapor so as to set up a concentration *plateau* of given height invariant with time and with distance along the column. A sample of solute having a symmetrical concentration profile is injected into the gas stream at the column inlet. After repeated partition in the column, the peak is eluted at the outlet, giving an elution chromatogram (Fig. 1). By using a sample of higher concentration of solute than that in the gas stream, a *positive peak* results: using a sample of lower concentration a

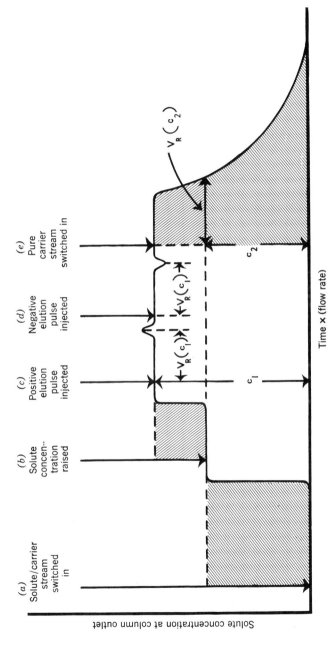

Fig. 1. Combined frontal and elution chromatograms. V_R is the retention volume at concentration c. The hatched areas represent amounts of solute sorbed by, or desorbed from, the stationary phase when the solute concentration is changed: (a) from 0 to c_2, (b) from c_2 to c_1, (e) from c_1 to 0. Areas hatched in the same direction are equal in area, to a first approximation (see Sec. II-A and III-D).

negative peak results. Clearly, if the gas stream contains no solute, only positive peaks are obtainable. When the elution peak is large the process is best considered in terms of two frontal analysis operations carried out in rapid succession, a front boundary being followed by a rear boundary, or vice versa.

B. Retention Theory

A brief statement of the salient features of the basic theory is given to facilitate the subsequent development.

Information on the physicochemical properties of a chromatographic system is obtained by comparing the boundary profiles, and times of appearance, at the inlet and outlet of the column. As the boundary passes along the column it is modified in a manner depending on (*a*) the equilibrium thermodynamic properties of the system; (*b*) changes in the velocity of the gas phase caused by the flux of solute molecules in and out of the gas phase wherever a concentration gradient exists (sorption effect); and (*c*) diffusional and other kinetic band-broadening mechanisms operating in the mobile and stationary phases (nonideality).

These three factors combine to determine the volume, V_R, of gas required to move a zone of given concentration on the boundary from inlet to outlet of the column. By making the assumptions that only factors (*a*) and (*b*) are operative and kinetic band-broadening is negligible, i.e., that the chromatographic process is "ideal" (the effect of nonideality is described later), Conder and Purnell (6) have shown that the general retention volume equation applicable at all concentrations of solute is, in its simplest form,

$$jV_R = V_R^0 = V_G + V_L\left(1 - J\left(\frac{2}{3}\right)y\right)\frac{dq}{dc} \tag{1}$$

y is the mole fraction, and c the concentration in milliliters per mole, of solute in the gas phase; q is the concentration of solute in the liquid or adsorbed phase; $J\left(\frac{m}{n}\right)$ is given in terms of the column inlet and outlet pressures, P_i and P_o, respectively, by

$$J\left(\frac{m}{n}\right) = \frac{n}{m}\frac{(P_i/P_o)^m - 1}{(P_i/P_o)^n - 1} \tag{2}$$

j is the gas compressibility factor of James and Martin (7) and is equal to $J\left(\frac{2}{3}\right)$; V_G is the volume of column occupied by the gas phase. In gas–liquid chromatography (GLC) V_L is the volume of liquid solvent in the column: in gas–solid chromatography (GSC) V_L is either the surface area or the mass of solid adsorbent in the column. The units of q and V_L must be consistent with respect to the amount of stationary phase present. V_R is measured as the product of the breakthrough time of a zone of concentration c and the gas flow rate at the outlet at the moment c breaks through.

In eq. (1) the factor (dq/dc) arises from effect (a) above: it is simply the slope of the partition isotherm, $q(c)$. The factor $(1 - Jy)$ arises from effect (b).

The equation has important consequences for both infinite dilution and finite concentration GC. At infinite dilution,

$$y \to 0$$
$$\frac{dq}{dc} \to \frac{q}{c} = K \tag{3}$$

where K is the partition coefficient of solute' between mobile and stationary phases. Equation (1) then reduces to the equation long familiar in gas chromatography,

$$jV_R = V_R{}^0 = V_G + KV_L \tag{4}$$

It is emphasized that eq. (4), like eq. (1), is applicable not only to GLC but also to GSC with appropriate definition of V_L and K.

At finite concentrations the retention volume given by eq. (1) varies with concentration because of curvature of the partition isotherm and change of gas velocity with concentration [effects (a) and (b)]. The resulting boundary profile in general takes one of two forms. A boundary which broadens markedly as it passes through the column and breaks through slowly at the outlet is said to be *diffuse*. A boundary which becomes steeper or maintains a steep profile as it passes through the column and breaks through rapidly at the outlet is said to be *self-sharpening*. The influence of effects (a), (b), and (c) on the boundary profile is described in the following sections.

C. Partition Isotherm

The part played by the partition isotherm, $q(c)$, in determining the frontal chromatogram is observed in the dependence of V_R on (dq/dc) in eq. (1). This relationship was discussed quantitatively before the advent of gas chromatography, first by Wilson (8), and later by Weiss (9), DeVault (10), and Glueckauf (11). The shapes of chromatograms were predicted for all five types of isotherm in the BET classification. Examples are shown in Figure 2. For a type I (Langmuir) isotherm (dq/dc), and hence V_R, decreases with increasing concentration. The chromatogram of a rear boundary is then diffuse, whereas a front boundary tends to sharpen itself as it progresses and produces a sharply stepped chromatogram. Conversely, a type II (anti-Langmuir) isotherm leads to a diffuse front boundary or a self-sharpening rear boundary. Further, as Glueckauf has shown (12), a linear isotherm gives front and rear

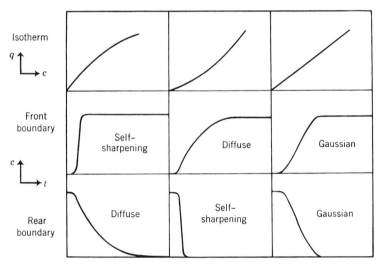

Fig. 2. The dependence of the boundary profile on the form of the partition isotherm.

boundaries which are both gaussian (the integrated normal curve of error), and have a singular point of inflection to be contrasted with the long, straight portion of a self-sharpening boundary, as shown in Figure 2. Isotherms having curvature in different directions in different concentration ranges give more complex chromatograms. Gregg and Stock (13) have observed examples of all five types of isotherm in the BET classification in the case of gas–solid chromatography.

D. Sorption Effect

The second factor influencing the shape of the frontal chromatogram is variation of gas velocity with concentration due to flux of solute molecules into or out of the gas phase as the boundary progresses. The effect was first described by Bosanquet (14,15) and has been further discussed by Schay et al. (16,17) and Peterson and Helfferich (18). The frontal chromatogram is influenced by the sorption effect through the factor $(1 - Jy)$ in eq. (1). The effect is therefore small at low concentrations but becomes important as y rises. In contrast to the effect of the partition isotherm, the sorption effect always leads to self-sharpening front and diffuse rear boundaries.

The form of a frontal chromatogram is thus seen to depend on whether the effects of partition isotherm and of sorption are mutually supporting or opposed. In the latter case either effect may predominate, depending on the magnitude of curvature of the partition isotherm. The overall criteria for the boundaries to be diffuse or self-sharpening have been discussed quantitatively by Peterson and Helfferich (18). The important conclusion for physical measurement, however, is that retention volume measurements can lead to accurate determination of the partition isotherm at finite concentration only if the sorption effect is taken into account, as in eq. (1).

E. Nonideality

All boundaries, whether diffuse or self-sharpening, suffer band broadening from several kinetic causes, of which the three most important are: (a) longitudinal diffusion of solute in the gas phase, (b) channelling and nonuniform lateral distribution of solute, and (c) slow mass transfer in the liquid phase, or slow rates of sorption and desorption from a solid surface. These effects give rise to so-called "nonideal" chromatographic behavior. Diffuse frontal boundaries are thus more diffuse in practice than would be predicted from the partition and sorption effects alone. Self-sharpening frontal boundaries possess an inherent sharpening mechanism which counteracts kinetic band broadening, but even in this case, however close to perfectly step-shaped the input profile, the chromatogram is always rounded at the beginning and end of the region of concentration change.

At the present time the theory of kinetic band broadening is less firmly founded than retention theory. Consequently, diffusion coefficients and other rate parameters determined from band shapes are of limited reliability. Further, it is difficult to predict quantitatively the effect of nonideality on boundary profiles, this being best investigated by experiment. Fortunately, there is every reason to believe that the situation will improve within the next few years and that it will then become possible to measure diffusion coefficients in gas and liquid phases by GC.

III. TECHNIQUES OF PHYSICAL MEASUREMENT

A. Introduction

The measurement of equilibrium thermodynamic properties by gas chromatography depends in the first instance on determining the amount of solute taken up by the stationary phase at a given concentration in the mobile phase. In practice, therefore, the retention data are used to calculate first the sorption isotherm (or partition coefficient at infinite dilution) using eq. (1) of Section II-B, and then other thermodynamic parameters.

A GC system may be used to measure solution and adsorption isotherms, collectively referred to as "sorption isotherms," in several different ways. All of these are based on one or other of the two basic modes of operation, elution and frontal analysis. The various techniques each offer distinct advantages and disadvantages.

Four techniques, two elution and two frontal, are closely related to each other in principle and take eq. (1) as a common starting point. These are the techniques described by Conder and Purnell (6) as "frontal analysis (FA)," "frontal analysis by characteristic point (FACP)," "elution by characteristic point (ECP)," and "elution on a plateau (EP)."

In the following sections, those aspects of the technique of elution chromatography which are relevant to measurements at both infinite dilution and finite concentration are described first, and are followed by an account of frontal and elution methods applicable at finite concentration.

B. Elution Methods

Equation (1) (Sec. II-B) gives the retention volume of a moving zone of solute *having constant concentration* along the column. To carry out an elution experiment at finite concentration, a constant concentration of solute is established along the column by setting up a plateau in a column designed to have as near zero total pressure gradient as possible. To avoid significant error, the total pressure drop should not exceed 0.5% of the outlet pressure. The latter condition is achieved in practice by using a column packing of very coarse mesh, as described in Section IV-F. At infinite dilution the plateau concentration is, of course, zero everywhere and therefore constant.

Very small solute samples are injected at the inlet and "ride" along the plateau to the outlet. The retention time is measured. Either positive or negative peaks (Sec. II-A-2) can be used at finite concentration, but clearly only positive peaks can be obtained at infinite dilution.

1. The Significance of Peak Shape and Concentration

Equation (1) is strictly applicable to the peak maximum only if the peak height is vanishingly small, so that the concentration of the peak maximum is equal to that of the plateau and therefore constant. This theoretical condition cannot be achieved in practice, but the retention volume will be unaffected if the sample size is sufficiently small to satisfy the conditions: (a) partition isotherm is essentially linear over the range of concentration covered by the peak; (b) gas velocity variation within the peak from the sorption effect is negligible; and (c) kinetic band broadening spreads the peak symmetrically.

These three conditions and other factors affecting the retention volume are considered in turn.

The effect of a nonlinear partition isotherm on a peak of finite height is to cause change of peak retention volume and concomitant peak asymmetry. The degree of asymmetry is measured by the skew ratio, η, which is the ratio of the slope of the trailing to that of the leading edge of the peak at the points of inflection (19). The skew ratios of positive and negative peaks are denoted respectively by η_+ and η_-.

It is often assumed that the partition isotherm is linear in GLC if the solution behaves ideally in the sense of Raoult's or Henry's law. This is not so. As Cruickshank and Everett (20) have shown, ideal solution behavior implies that the partition isotherm is of the anti-Langmuir type, which gives an eluted peak having $\eta_+ > 1$. This is shown in Figure 3. A peak having $\eta_+ < 1$ is obtained only in the case of a negative deviation from Raoult's law of such magnitude as to be very rare in noncomplexing GLC systems. Thus, irrespective of the sign of moderate deviations from Raoult's law, $\eta_+ > 1$, as regards this effect alone. In GSC, in contrast, isotherms are often of the Langmuir type, and isotherm curvature tends to skew the peak in the direction $\eta_+ < 1$.

The sorption effect always results in $\eta_+ < 1$, since gas in the region carrying the peak is moving faster than the rest of the gas stream on either side. The effect of sorption is thus opposed to that of isotherm nonlinearity in GLC, while both frequently act together to give tailed peaks in GSC.

When nonideality is dominated by longitudinal gas-phase diffusion and lateral nonuniformity of concentration profile, the effect is merely to spread symmetrically an already symmetrical peak, without affecting the position of the peak maximum. This statement is not quite correct: there is always a slight tendency toward peak asymmetry in the direction

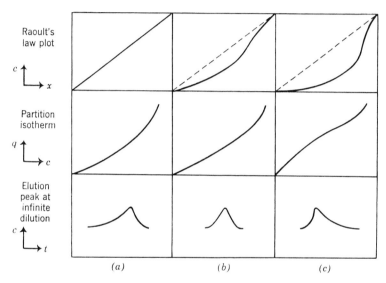

Fig. 3. The dependence of peak shape on deviations from ideal solution behavior: (a) ideal solution; (b) moderately large negative deviation; (c) very large negative deviation.

$\eta_+ < 1$ occasioned by the difference in residence times between front and rear sides of the peak, because the extent of band broadening arising from both partitioning and kinetic effects is proportional to the residence time. Depending on the retention volume and number of plates in the column, however, asymmetry from this source is usually small.

When, on the other hand, nonideality is dominated by nonequilibrium, through insufficiently rapid mass transfer in the stationary phase, peak asymmetry again results, though in this case without affecting the position of the peak maximum (12). Such asymmetry is small unless unusually short columns or very high flow rates are used (12).

Consideration of the effect of nonideality on peaks already asymmetric because of the nonlinearity and sorption effects is simplified by using the fact that under certain limiting conditions the three effects are independent and additive (21).

The effect of temperature changes accompanying sorption and desorption of solute has been investigated by Scott (22). A positive peak is at a higher temperature than the operating temperature of the column, so that the retention volume is reduced and $\eta_+ < 1$. The magnitude of the effect increases with increasing sample size, increasing flow rate, and decreasing partition coefficient, and can be quite large for solutes of short retention.

Pressure changes accompanying sorption and desorption of solute have been investigated by Haarhoff and van der Linde (23). The effect appears to be very much smaller than the temperature effect.

Asymmetry in the recorded peak profile can arise also from the finite response time of the detector and readout system. The apparent time of appearance of the peak is delayed and $\eta_+ < 1$. When retention is measured relative to an air peak the apparent retention volume is reduced by slow response, because the effect of the latter is greater for the air peak than for the solute peak.

With GLC, sorption of solute at either the liquid–solid or liquid–gas interface can have a major effect on retention volume and peak symmetry in some cases. These effects are discussed in Sections V-F and IX-B.

The influence of four of the aforementioned factors on the measured retention volume and skew ratio is shown schematically in Figure 4 for the case of elution on a plateau, of which elution at infinite dilution constitutes a particular case. At infinite dilution only the upper part of each diagram in the figure applies since only positive peaks are obtainable. The retention volume plots are shown linear but only the signs of the gradients of the plots are intended to be significant. The exact form of the variation of V_R and η over a larger range of concentration near infinite dilution has been derived by Haarhoff and van der Linde (21). The scheme of Figure 4 is consistent with practical experience (24). For very small samples, equivalent to 0.01–0.1 μl of liquid, the author has found values of η_+ and η_- both lying between 0.7 and 1.0 for alkanes of widely differing solubility in squalane solvent. This was with a katharometer of 2 sec response time, column lengths varying from 1 to

8 ft, and flow rates of 20–100 ml/min. Cruickshank, Everett, and Westaway (19) have also observed limiting values of η_+ of about 0.8 at zero sample size. At excessively high sample concentrations, skew ratios as high as 3 can be obtained (19), indicating the overriding effect of nonlinearity.

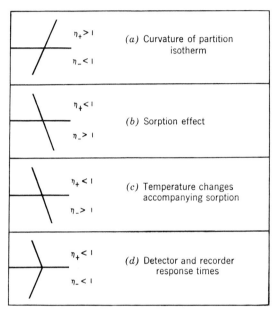

Fig. 4. The predicted effect of four factors on the variation of retention volume and skew ratio η, with sample size, for positive and negative peaks. In each case the abscissa is the retention volume, the ordinate is the peak height and the abscissa axis is at zero peak height.

The significance of the foregoing considerations for physical measurement is twofold. First, in order to measure the retention volume accurately, it is very important to use samples having the smallest possible peak height. In this way, the effects on the peak retention volume of nonlinearity, sorption effect, and slow detector response are minimized. It is commonly suggested that the retention volume at infinite dilution should be obtained by extrapolating to zero peak height from measurements over a range of peak heights. The extrapolation is said to be linear (21,25), although the author has observed nonlinear plots. In order to obtain such a plot, however, it is necessary to use larger peak heights than that which gives the smallest practicable signal-to-noise ratio. The extrapolation procedure therefore defeats its own purpose to some extent, especially since a comparatively large concentration range is often required to reveal a distinct trend in the plot through the small random variations in the measurements. It is arguable whether extrapolation over a concentration range offers any great advantage over the alternative procedure of taking several (say, two to four) measurements using the lowest conveniently attainable peak height each time. A method of calculating the retention volume at zero sample size by making measurements on an asymmetrical peak chromatogram has been given by Haarhoff and van der Linde (21).

Secondly, it is evident that the degree of peak asymmetry provides an indication of the reliability of the measured retention volume. The available evidence (19,24) suggests that apparent skew ratios in the region of 0.7–1.0 are "normal" at zero peak height. This accords with expectation because only the residence time and recorder response effects are operative at zero peak height. Skew ratios differing markedly from these values should be taken as evidence that the measured retention volume does not accurately reflect true infinite dilution conditions. On the other hand, it should not be too readily assumed that, when skew ratios lie in the suggested range, the measured retention volume is necessarily reliable.

2. Sample Input

The influence of the mode of sample injection on peak input profile has been discussed by Porter, Deal, and Stross (26) and Haarhoff and van der Linde (21). There are two limiting types of injection. In one the sample is charged as a plug, and in the other complete mixing occurs in the sample chamber at all stages after admission of carrier gas. In the first case, the mode of injection does not lead to input peak asymmetry and there is no correction to be made to the retention volume measured relative to an air peak incorporated in the sample. This statement is subject to the provision that the input bandwidth does not exceed about one quarter of the emergent bandwidth, for otherwise the simple plate theory of GC breaks down (12).

In the second case, the concentration of vapor emerging from the sample chamber falls off exponentially, giving rise to a tailed peak. If the input bandwidth is not very small, the retention volume then requires a correction for input bandwidth, since the peak profile changes as the concentration falls during passage through the column. This may therefore be considered as a further mechanism contributing to variation of retention volume with sample size.

In practice the input concentration profile lies somewhere between these two limiting cases, depending on the particular method of injection employed and the quantity of sample injected. There is no simple way of calculating the correction to be applied to the retention volume for a nonsymmetrical input distribution, but if the input bandwidth is fairly small in comparison with the emergent bandwidth—again, one quarter of the latter seems a reasonable maximum value in most cases— the correction will be negligible. It is not advisable, however, to try to reduce the input bandwidth more than necessary, for this raises the concentration of solute at the column inlet required to produce a detector signal of given size at the column outlet. Retention volume and peak symmetry are then affected as described in the previous section.

3. Sample Size

The effect of the discussion of the previous two sections in determining permissible sample size is illustrated by the following simple calculation based on that given by Purnell (27).

A column, 1 m in length, having an efficiency of 1000 theoretical plates, gives an emergent bandwidth of 6.5 cm. If the input bandwidth is to be less than a quarter of this figure and the column contains 1 g of solvent of molecular weight 400, the permissible input bandwidth in terms of column length takes in only 7.5×10^{-5} moles of solvent. The partition isotherm cannot be expected to be adequately linear over a solute concentration range of more than 1 mole %. Assuming that the solute has a molecular weight of 100 and a high partition coefficient, the maximum permissible sample size for the column quoted is then of the order of 1 μmole, or about 0.1 μl of liquid solute of molecular weight 100. This is much smaller than has often been used in the past.

A similar calculation for GSC suggests that the upper limit of permissible sample size lies in the region of 0.01–1 μmole, depending on the surface area of the adsorbent.

Calculations for the sorption effect and for the effect of temperature changes accompanying the peak, using Scott's experimental results (22) for the latter, suggest an upper limit to the permissible sample size of about 1 μmole in both cases, in GLC.

Since nonlinearity, the sorption effect, and the temperature effect probably constitute the most important intracolumn sources of peak assymmetry, it is concluded that the maximum permissible sample size for packed columns of conventional specification is about 1 μmole in GLC, and may be very much smaller in GSC.

There is no practical difficulty in introducing vapor samples several orders of magnitude smaller than this. The only limitation is the sensitivity of the detector. With most katharometers, sensitivity in nitrogen is marginal with sample sizes greatly below 1 μmole, but sensitivity in helium or hydrogen is much higher. With more sensitive detectors, there is no obstacle to achievement of desirably low sample sizes.

The term sample size is usually taken to refer to the total amount of solute or solutes injected, whether measured in μmole, mg, μl, or other units. The quantity is proportional to the product of the input bandwidth and the concentration of the peak maximum at the inlet, and in some cases it may be desirable to know the latter quantities as well. The concentration can be calculated from the sample size if the theoretical plate height, amount of solvent or adsorbent in the column, and partition coefficient are also specified. The sample concentration at the outlet is smaller than that at the inlet and therefore less critical, and it should be noted that the concentration over the greater part of the column length will be closer to the outlet concentration than to that at the inlet.

In conclusion, when presenting results, it is clearly essential to include some statement of sample size. Without such information, very little confidence can be placed in the results. The measured retention volume can be in error by 10% or more at sample sizes of only a few tens of micromoles of solute.

4. Determination of Retention Volume

It has been suggested by Everett and co-workers (19,28) that the thermodynamically significant retention volume is not that of the peak maximum, V_R, but the initial retention volume, V_I, i.e., that of the point of intersection of the baseline with a tangent to the leading edge of the peak at the point of inflection. This view is quite without theoretical foundation. It is evident from the discussion of the preceding sections that the equilibrium properties of the system determine only the peak maximum retention volume. The residence time of other concentration zones in the peak depends on the extent of nonideality and on the gas flow rate, and is a function of the number of theoretical plates in the column.

The initial retention volume hypothesis was put forward on empirical grounds, in particular the observation that V_R increased with solute concentration much more rapidly than V_I, and that activity coefficients in solution calculated from V_I were in much better agreement with results obtained by static measurements than were those calculated from V_R.

The reliability of these results, however, is open to considerable doubt because of the excessively large samples employed, ranging from 5 to 200 μmole of solute. Extrapolation from such large samples is not generally a valid procedure. Indeed, the observation that V_I increased, rather than decreased, with increasing sample size, suggests the effect of excessive feed volume and lengthy times of evaporation resulting from the use of large samples. Measurements based on V_R for the same systems as used by Everett et al. have been found by Conder and by Cruickshank et al. (24,29) to be in excellent agreement with the results of static measurements (30) when sufficiently small samples are employed.

C. Frontal Analysis by Characteristic Point (FACP)

In the frontal technique of FACP, the isotherm is calculated from the movement of a characteristic point on a single, diffuse, frontal chromatogram. The term characteristic point was used by Glueckauf (11) to refer to a zone of constant concentration on a moving, diffuse boundary. The locus of the characteristic point as the concentration varies at constant time is the boundary itself. Equation (1), Section II-B, gives the retention volume of such a characteristic point of concentration c. The conditions under which the equation is derived (6) require that (dc/dV_R) be finite. It is characteristic of a self-sharpening boundary that $(dc/dV_R) \to \infty$. The FACP technique therefore involves use of a diffuse boundary, whichever of the two boundaries, front or rear, this may be in a particular case.

The method was first developed by Glueckauf (11,31) for measuring partition isotherms in liquid–solid chromatography. Glueckauf's theoretical treatment thus omits considerations particularly relevant to gas chromatography, viz., gas compressibility, variation of flow velocity along the boundary due to the sorption effect, nonsharp boundary input profiles, and the contribution of gas holdup to total retention. For this reason, the procedure of Gregg and Stock (13), who applied Glueckauf's equations directly to gas–solid chromatography, allows accurate measurement of sorption isotherms only at low solute concentrations. The factors just mentioned are taken into account in the following procedure.

Two chromatograms are shown in Figure 5, one for a diffuse front and the other for a diffuse rear boundary. Experiment has shown (24) that the boundaries produced at the column inlet have a profile which is not very close to the ideal step form frequently assumed, even when special valves are employed for the purpose. It is essential to take account of this fact when using the frontal techniques. A second detector is therefore incorporated at the column head and the outputs of

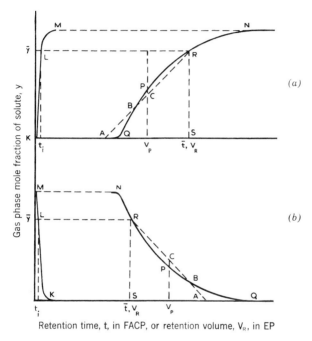

Fig. 5. FACP chromatograms. The diagram also shows the constructions required to calculate the results of EP measurements by the third method described in Section III-E (6).

both detectors are displayed on the same recorder, giving the composite chromatogram shown in Figure 5, where KLM represents the input boundary profile and $QBPRN$ the emergent boundary profile.

To measure a partition isotherm, a boundary covering a concentration range not less than that required to be measured is passed through the column. Several suitably spaced points R (Fig. 5) are chosen on the chromatogram and lines LR parallel to the time axis are drawn to intersect the trace KLM in L. One of two calculation procedures may then be followed, depending on the experimental conditions.

In the first method the flow rate of gas at each concentration corresponding to a particular position of R is calculated (6) and multiplied by the retention time, LR, to give the retention volume, V_R. A plot of $(V_R^0 - V_G)/(1 - Jy)$ against c is constructed, c being calculated from y using the virial expansion for an imperfect gas. From eq. (1),

$$qV_L = \int_{c=0}^{c=\bar{c}} \frac{(V_R^0 - V_G)\, dc}{1 - Jy} \tag{5}$$

Measurement of the area under the curve for each of several values of $\bar{c}$ thus gives a series of corresponding values of $\bar{q}$, from which the partition isotherm can be plotted.

In the second method the necessity for constructing a separate plot to obtain $\bar{q}$ is avoided by first integrating eq. (1) to give an expression for $\bar{q}$ in terms of areas measured directly on the chromatogram. This can be done only if certain approximations are made. A semi-empirical treatment has been given by Conder and Purnell (6), who have shown that in general it is possible to choose experimental conditions so that the approximations lead to negligible error in the result. The conditions are that the pressure drop along the column must be less than 5% of the outlet pressure, that the retention volume must be greater than 10 times the gas holdup, and that the input boundary must be adequately sharp. The integrated equation obtained (6) permits direct calculation of $\bar{q}$ by measuring the areas $KLRPBQ$ and $QBPRS$ on the chromatogram. This is a very convenient and rapid procedure and is accurate to better than 1–2% at values of the gas-phase mole fraction of solute up to 0.5. For more volatile solutes the first method of calculation should be used.

The advantage of the FACP technique is that complete partition isotherms can be determined in a single experiment. Other chromatographic and nonchromatographic techniques require a separate experiment to determine each point on the isotherm.

D. Frontal Analysis (FA)

The FA technique is related to FACP. The characteristic point R in Figure 5 is taken to be at the plateau concentration, i.e., at N. The total area $KLMNRPBQ$ bounded by the chromatogram is measured and $\bar{q}$ is obtained by the second calculation procedure described in the previous section.

In this case it is possible to use either a diffuse or a self-sharpening boundary for the measurements (6). A further point of difference between FA and FACP is that FA requires a separate experiment to determine each point on the partition isotherm. The points may be determined in one of two ways. The change in concentration effected by introducing the boundary may be carried out between zero concentration and the concentration in question each time. Alternatively, the concentration may be changed by successive increments or decrements, each new point on the isotherm being located in relation to the previous point. The second method is quicker since the concentration does not have to be brought back to zero each time, yet the first method has the advantage of allowing two determinations of each point on the isotherm in the same run, one from the front and one from the rear boundary, thus permitting a direct check on the possibility of hysteresis in GSC. The second method is also less accurate, since errors are cumulative as successive isotherm points are determined, but is still preferable if detector response is insufficiently linear.

A simple comparison between the methods of FA and FACP may be made by referring again to Figure 1, Section III-A. The chromatogram shown results from the passage of two successive, self-sharpening front boundaries, followed by a single diffuse rear boundary which returns the solute concentration to zero. Areas hatched in the same direction are equal to a first approximation, i.e., if the sorption effect and lack of sharpness in the boundary input profile is neglected. Two points on the isotherm can be determined in the FA manner by measuring the hatched areas on the left-hand side of the figure. The sum of these two areas is equal, again approximately, to the total hatched area on the right-hand side of the figure, which could be used in a FA calculation to repeat the determination of the isotherm point at concentration c_2. The diffuse boundary can also be used for FACP calculation, in which case the characteristic point of concentration c_2 is equivalent to the FA plateau of the same concentration on the left-hand side of the figure.

A slightly different, but essentially similar, form of the FA technique was used by James and Phillips (1), and later by Perrett and Purnell (32), to measure gas–solid adsorption isotherms. Only self-sharpening boundaries were used and, instead of measuring areas, the retention time at plateau half-height on the chromatogram was determined. Since V_R is independent of concentration for a self-sharpening boundary, eq. (5) of the previous section shows that the product of V_R and the plateau concentration gives the amount of solute sorbed by the stationary phase. This form of the FA technique is subject to the same sources of approximation as the FACP technique of Gregg and Stock (13). When, as in the approach previously described, the simplifying assumptions are not made, the treatment leads perforce to measurement of areas in place of retention times, which in turn allows use of diffuse, as well as self-sharpening, boundaries.

E. Elution on a Plateau (EP)

Like the frontal methods, the EP method is based on eq. (1). A plateau of constant concentration along the column is set up and the retention volume is determined by using a number of very small positive and negative peaks, as already described in Section III-B-1. The plateau concentration is then changed and V_R is determined at a different concentration. The EP technique thus has one feature in common with FA, in that a series of experiments must be carried out for each concentration.

Values of V_R so obtained may be used to calculate partition isotherms in one of three ways. The first method, due to Stalkup and Kobayashi (33), and also used by Chueh and Ziegler (34), essentially involves a step-by-step iteration procedure, which may be illustrated in terms of eq. (1) as follows. The value of K ($=q/c$) at $c_0 = 0$ is obtained from an experiment at infinite dilution. A trial value of K is then assumed at the next higher plateau concentration, $c_1 = c_0 + c$. dK/dc is set equal to K/c between c_0 and c_1, dq/dc is calculated from eq. (1), and a better value of K is then obtained from the relation

$$K = \frac{dq}{dc} + c\frac{dK}{dc} \qquad (6)$$

The new value of K is compared with the initially assumed value of K. Adjustments are made until agreement between the assumed and calculated K is finally achieved. K at other values of c is calculated by the same process. The method is seen to be cumbersome and requires a large number of fairly closely spaced values of c.

The other two EP calculation procedures both use graphical construction, which greatly reduces the amount of time and labor involved.

The second method (6,18) is essentially the same as the first method of calculation previously described for FACP using eq. (5). Since the column pressure gradient is virtually zero, $j = J = 1$, and q is obtained by measuring the area under a plot of $[(V_R - V_G)/(1 - y)]$ against c.

The third method (6) provides an alternative to the last method at mole fractions of solute in the gas phase up to 0.5. The retention data are used to construct the equivalent FACP chromatogram, making due allowance for variation of flow velocity with height on the boundary due to the sorption effect. The partition isotherm is then calculated from areas measured on the equivalent chromatogram according to the second method of calculation described in Section III-C for FACP.

At first sight, it may seem surprising that an EP experiment at a single plateau concentration does not allow immediate calculation of the corresponding point on the isotherm, especially since K can be calculated from a single elution run at infinite dilution [eq. (4), Sec. II-B]. The reason is that V_R is expressed in eq. (1), not in terms of q, but in terms of dq/dc. It is necessary to have values of V_R at several concentrations so that dq/dc is known as a function of concentration, when q can be obtained by integration. In contrast to EP, both frontal techniques permit calculation of an isotherm point from a single experiment because the complete information required to integrate dq/dc is contained in a single chromatogram, provided the latter starts or ends at zero solute concentration.

F. Elution by Characteristic Point (ECP)

The name ECP has been given (6) to a most ingenious and simple technique introduced by Cremer (35), and also by Huber and Keulemans (36). A large elution peak is passed through the column and the isotherm is calculated from the shape of the diffuse side of the peak. In essence, the peak is regarded as composed of two boundaries, the rear following immediately upon the front. One boundary is self-sharpening and the other diffuse.

The following comparison of the properties of elution and frontal chromatograms serves to explain the method. We assume that the sorption effect can be neglected, and further simplify matters by considering only ideal chromatography, in which the only band-broadening mechanism is partition. The result is shown in Figure 6. For linear chromatography the midpoint of the frontal breakthrough curve and the peak maximum have the same retention time, as shown in Figure 6a. A close approximation to this situation can be achieved with a very low solute concentration. If the isotherm is made increasingly nonlinear, the front of the peak sharpens and the rear of the peak and the frontal boundary become more diffuse until the peak maximum coincides with that point on the boundary having the same concentration, as in Figure 6b. Thus, if the peak height and frontal step height are the same, the peak maximum moves from coincidence with the midpoint of the boundary in the first case, to coincidence with the start of breakthrough of the boundary in the limiting second case. The phenomenon is normally observed as the concentration is raised from a very low value.

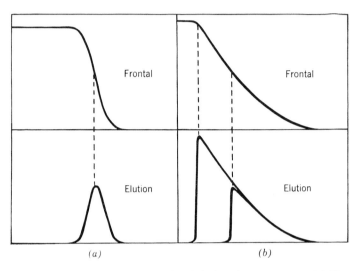

Fig. 6. The relation between frontal and elution chromatograms. (a) Chromatograms obtained with a linear partition isotherm. (b) Chromatograms obtained with a nonlinear partition isotherm. (The sorption effect is not taken into account.)

In view of the relationship between FACP and ECP, it is not surprising that the equation derived by Cremer and by Huber and Keulemans is closely related to that derived by Glueckauf (11,31), already referred to in Section III-C, and is inadequate for accurate GC application for the same reasons. More accurate results might be obtained by using either method of calculation previously described for FACP. Such refinement, however, is unlikely to be warranted as the method is in any case limited in accuracy and applicability by additional factors.

In the first place, ECP is capable of covering only a small part of the partition isotherm because of the large fall in concentration as the peak passes through the column. Secondly, nonideality, as well as the partition isotherm, contributes to peak profile, and because the concentration change is small, the relative contribution from nonideality may be much larger than in FACP. Bachman, Bechtold, and Cremer (37) devised two empirical procedures to correct for nonideality and obtained isotherms within 5% of the true ones. Knözinger and Spannheimer (38), however, suggested that the procedures are not generally valid and advised a return to the approach of Huber and Keulemans (36), who simply suggested using long columns to reduce the relative contribution of nonideality, and choosing the flow rate in the region of minimum plate height. Using 1-m columns in this way, Huber and Keulemans obtained isotherms deviating only 2% from the statically measured curves. Finally, it should be noted that the technique is applicable in its simple form only if the diffuse side of the peak is the rear side, for the velocity of the front side is affected by release of solute into the gas stream occurring at the rear side.

It is evident that ECP, in contrast to the three methods already discussed, is not a suitable technique for measuring partition isotherms over a large range of concentration. Its advantage lies in great experimental simplicity. As with FACP, an isotherm can be determined in a single experiment, yet no saturator or stream-switching valve is required. The same apparatus can be employed that is ordinarily used for elution at infinite dilution, and this may be of commercial quality. ECP is thus ideally suited to the purpose of rapid and convenient characterization of adsorbents for GC separations.

G. Schay's Frontal Method

A method described by Fejes, Fromm-Czaran, and Schay (17) depends upon using self-sharpening frontal boundaries. Such boundaries achieve a "stationary" form in the column, in which each point on the boundary travels forward at the same velocity, instead of a different velocity as in the diffuse case. The stationary form is determined by opposing effects: on the one hand nonlinearity overcomes the sorption effect in tending to sharpen the boundary, while on the other hand nonideality tends to spread the boundary. By working in a region of sufficiently low flow rate where longitudinal gas phase diffusion rather than slow mass transfer is the main contributor to nonideality, points on the partition isotherm can be determined if the effective gas phase diffusion coefficient is known. The latter is determined from the boundary profile in a region where the isotherm is linear.

Although contributions to nonideality other than longitudinal diffusion are not taken into account, the method has given results in very good agreement with isotherms determined by conventional static methods (17).

H. Elution of Isotopes on a Plateau

All the methods described so far have made use of the retention time of a given concentration zone. In general, the actual molecules of solute travel at a different rate from that of a concentration zone (39). Whereas the rate of travel of a concentration zone is given by eq. (1), Section II-B, the rate of travel of individual molecules at the same plateau concentration is given by

$$V_R{}^0 = V_G + KV_L \qquad (7)$$

K being the partition coefficient of solute at the plateau concentration. This equation is identical with the familiar eq. (4) applicable to a concentration zone at infinite dilution. At any given concentration, therefore, the retention volume of a *concentration zone* is governed by the *tangent* to the partition isotherm, dq/dc: for the *individual molecules*, it is governed by the *chord*, q/c $(=K)$, from the origin to the isotherm point in question.

If the retention volume of the molecules is determined at a particular concentration, an isotherm point is immediately calculable. There is no need to generate the isotherm from a series of values of dq/dc, as in the previously described EP technique. The advantage, however, is one of simplification of calculation, rather than of reduction of experimental labor, since one usually requires not an isolated point on the isotherm, but the complete isotherm, and hence measurements must be made at each of several concentrations in either case.

To measure the retention of individual molecules, a plateau of the desired concentration is first set up in the column. A small sample having the same total concentration, but tagged with a detectable isotope of the solute, is injected and its retention time is measured (33). If the two concentrations were not the same, both a concentration pulse and an isotopic pulse would travel down the column, but at different speeds.

The detector must be sensitive to the isotopes used. Nonradioactive isotopes can be detected with a gas density balance if the difference in mass is sufficient. Better sensitivity can be obtained by using radioactive isotopes and detecting them by their ability to ionize the surrounding gas and produce a current under the influence of an applied potential gradient. As is true for all elution techniques, the amount of isotope in the injected sample must be small and yet admit of ready detection. The method therefore does not avoid the sample size problem discussed in Section III-B.

The main disadvantages of the method are the difficulty of obtaining suitable isotopes in every case, the experimental complications involved in handling many radioactive samples, and the limited choice of method of detection. For general use the disadvantages are likely to outweigh the minor advantage of simpler calculation of the data.

I. Entrainment—GC Method

A very different approach from the foregoing has been developed by Burnett (40) for solution studies, and makes use of the capacity of GC to measure accurately very small quantities of materials.

The solution is contained in a special cell through which is passed an inert entraining gas at constant flow rate. The quantity of solution is sufficiently small to ensure that the concentration of solute decreases at a measurable rate. The effluent gas, saturated with solute and solvent at their respective partial pressures, is analyzed every few minutes gas chromatographically. The detector is previously calibrated for concentration against peak height. The effect of mixing in the dead space above the solution can be adequately corrected for.

Burnett was able to measure the partition coefficients at infinite dilution of C_1–C_4 alcohols in water and of C_5–C_9 alkanes in squalane, with an experimental precision of about 1% or better. The initial concentrations of solute in solution were of the order of 0.1 mole %, which is comparable with the closeness of approach to true infinite dilution obtained by elution GC with detectors of moderate sensitivity such as katharometers. At such low concentrations it was possible to determine partition coefficients of several solutes simultaneously in the one solvent with insignificant effect on the results.

It should be possible to extend the technique to finite concentrations, since entrainment leads to very little absolute change in a given concentration in solution during the period of a run. In comparison with classical static and entrainment methods, the method offers the same advantages of speed and attainment of very low concentrations as do the other GC methods previously described. In comparison with the latter, it has the advantage of being equally applicable to volatile and involatile solvents. Further, since no solid support is required and the liquid surface-area-to-volume ratio is small, there are no significant contributions from surface effects to interfere with studies involving strongly polar solutes or solvents.

J. Choice of Technique at Finite Concentrations

For general purposes, only four finite concentration techniques need be considered, viz., FACP, FA, EP, and Schay's frontal method. ECP and the isotope elution method are of limited use for accurate work, for reasons already discussed.

Schay's method requires very low gas flow rates, necessitating inconveniently long retention times for solute/solvent systems of moderate or high solubility. The method has been used only for solutes of low solubility or adsorptivity (17).

The FACP and FA techniques have so far been tested experimentally only with solutes of saturation vapor pressure well below 1 atm at the operating temperature, implying fairly low ranges of gas-phase concentration (up to 0.2 mole fraction of solute). The systems concerned were n-hexane in squalane and n-heptane in di-n-nonyl phthalate, and the results (24) were in good agreement with static measurements, to within the desired 1–2%. For FACP, columns at least 5 ft in length should be employed to reduce the effect of nonideality on boundary profile to negligible proportions. FACP offers a considerable saving in experimental time over the other techniques, since a complete isotherm can be measured in one experiment, though if the concentration range covered is large, detector response may be inadequately linear. FA puts less strain on the assumption of linear detector response if the concentration is raised stepwise from one isotherm point to the next.

Although all the techniques are much quicker in application than classical methods, the EP technique, like FA, is not as economical on experimental time as FACP, the number of different plateau concentrations required to cover a given concentration range depending on the method of calculation used. On the other hand, if the data are calculated by either the second or third method given in part E, no more points are required than in the FA case, and the desired accuracy of 1–2% or better should still be attainable.

Whereas linearity of detector response is important for the frontal methods, EP demands only good sensitivity of detection. A further point in favor of EP is that small amounts of impurity in the volatile component will tend to concentrate in either the adsorption or desorption frontal boundary and so affect the measurements. Slight amounts of impurity should have less effect on the EP results. Finally, the frontal techniques would be expected to be much more prone than EP to the effect of temperature changes accompanying passage of the boundary, particularly when self-sharpening boundaries are employed. Nevertheless, for solutes of moderately long retention at mole fractions up to 0.6 in solution, no such significant effects have been found (24).

IV. APPARATUS AND EXPERIMENTAL PROCEDURE

Two great advantages of gas chromatographic methods of physical measurement are experimental simplicity and speed of operation, for the apparatus required is basically the same as that commonly used for GC analytical work. The main difference is that temperature, pressure, flow rate, and column specification must generally be controlled and measured within closer limits. For the most accurate work commercial analytical equipment is usually inadequate without modification and it is often better to build a gas chromatograph for the purpose. Further, measurement at finite concentrations, as opposed to infinite dilution, requires provision for introducing solute continuously into the carrier gas, and for switching different gas streams into the column. Once a chromatograph meeting the necessary requirements has been constructed, results can be obtained rapidly and easily.

A. Accuracy

When proper precautions are taken, specific retention volumes should be measurable with a precision of 1–2% between different workers or with different apparatus. Relative retention volumes should be measurable with greater precision, to considerably better than 1%. These figures might be regarded as optimistic in view of the results of correlation tests (41) in which different laboratories have carried out retention determinations. These tests, however, were carried out under widely differing chromatographic conditions. If appropriate precautions are taken to ensure more accurate determination of retention volumes, the precision of results obtained in different laboratories should be considerably improved, and this aspect of physical measurement has been emphasized in Section III.

Experience shows that a precision of about $\pm 0.3\%$ or better can readily be achieved for measurement of specific retention volumes under a single set of experimental conditions. However, the figures given in the previous paragraph are more likely to reflect the real accuracy attained.

B. Flow System

A convenient chromatographic arrangement, suitable for measurement at both infinite dilution and finite concentration, is shown in Figure 7. Carrier gas, for example hydrogen, helium, nitrogen, or argon,

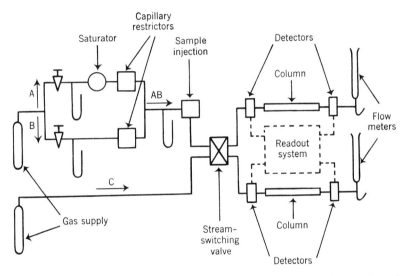

Fig. 7. A gas chromatograph suitable for all frontal and elution modes of operation.

is drawn from cylinders and dried by passing through a tube containing silica gel or Linde molecular sieve 4A. Three gas streams are used, each controlled by a needle valve. Stream A is passed through a solute vapor saturator maintained at a suitable temperature, and subsequently combined with stream B. The resulting AB stream can be made to contain any desired concentration of solute by adjusting the needle valves controlling flow. Capillary restrictors are incorporated in conjunction with manometers to monitor flow rate for calculation of the composition of the AB stream. Provision is made for sample injection by hypodermic syringe or sampling valve. A stream-switching valve allows the solute-containing stream AB and pure carrier gas stream C to be interchanged between the two columns. When the two columns are matched in pneumatic impedance, this arrangement causes minimum disturbance to flow on operating the valve. Detectors are situated at both inlet and outlet of each column so that the boundary input profile to the column can be observed as well as the chromatogram at the outlet. With flow-sensitive detectors, such as katharometers, it is in any case advantageous to mount channels in pairs in this way to provide some compensation for fluctuations in temperature and flow rate. While there is no great need to attach detectors to the second column, it is an added convenience to be able to use both columns for measurement. The output from each pair of detectors is fed via suitable amplifier–attenuator circuitry to a recorder. Expense can be saved by using only one recorder with provision for switching in either detector output. Finally, both gas streams are passed through flow meters.

The various experimental requirements are now discussed in turn.

C. Temperature Control

The properties and performance of a column depend markedly on temperature. For analytical work, temperature control to about $\pm 1°C$ is usually adequate. For accurate physical measurement, however, the temperature should be controlled and known to at least $\pm 0.1°C$. Certainly, temperature fluctuations with time should not exceed this figure. In some cases a rather larger variation of temperature with position along the column may be tolerated, provided an appropriately weighted mean temperature can be accurately calculated.

To thermostat the column within these limits, some form of stirred air or liquid bath is required: vapor jackets give inadequate constancy of temperature. Stirred liquid baths readily provide the desired temperature constancy, except that it is not easy to provide thermostatting right up to the ends of the column, especially if dead spaces at each end of the column must be kept to a minimum, as is sometimes necessary. If the whole column is immersed, including connecting tubing, care must be taken that the bath liquid does not get into the column.

The most satisfactory approach is to use a forced circulation air thermostat. Designs used in commercial instruments frequently have large temperature gradients within the oven. A great improvement is effected if the circulation rate is increased to give turbulent flow. An easily constructed design which has been much used in one laboratory

(42) can be made to give temperatures constant to better than 0.1°C throughout the space in which the columns are mounted.

D. Pressure and Flow Control

Manometers are not often incorporated in analytical gas chromatographs. For purposes of physical measurement, the pressures at both inlet and outlet of the column must be known in order to calculate the gas compressibility correction factor. The outlet pressure is usually atmospheric, though it should be checked that the detector and flow meter do not cause appreciable restriction in the flow line. If this is not the case, a correction is most easily made by calibrating this part of the flow line so that the pressure drop is always known at any given flow rate.

To read the column inlet pressure, a mercury manometer is incorporated near the inlet. However, sampling devices and stream-switching valves must be placed between the manometer and column inlet, since otherwise the dead volume in the manometer connection causes extra peak tailing and diffuseness of boundaries. If the valves cause appreciable restriction to flow, a calibration correction must again be made.

Manometers constructed in glass tubing should have an internal tube diameter of 7 mm or more, in order to minimize capillary error due to nonuniformity of the bore. Column inlet and outlet pressures should be measurable to at least 1 mm of mercury. Pressures on manometers used as capillary flow meters may need to be measured with greater precision, depending on the size of the capillary restriction.

It is advisable to use two-stage pressure regulators at the cylinder heads in conjunction with needle valves for good flow control. If the column used presents a substantial impedance to flow, this will also help to maintain constancy of flow rate.

For measurement of flow rate, it is essential to use a soap-bubble flow meter, or a capillary flow meter calibrated with a soap bubble meter. Rotameters are much too inaccurate for the purpose. The flow meter should be thermostatted to better than $\pm \frac{1}{2}$°C. When measuring with a soap bubble flowmeter, the walls should be well wetted, if necessary by sending many bubbles completely through the burette before measuring. Any dryness of the walls will lead to irreproducible flow rate determinations because the carrier gas in the burette is not saturated with water vapor. When helium or hydrogen is used as carrier gas, precautions should be taken to ensure that no air is present in the burette during measurements, since the light gases can diffuse through soap bubbles.

E. Sample Injection

The essential requirement for sample injection is that the sample size should be very small. More precisely, as discussed in Section III-B, this means that (a) the excess of solute concentration in the sample above or below that in the gas stream should be small, (b) the peak profile must be almost symmetrical, and (c) the input bandwidth of a symmetrical peak may be as large as one quarter of the emergent bandwidth, but must not exceed this value.

Introduction of liquid samples to give positive elution peaks is conveniently accomplished by injection with a hypodermic syringe through a rubber septum into a heated chamber where the sample is vaporized. Rapid vaporization is important to reduce peak tailing. Some tailing is likely to occur even at high chamber temperatures through continuous mixing of vapor with carrier, but the measured retention will not be effected if the input bandwidth, as observed with the detector at the column inlet, is considerably less than one quarter of the emergent bandwidth. With this form of injection, preliminary retention measurements should be made at different chamber temperatures to make sure that the results are not affected by heating of the gas stream at the temperature to be used. As shown in Section III-B-3, liquid samples containing only one component should not generally exceed about 1 μmole in size for $\frac{1}{4}$-in. diameter packed columns with 10–20% liquid phase loading. The corresponding upper limit for GSC varies between about 0.01 and 1 μmole.

Injection of the solute as a vapor is a technique which leads readily to introduction of both positive and negative peaks. Either a sampling valve or syringe injection may be used, but the latter is generally preferable. Sampling valves often place substantial impedance in the flow line, which causes difficulties with flow control and pressure measurement. Moreover, in the case of finite dilution GC, operation of the sampling valve may produce transient flow disturbances which lead to propagation of spurious peaks and transient concentration changes along the column. Such disturbances may also be observed, but to a lesser extent, when syringe injection is used, since the volume of a diluted vapor sample is often of the order of 100 μl or more for a packed column. If one experiments with capillary restrictors or ballast volumes placed at different positions in the flow line, it may be found possible to reduce or prevent spurious concentration changes (24).

Vapor injection requires preparation of a separate reservoir of mixed carrier gas and solute vapor in equilibrium with liquid solute maintained at a suitable temperature. Samples are transferred from reservoir to flow line by syringe or sampling valve. The peak height, whether positive or negative, is controlled by varying the reservoir temperature, and/or by varying the sample volume and speed of injection. The latter techniques are effective because the extent of dilution of sample by the gas stream depends on the volume and period of injection. In fact, negative peaks can readily be produced by injecting small quantities of pure carrier gas alone, subsequent mixing with the gas stream ensuring a small negative peak height.

Although vapor injection may cause less strongly tailed peaks than liquid or solid injection, it is more important than in the latter cases to ensure that the maximum permissible feed bandwidth of one quarter of the emergent bandwidth is not exceeded, on account of the larger volume of diluted sample injected. For introduction of very small sample sizes, vapor injection is more convenient than liquid injection, an advantage which is particularly important with capillary columns.

When working at high pressures, some form of sampling valve, such as those described by Scott (43) and Pratt and Purnell (44), is essential.

Whichever mode of sampling is employed, a very great saving in time can often be achieved by injecting the samples as mixtures, rather than singly. The mixtures should be so made up that each component is fully resolved on emerging from the column. Amaya and Sasaki (45) found that mutual interaction between two components injected as a mixed sample of 25 μl liquid affected retention volumes by 6% in one case with columns of moderate length. This observation and the author's own experience suggest that, provided the sample size of each component in the mixture is kept within the limits previously suggested, the effect on the retention volumes is quite negligible.

Finally, it is convenient to incorporate a nonsorbed sample peak in each chromatogram by injecting air or other suitable inert gas with the sample.

F. Production of the Boundaries

The theories of frontal analysis (FA) and of the second FACP procedure outlined in Section III require that the input boundary should be as sharp as possible. It is not always realized that unless special arrangements are made to produce sharp, step-shaped boundaries, the flow system will often take several minutes to settle down again after the needle valves have been readjusted. Accurate measurement is impossible with such a system. One method of obtaining sharp boundaries is to set up two gas streams having different solute concentrations, but matched flow paths, through matched columns. The gas streams are then instantaneously changed between the columns with minimum disturbance to the flow pattern. An experimental arrangement for this purpose has been shown in Figure 7, and a suitable gas-stream switching valve is described elsewhere (24).

G. Columns

Either packed or capillary columns may be used, but the former are usually preferred for reasons of experimental convenience. Packed columns are best constructed in stainless steel or glass tubing, as copper tubing can lead to adsorption of solute on the oxide surface of the walls. In contrast to the analytical case, preparation of the column in such a way as to give maximum column efficiency is not generally necessary, unless kinetic band broadening is actually the object of investigation. It is important, however, that the amount of stationary phase in the column should be accurately known, and the materials should be carefully weighed out, treated, and packed with this end in view. Accounts of the coating and packing procedures are given in standard textbooks (see, e.g., ref. 46).

When using a stationary liquid phase, consideration must be given to the choice of support material (47,48). Much has been written on the subject, but for physical measurement the main consideration is usually support adsorptivity, which results in falsely high values of the measured solute retention volume. Of the diatomaceous earth supports, Celite is less adsorptive than firebrick, and adsorption can be further considerably reduced by treatment with hexamethyldisilazane (49). Polymers of tetrafluoroethylene and trifluorochloroethylene, such as Teflon, Kel-F, and Fluoropak, are commonly stated to be the most inert support materials (50), although Fluoropak is not always suitable because of its low surface area and capacity for taking up liquid. In some instances metal helices (51) and diatomaceous earths coated with silver (43) have been used as support materials. The effect of support adsorptivity is further considered in Section IX.

At infinite dilution, support of any convenient mesh size can be used. Size 60–80 ASTM is convenient, the peaks being sufficiently narrow for convenient location of the peak maximum. For EP, whether using a concentration pulse or an isotope sample, the pressure gradient must be very small indeed, and the support should preferably be 10–20 mesh ASTM, but 20–30 mesh may be used with columns of 1–2 ft in length at very low flow rates (below 20 ml/min). For the frontal methods the pressure gradient may again have any value, except when it is intended to use the second method of calculation of the data described in Section III-3, involving a diffuse boundary. In this case, a mesh range of 30–40 is suitable for columns of up to 4 ft in length at flow rates up to 40 ml/min; 20–30 mesh should be used for longer columns or higher flow rates.

H. Detector and Readout System

The choice of detector depends on several factors, depending upon the type of measurement to be made. For frontal analysis, detectors must be incorporated at both ends of the column, and a linear detector response is mandatory. For elution measurements involving only the peak retention volume, there is no need to monitor inlet peak profile unless the experiments are to be carried out in such a way that feed volume or inlet peak assymmetry becomes critical.

In all cases, the response of the whole detector and readout system must be rapid if it is not to influence the measurements. This implies, in particular, that the effective internal volume of the detector must be small in comparison with the retention volume to be measured. Thermal conductivity detectors are therefore not generally suitable for use with capillary columns. These detectors are, however, very convenient for packed columns, are inexpensive, and require only simple instrumentation. One detector channel is mounted at the column inlet and the other at the outlet, thus both providing for monitoring of sample input profile and partly compensating for flow rate sensitivity. The filaments are connected as adjacent arms in a Wheatstone bridge circuit, so that input and output solute concentration profiles are displayed successively on the same recorder. Sensitivity of detection is quite satisfactory with the lighter carrier gases, helium and hydrogen. With heavier carrier gases, sensitivity may be marginal at the small sample sizes used in elution, and difficulty is sometimes experienced with peak inversion. On the other hand, since good gas flow control is in any case required for reasons of precise measurement, the susceptibility of katharometers to flow variation is not disadvantageous when physical measurement is the object of the work. To produce a steady signal, the katharometer walls need to be thermostatted.

Katharometer sensitivity with the elution techniques is less likely to be adequate for GSC than for GLC. For this reason, if nitrogen is to be used as carrier gas, detectors of higher sensitivity such as the electron capture, argon β-ray or flame ionization detector may be preferred. Extended linearity of response is unnecessary in view of the small sample sizes used.

For measurement using frontal analysis techniques, a linear detector response is required. Over not too large concentration ranges the response of a katharometer is virtually linear for the lighter carrier gases, hydrogen and helium. Larger ranges of concentration will require use of a flame ionization detector, which offers linear response over a larger range of concentration than other conventional detectors. This detector also has very high sensitivity, though the advantage is more significant for elution than for frontal GC. The disadvantage is that it consumes the gas stream and cannot therefore be used at the column inlet. Furthermore, special arrangements must be made for measuring carrier gas flow rate with this detector.

It is concluded that katharometers are generally the most suitable type of detector for physical measurement, flame ionization detectors being used when necessary for frontal analysis. Other types of detector may offer advantages where a higher sensitivity is required, e.g., for elution measurements in GSC, or with capillary columns.

In order that the detectors should monitor the actual solute concentration profiles at the column inlet and outlet, the column–detector connections should be so designed as to minimize the volume of the flow line linking column and detectors.

V. SOLUTION AND ADSORPTION BEHAVIOR

A. The Place of GC in Thermodynamic Studies

Most conventional techniques of studying solution and adsorption phenomena suffer from the disadvantage that precision of measurement varies with concentration. For example, when vapor pressure versus composition of sorbed phase is measured using a tensiometer method the proportional experimental error is high at low concentrations of the more volatile component. Often it is the region of dilute solution or of low surface coverage that is of most interest. The precision of measurement of the GC technique is independent of concentration from infinite dilution up to large finite concentrations. GC therefore not only offers a rapid and convenient alternative to more conventional methods, but is particularly valuable in the regions of low concentration and infinite dilution where other methods are inaccurate or cannot be used at all.

The experimental objective is a thermodynamic description of the system. The various thermodynamic parameters involved can be measured by several different basic types of experiment, viz., vapor pressure measurement, calorimetry, dilatometry, and compressibility measurement. GC is, in essence, a technique of vapor pressure measurement. The latter is the most basic of the various approaches and gives the greatest amount of information, since free energies, enthalpies, and entropies can all be derived. Enthalpies, however, are more accurately determined by direct calorimetry, and in general all types of experimental approach must be adopted for a more comprehensive description of the system.

In an excellent account of the experimental study of solutions, Everett (52) argued that the activity coefficient should be the primary point of comparison between theory and experiment. In general, it suffices to calculate the activity coefficient of only one component of a binary system from the total vapor pressure, for the two activity coefficients are related through the Gibbs–Duhem equation.

As is so often the case when a particular physical property is being measured, interference from other effects in the system under study must be taken into account. This applies in GC particularly when some bulk property of a liquid stationary phase is under investigation, for the retention is additionally affected by interactions in the gas phase and by possible adsorption of solute at either the liquid–gas or liquid–solid interface. The circumstances under which such complications need be considered, and the correction procedures to be used when necessary, are discussed in the following sections and in Section IX-A-2.

B. Correction for Gas Imperfection

The methods described in Section III lead to evaluation of the amount of sorbed solute as a function of gas-phase composition. In GSC, it is usual to plot the results directly as the adsorption isotherm, whereas in GLC the activity coefficient in solution is of more interest.

When the greatest accuracy is not required, the activity coefficient, γ, of the solute (reference state: $\gamma = 1$ for pure solute) can be calculated directly from the measured specific retention volume, V_g, by means of the equation

$$V_g = 273R/\gamma p^\circ M_1 \qquad (8)$$

R is the gas constant, p° is the saturation vapor pressure of solute at column temperature, and M_1 is the molecular weight of the solvent.

For greater accuracy, the effect of imperfection in the gas phase must be taken into account. The error is otherwise in the region of 1–5% for most systems encountered in GC. Several authors have attempted to make the correction either by replacing p° in eq. (8) by the fugacity of the pure solute, or by using equations applicable to static tensiometer methods of measuring γ. Both procedures give at best only an approximate correction, since the fugacity of the pure solute vapor is not equal to that of the solute diluted with carrier gas at the same partial pressure of solute.

When gas imperfection is taken into account, it can be shown (6,24) that

$$\ln \gamma = \ln \left[\frac{y P_o (n_1 + n_2)}{p^\circ n_2} \right]$$

$$+ \left[\frac{P_o}{jRT_c} \right] [B_{22} - (1 - y)^2 (B_{22} - 2B_{23} + B_{33}) - \bar{v}]$$

$$- \left[\frac{p^\circ}{RT_c} \right] [B_{22} - v^\circ] \qquad (9)$$

The symbols are defined as follows:

γ Activity coefficient at zero total pressure
y Mole fraction of solute in gas phase at the column outlet
P_o Column outlet pressure
p° Saturation vapor pressure of solute in absence of carrier gas
n_1 Moles of solvent in stationary phase
n_2 Moles of solute in stationary phase
j Gas compressibility correction factor (Sec. II-B)
T_c Column temperature
B_{22} Second virial coefficient of pure solute vapor at T_c
B_{23} Mixed second virial coefficient of solute and carrier gas at T_c
B_{33} Second virial coefficient of pure carrier gas at T_c

$\bar{v}$ Partial molar volume of solute in solvent

v° Molar volume of pure solute

An infinite dilution this equation reduces to the equation (cf. 53,54)

$$\ln \gamma = \ln \left[\frac{273R}{V_g p^\circ M_1}\right] + \left[\frac{P_o}{jRT_c}\right][2B_{23} - \bar{v}] - \left[\frac{P^\circ}{RT_c}\right][B_{22} - v^\circ] \quad (10)$$

Unfortunately the virial coefficient data required to make the gas imperfection correction are very often not available. This difficulty is, of course, common to all methods of studying solutions by vapor pressure measurement. Where relative retentions only are required, as in studying variation in solution behavior among solutes of closely similar chemical type, the correction is of similar magnitude for each solute, and can frequently be neglected.

C. Solution Studies

Measurement of γ at two or more different temperatures allows calculation of other thermodynamic quantities (55). The partial molar excess free energy, enthalpy, and entropy of solution of the solute component are given by the equations

$$\Delta G^E = \Delta H^E - T \Delta S^E = RT \ln \gamma \quad (11)$$

$$\Delta H^E = - R \frac{d \ln \gamma}{d(1/T)} \quad (12)$$

The accuracy with which heats can be measured depends on the size of temperature range employed. Nevertheless, the temperature range should not be too large because ΔH itself varies with temperature. There is an optimum size of range for which uncertainty through determining only a mean value of ΔH is balanced by the experimental error. Since two temperatures are required, determination of ΔH is essentially a relative retention method.

Assuming a precision of 0.2% in determination of γ carried out in a single series of experiments, the resulting precision of measurement of ΔH is 50 cal/mole over a $10°C$ range at room temperature and 13 cal/mole over a $50°C$ range. If ΔH varied with temperature by 5 cal/mole/$°C$, a $10°C$ temperature range would be suitable. The precision of measurement of ΔS would then be 0.20 eu, though the error in measurement of ΔS is likely to be larger, since ΔS depends on absolute, as well as relative, retention measurements, and systematic errors in temperature and other parameters play a larger role than in the case of relative retention measurements.

The deviation from Raoult's law is expressed (30,56) as the sum of two independent contributions to γ:

$$\ln \gamma = \ln \gamma_a + \ln \gamma_t \qquad (13)$$

γ_a, the "athermal" activity coefficient, is independent of temperature and arises from differences in size between solute and solvent molecules. The Flory–Huggins expression (30) relates γ_a to the ratio of molecular sizes, r, which can be taken as the ratio of molar volumes of the two components. Thus, at infinite dilution

$$\ln \gamma_a = \ln \frac{1}{r} + \left(1 - \frac{1}{r}\right) = -\frac{\Delta S_a^E}{R} \qquad (14)$$

γ_t, the "thermal" activity coefficient, is temperature dependent and is associated with the interaction energies between the molecules:

$$\ln \gamma_t = \Delta H^E/RT - \Delta S_t^E/R \qquad (15)$$

According to this model, there are two contributions to the excess entropy of mixing, one configurational and the other arising from the temperature dependence of the interchange energy, w (56). In the regular solution theory, $(\Delta S^E = \Delta S_a^E + \Delta S_t^E)$ is assumed to be zero, and ΔH^E is related via the solubility parameters to the latent heats of evaporation and partial molar volumes of the components. The assumption is unsatisfactory for solutions typically encountered in GLC, where, because of the difference in size between solute and solvent molecules, ΔS_a^E at least is usually far from zero. A better approximation, which has met with some success in GLC (57–59), is to calculate γ_a from the Flory-Huggins eq. (14) above, and γ_t from the regular solution theory, assuming $\Delta S_t^E = 0$.

Some values of γ calculated in this way from eq. (13) are compared with GLC-measured values in Table I for benzene in polyphenyl

TABLE I

Comparison of Activity Coefficients Predicted from the "Flory–Huggins Plus Regular Solution" Model with Those Measured by GLC, for Benzene at Infinite Dilution in Three Solvents at 90°C

Solvent	$\ln \gamma_a$	$\ln \gamma$, calc.	$\ln \gamma$, obs.
Biphenyl	-0.193	0.084	0.105 ± 0.003
m-Terphenyl	-0.432	0.025	0.020 ± 0.008
o-Terphenyl	-0.432	0.092	-0.063 ± 0.006

solvents, taken from the work of Clark and Schmidt (60). The precision of the GLC measurements shows up the inadequacy of the "Flory–Huggins plus regular solution" model. Clark and Schmidt have considered further factors not taken into account in the foregoing model, and have used the GLC data to calculate the parameters in more recent theories of solution.

Although this aspect of GC measurement has been little explored there is no doubt that GLC will play an increasing role in future solution studies.

D. Liquid Crystals

GC is a very suitable technique for studying liquid crystals, since such molecules, by their nature, are long and extended and of high molecular weight, and make suitably involatile stationary phases. Because of the partly ordered structure of the mesophase, solute retention time depends very much on the shape of the solute molecule, with specific energy effects playing very little part. For example, p-xylene fits better into the mesophase lattice than m-xylene and has a greater retention. Thus, an important application of these studies is likely to be the development of new and better stationary phases for separating structural isomers.

The smectic mesophase can be visualized as a two-dimensional solid, and the nematic mesophase as one dimensional. It would therefore be expected, as Dewar and Schroeder have found (61), that m and p isomers are better separated on the smectic than on the nematic phase, though in another case (62) no such distinction has been observed.

Plots of retention volume against temperature (Fig. 8) usually show a discontinuity at the temperature of transition between the anisotropic liquids, whether the mesophase is smectic, nematic, or cholesteric (61–65). Solubility is greater in the isotropic liquid, sometimes very much so (65). However, Kelker (62,63) and Barrall, Porter, and Johnson (65) have observed some cases in which there is merely a slope change, and no discontinuity, in the retention plot at the transition temperature. Measurement of the slopes of the plot above and below the transition point gives the corresponding heats of solution of the solute (eq. (17), Sec. VI-A) and hence the heats of mixing in the mesophase and isotropic liquid. For p, p'-disubstituted-azoxybenzenes, Kelker (62) found that both heats of mixing were positive, the anisotropic value being some few kilocalories per mole larger than the isotropic value. He also made the very interesting discovery (62,63) that the plots of log V_g vs. $1/T$ for a given solute are collinear for the isotropic liquids of several mesomorphic materials of different types, a result which has been confirmed by Barrall et al. (65). This implies that the mesomorphic materials behave as almost identical solvents in the isotropic liquid phase. On theoretical grounds such behavior might be expected of long molecules in which the heat of mixing is small, and may not be restricted to mesomorphic materials.

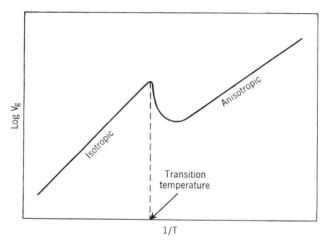

Fig. 8. Plot of the logarithm of the specific retention volume against the reciprocal of the absolute temperature for a liquid crystalline stationary phase.

The transition temperature of a mesophase is not a definite quantity but depends on the property used to observe and define the transition. The retention volume observed in GC provides an independent method of defining the transition. Barrall et al. (65) found that GC values of the transition temperature were on the whole lower than those given by differential thermal analysis and by optical methods. This could be due to different substrate effects from the material supporting the mesophase, or it could reflect the fact that GC defines a transition temperature in terms of solution phenomena and that insertion of solute molecules tends to break down the lattice structure. In this connection, it may be noted that increase of sample size leads to a very rapid increase in retention volume and peak asymmetry (63).

Interest in liquid crystals has so far been largely confined to thermo-tropic mesomorphism. Very little work has been done on lyotropic mesomorphism (66), in which the mesophase is created by treating the mesomorphic solid with a solvent, excess of solvent giving an isotropic solution. GC may have a considerable role to play here, in both infinite dilution and finite concentration forms of the technique.

E. Gas–Solid Adsorption and Surface Area Determination

As in GLC, so in GSC, free energies, heats and entropies of adsorption can be calculated from the adsorption isotherm. Equations are given by Hayward and Trapnell (103). Further, by making the usual BET plot, the available surface area can be determined if the area occupied by an adsorbed molecule is known.

It should be borne in mind that the effective area so determined may depend on the nature of the adsorbate. Thus, Perrett and Purnell (32) found that their measurements of the surface area of pink diatomaceous earth supports using benzene and acetone gave half to two-thirds the value found by other workers using low temperature nitrogen adsorption. As in a similar case discussed in part F, the most probable explanation is that, whereas the smaller molecules are readily accommodated in narrow pores of the support, the larger molecules are excluded or contact both walls simultaneously.

The use of GSC to determine gas–solid interaction potentials has been described by Murphy (68).

F. Liquid Surfaces

Because the solvent is spread as a very thin layer with a very high surface-to-volume ratio, GLC is particularly suitable for studies of the liquid surface. The phenomenon of adsorption of solute at infinite dilution at the gas–liquid interface in GLC was first discovered and investigated by Martin (69,70), who expressed his results in terms of the equation

$$V_N = V_R{}^0 - V_G = KV_L + k_a A_L \qquad (16)$$

where A_L is the liquid surface area, and k_a is an adsorption coefficient for the liquid–gas interface.

The term $k_a A_L$ is usually negligible for systems in which the activity coefficient of the solute is less than about 10 for columns of greater than 5% liquid loading (71). This fact makes possible the determination of bulk thermodynamic quantities as described in the preceding sections. With polar solvents, where the activity coefficient may be very high, adsorption becomes important and can far outweigh bulk solution at low liquid loadings (72).

It is possible to obtain approximate values of K and $k_a A_L$ from GC data alone by assuming that A_L is independent of liquid loading and plotting V_N against V_L. This assumption is justified by the empirical finding (73) that A_L on diatomaceous earth supports diminishes by about 10% for a 5% increase in liquid loading so long as the latter is greater than about 2%.

If the area of available liquid surface is measured independently, both K and k_a can be obtained by plotting V_N/A_L against V_L/A_L. One way to measure A_L is to freeze down the packing, measure the adsorption isotherm of nitrogen or other inert gas on the frozen surface of the stationary phase and determine the area from the BET plot. Pecsok, Yllana, and Abdul-Karim (72) found this method more satisfactory than the continuous-flow method of Nelsen and Eggertsen (74) because the abrupt lowering of temperature required in the latter case appeared to cause cracking of the liquid surface with consequent increase in area. There is, however, no certainty that surface areas measured in this way are in fact the required values of A_L. Martire, Pecsok, and Purnell have shown (71,73), by measuring K and k_a by static surface tension and tensiometer methods with the bulk liquid, that values of A_L determined with the frozen surface are about twice too large. They attribute the discrepancy to the small pore size of the solid support, which makes the effective area larger for adsorption of permanent gases than for organic molecules. It seems reasonable to assume that, provided the same organic adsorbent is used for measurements on both the liquid and the "frozen liquid," the two surface areas should agree. Further work is needed to test this assumption. If it is found to be justified, GC will offer a means of studying liquid surfaces capable of considerable accuracy.

VI. PHYSICAL PROPERTIES OF SINGLE SUBSTANCES

Gas chromatography provides a means of determining physical properties by using the material under investigation as the solute in GLC at infinite dilution. The method is rapid, uses only very small quantities (even trace amounts) of the material and does not require the sample to be pure. High molecular weights can be determined by using the material as the stationary phase.

Measurements of this type generally are required to be less precise than studies of solution or adsorption thermodynamics. Speed and convenience are of more importance here than the highest accuracy, for which classical methods are available. Often the measurements involve comparison between members of an homologous series. The size of the gas imperfection correction varies but little and regularly for members of such series, and the correction is usually neglected.

A. Latent Heat of Vaporization

Latent heats of vaporization can be determined by one of two GC techniques.

The first method simply requires measurement of the specific retention volume at two or more temperatures. ΔH_v is the desired molar latent heat of vaporization of the pure solute. ΔH_s is the partial molar heat of vaporization of the solute at infinite dilution and is equal to $(\Delta H_v - \Delta H^E)$. From eqs. (8) and (11) and the Clausius–Clapeyron equation, it is easily shown that

$$\ln V_g = \Delta H_s/RT + \text{const. (w.r.t. } T) \qquad (17)$$

A solvent is chosen which, together with the solute, gives a system for which $\Delta H^E \simeq 0$. Usually this simply means using a nonpolar solvent such as squalane. The retention volume of the solute whose latent heat is required is measured at two or more temperatures and $\Delta H_v \simeq \Delta H_s$ is calculated from the slope of a plot of $\ln V_g$ against $1/T$. The plot is substantially linear, since ΔH_v varies little over a small temperature range.

The second method has been described by Mackle and co-workers (75,76). Constant-volume samples of saturated vapor at different temperatures T are injected into a column and the peak height is plotted against $1/T$. With a detector of linear response the peak height is proportional to the saturation vapor pressure, so that ΔH_v can be calculated from the slope of the plot. The results compare well with ebullioscopic determinations.

B. Boiling Point

Once ΔH_v has been measured, the boiling point can be estimated from Trouton's rule:

$$\Delta H_v/T_b \simeq 23 \text{ cal/mole/°C} \qquad (18)$$

Since ΔH_v is dependent on temperature, the temperature range used for the determination should be in the region of T_b. Trouton's rule is quite well obeyed by most organic compounds, except for some substances in which association occurs in the liquid state, e.g., alcohols, for which the Trouton constant is around 28–29.

C. Vapor Pressure

To measure the vapor pressure of a volatile material at a given temperature, a nonpolar solvent is again chosen so that $\Delta H^E \simeq 0$. For an homologous series of solutes, or other series of close structural similarity, it then follows from eq. (17) and the Clausius–Clapeyron equation that at constant temperature,

$$\ln V_g = k_1 \ln p^0 + k_2 \qquad (19)$$

A plot of $\ln V_g$ against $\ln p^0$ for the series is linear and has been termed a "family" plot by Purnell (77). The unknown vapor pressure of one solute relative to the known values for other solutes in the series is read off from the plot. It is advisable not to use the very lowest members of the series, since they often do not conform to the family behavior of the rest of the series.

D. Molecular Weight

Equation (8), Section V-B, for the specific retention volume at infinite dilution contains the activity coefficient of the solute and the molecular weight, M_1, of the solvent. Martire and Purnell (78) have developed a simple method of measuring M_1 by making use of the Flory–Huggins expression for γ, eq. (14), Section V-3. The inadequacies of the theoretical model are partly overcome by comparing the relative retention, R_b, of two solutes in the solvent "b", whose molecular weight is required, with the relative retention, R_a, in a solvent a of known molecular weight belonging to the same family as the unknown. In this case,

$$\frac{1}{M_b} = \frac{\rho_a}{\rho_b M_a} - \frac{\ln (R_a/R_b)}{\rho_b \, \Delta v^\circ} \qquad (20)$$

The information required to calculate M_b therefore consists of the densities, ρ_a and ρ_b, of the two solvents, the difference, Δv°, between the molar volumes of the pure solates, and the molecular weight, M_a, of the reference solvent. The solutes used should be nonpolar, e.g., two normal paraffins.

The method is most accurate for materials of moderately high molecular weight and of a nonpolar or slightly polar nature. Thus the molecular weight of squalane (relative to eicosane) was determined (78) to be 422, in excellent agreement with the actual value of 422.8, while that of polyethylene glycol, PPG 1200 (relative to PPG 400, M.W. 409), was found to be 1220, which compares with a value of 1260 determined by cryoscopy. For more polar solvents the method is rather less accurate, because of the limitations of the theoretical solution model employed. Accuracy also diminishes with increasing molecular weight, a feature also of cryoscopic measurements.

E. Structural Assignment

The existence of regular patterns of retention volume behavior between series of solutes and solvents has been exploited in structural investigations. Hively (79) has studied retention volume behavior to deduce the assignment of 3-methyl-2-hexene and 3-methyl-3-hexene. Halpern, Westley, and Weinstein (80) used GC to investigate steric effects about the amide bond. Further discussion of this topic is outside the scope of the present review.

VII. COMPLEXING EQUILIBRIA

A. Studies of Simple Systems

Although only a few GC studies of complexing equilibria have so far been carried out, the technique promises to become one of the main tools for studies in this area.

The first quantitative GC study was that of DuPlessis and Spong (81), who measured the dissociation pressure and the quantity y for the equilibrium:

$$Ag^+(NH_3)_x + yNH_3 \rightleftharpoons Ag^+(NH_3)_{x+y}$$

The stationary phase was benzyl cyanide containing a small proportion of silver nitrate. Injected samples of ammonia were at first absorbed irreversibly with formation of $Ag^+(NH_3)_x$. Subsequent injection of ammonia samples gave rise to emergent sample profiles which depended markedly on sample size. Large samples gave a large elution peak with a long, flat shoulder or plateau on the trailing side, rather like the profile of a straight-backed chair viewed from the side. With decreasing sample size, the "back" of the "chair" diminished in height until it disappeared, when the width of the plateau began to narrow. At the lowest sample sizes the plateau gave way to a small normal elution peak of lower height.

These phenomena were explained as follows. At the largest sample sizes there is sufficient ammonia to saturate the column with ammonia and convert all $Ag^+(NH_3)_x$ to $Ag^+(NH_3)_{x+y}$. The plateau thus corresponds to the passage of an adsorption, followed by a desorption, frontal boundary, ammonia being in equilibrium with both complexes in the plateau zone. The "back" of the "chair" is the excess ammonia travelling as a normal elution peak ahead of the plateau. At the lowest sample sizes the dissociation pressure is never reached and a normal elution peak is again obtained, but for a different solvent system containing only the lower ammine.

On the basis of this interpretation, the dissociation pressure and y were calculated from the area under the plateau. The dissociation pressure was found to be $5.7 \pm 0.42 \times 10^{-3}$ atm. The fact that y was 0.5 ± 0.056 for a wide range of column lengths, liquid loadings, flow rates and sample sizes, provides some confirmation of the interpretation of the sample profile and to that extent serves to validate the method for use with other complexing systems of this type. The method is likely to be useful, however, only for cases in which the dissociation pressure is very low; otherwise the dissociation pressure is never reached in the column and only a normal elution peak is observed.

This type of chromatographic behavior must be regarded as a special case for a reason which does not appear to have to have been discussed hitherto. According to the Gibbs phase rule, the phenomenon of an invariant dissociation pressure at a given temperature in a system of three components (ignoring the carrier gas) is observed only when four phases are present. Thus, in addition to the gaseous and solution phases, there must be two further immiscible phases, one composed only of the lower, and the other of the higher, ammine. At pressures lower or higher than the dissociation pressure, the solubility product of the higher or lower ammine, respectively, is not achieved. System behavior of this type, therefore, will be observed only where the "stationary phase" in the presence of sufficient solute is in fact composed of three immiscible phases in intimate contact, a somewhat unusual situation. This same "abnormal" chromatographic behavior will furthermore be observed however much complexing additive (in this case $Ag^+(NH_3)_x$) is present, and will not be restricted to lean columns.

DuPlessis and Spong's observation of a pronounced tail at the rear of the plateau provides an interesting example of the effect of complexing in causing a large negative deviation from Raoult's law for solution of ammonia (see Sec. III-B-1).

A system of similar type but in which only normal elution peaks have been observed is:

$$\text{Olefin} + Ag^+ \rightleftharpoons Ag^+ \cdot \text{olefin}$$

in ethylene glycol solution. In this case the complex ion, and perhaps both ions, remain in solution and the equilibrium is described by the equation

$$K_R = K_R^0[1 + K_1(Ag^+)] \tag{21}$$

where

$$K_1 = \frac{(Ag^+ \cdot \text{olefin})}{(Ag^+)(\text{olefin})} \tag{22}$$

The partition coefficient, K_R, is determined from the retention volume of the olefin in silver nitrate/ethylene glycol, and K_R^0 from the retention volume of the olefin in ethylene glycol alone. The stability constant, K_1, is then calculated from eq. (21).

Muhs and Weiss (82) and Cvetanović, Duncan, Falconer, and Irwin (83), determined K_1 by this simple technique for a large number of olefins and so were able to study in detail the influence of structural factors on the complexing.

Gil-Av and Herling (84) showed that since γ_{olefin} can also be measured gas chromatographically (Sec. V-B), one can calculate $K_1/\gamma_{\text{olefin}}$, which is proportional to the thermodynamic equilibrium constant,

$$K_e = \frac{K_1 \gamma_{\text{complex}}}{\gamma_{Ag^+} \cdot \gamma_{\text{olefin}}} \tag{23}$$

$(\gamma_{\text{complex}}/\gamma_{Ag^+})$ can be considered, to a first approximation, to be independent of ionic strength and to change relatively little with the nature of the olefin in a series of olefins. On the other hand, γ_{olefin} varies with ionic strength, and plots of K_R against (Ag^+) are effectively linear only over a very small range of (Ag^+). Therefore, when K_R^0 is determined, an inert salt of the same ionic strength as the complexing material should be added to the solvent (85).

The extent of agreement between GC-determined values of the

TABLE II

Comparison of GC-Evaluated K_1 for Olefin–AgNO$_3$ Complexing in Ethylene Glycol Solution

	K_1, liters/mole, at 40°C	
Solute	Ref. 83	Ref. 82
Propylene	5.9	9.1
But-1-ene	6.8	7.7
Pent-1-ene	5.2	4.9
3-Methyl-but-1-ene	6.1	5.1
cis-But-2-ene	3.9	5.4
cis-Pent-2-ene	4.4	4.3
trans-But-2-ene	1.4	1.4
trans-Pent-2-ene	1.4	1.1
2-Methyl-but-1-ene	3.5	3.0
2-Methyl-but-2-ene	0.9	0.8
2,3-Dimethyl-but-2-ene	0.3	0.1
Cyclopentene	7.2	7.3
1,3-Butadiene	3.6	4.2

stability constants is shown by the comparison in Table II. The agreement is reasonable, being within 20% with the exception of propylene. It has been pointed out (85) that the discrepancies may be partly due to the fact that both groups of workers neglected to maintain constant ionic strength in their systems and evaluated K_1 via a lengthy extrapolation, and subsequent tangent drawing, to $(Ag^+) = 0$ from about $(Ag^+) = 1M$.

B. Complexing in General

Studies of complexing by GC are not limited to the cation–ligand case. Complexing by hydrogen-bonding or by charge-transfer between organic molecules is equally amenable to investigation. Included are cases where the terms "association" or "dissociation" are more commonly used to describe the phenomena.

Littlewood and Willmott (86) have studied the retention of alkane and polar solutes in solvents consisting of squalane with 1-dodecanol or lauronitrile as additive. In these systems, both solute–solvent and solvent–solvent association can occur through hydrogen-bonding. The retention volume varies linearly or nonlinearly with the proportion of additive, depending on the nature of the solute and solvent, and the authors have set up models of the association mechanisms which explain the results and lead to determination of both association constants.

The existence of charge-transfer complexes in solution between aromatic solutes and alkylated halophthalates was postulated by Langer and co-workers (58,59,87,88) on the basis of gas chromatographic measurements of activity coefficients. Recently, Cadogan and Purnell (85) have measured the stability constants of the complexes in the same way as described in the previous section for silver-olefin complexes, by using the halophthalate as an additive in squalane solvent.

All the work on complexing so far discussed, with one exception (86), has concerned the case in which the complexing occurs between solute and an additive dissolved in the solvent. Purnell (85) has given a general classification and theoretical treatment for the possible types of complexing in a three-component system consisting of solute, solvent, and additive. Provided the solute is volatile, and the solvent and additive are involatile, GC can be used to study examples of any one of these classes.

In many cases of complex formation, not one, but several, complexes exist together in equilibrium. In place of an equation such as eq. (21), expressions for the measured partition coefficient, K_R, are obtained which are polynomials, the terms containing different powers of the concentrations of the solute and other components (85). In order to solve these equations and determine each of the stability constants, values of K_R must be determined at each of several solute concentrations, and recourse is therefore made to one of the finite concentration techniques already discussed.

C. Advantages and Disadvantages of the GC Method

The GC technique is complementary to existing partition and spectroscopic methods, and as such opens up new avenues of investigation. It is available over a very wide range of stability constants and may even extend the range over which reasonable accuracy can be achieved (85). In the study of cation–ligand complexes, nonaqueous systems are ideal for GC while being difficult to study by liquid–liquid partition. Thus previously unexplored areas, such as the study of hydrolyzable or water-insoluble complexes, become accessible (89).

One possible limitation of the method is that complexing may be slower than the chromatographic process, resulting in failure to attain equilibrium. Whereas it is now well established that mass transfer in the liquid phase occurs sufficiently rapidly for interphase equilibrium to be achieved within the short time of passage of the peak, this is not necessarily true of the complexing reaction. Nevertheless, for most complexing systems equilibration occurs very rapidly and is unlikely to cause difficulty; a simple practical test is to vary the flow rate and check that the results are unaffected.

A second limitation arises in cases where the mixture of solvent and additive possesses mix solvency properties of some sort. A unique value of K_R^0 cannot then be determined, and the inadequacy of present solution theories hinders any corrective measures. This difficulty is less likely to be encountered with ionic additives (85).

VIII. SECOND VIRIAL COEFFICIENTS OF GAS MIXTURES

Measurement of second virial coefficients of gases by conventional $P-V$ methods is often slow and laborious. Very few determinations of the second virial coefficients of gas mixtures have been made, and these mostly for mixtures of two simple molecules, both showing deviations from the principle of corresponding states. GC provides a means of determining mixed second virial coefficients at least as accurately as conventional methods and is considerably more rapid in application. The results not only facilitate the accurate determination of thermodynamic parameters in solution and gas–solid adsorption by GC, but open up the possibility of rapid progress in the study of molecular interactions in the gas phase.

The mixed second virial coefficient, B_{23}, in a gaseous mixture of two components, 2 and 3, is related to the second virial coefficient, B, of the mixture by the equation

$$B = y^2 B_{22} + 2y(1 - y)B_{23} + (1 - y)^2 B_{33} \qquad (24)$$

y is the mole fraction of component 2, and B_{22} and B_{33} are the respective second virial coefficients of the pure components.

The GC method of determining B_{23} was first described by Desty, Goldup, Luckhurst, and Swanton (53). It depends on using one component as the carrier gas, and the other component as the solute at infinite dilution. The retention volume is measured over a range of column pressure extending to several atmospheres. The procedure has very recently been refined by Cruickshank, Windsor, and Young (29,90), who also give a description of the apparatus required for high pressure work. Using pressures up to 25 atm, these authors have determined B_{23} with a precision of 6 ml/mole, which compares well with that of the best conventional methods. Any systematic error also appears to have been small. Cruickshank et al. used packed columns, whereas Desty et al. used capillary columns, and it is encouraging that both sets of results are in good agreement.

The method is particularly suited to the measurement of B_{23} for mixtures of a permanent gas and a substance which is a vapor or liquid at normal temperatures. Such systems provide a good test of the theory of deviations from perfect gas behavior, and Cruickshank et al. have shown that, while their results are in excellent agreement with the predictions of the Hudson and McCoubrey combining rule for the critical temperature, the geometric mean rule is considerably in error.

Studies of gas imperfection and solution thermodynamics could in principle be significantly affected by solution of carrier gas in the stationary phase. Cruickshank et al. (29) and Conder and Langer (91) have found no difference in the measured gas imperfection when different solvents are used and have therefore concluded that the extent of solution of the carrier gas is negligible.

IX. EVALUATION OF THE GC APPROACH

It will be seen that the variety of types of study which can be carried out by gas chromatography is very wide indeed. It is part of the great appeal of GC that many types of information, ranging from rough estimates of boiling points to the more accurate data required to study current theories of molecular interactions in solution and in gases, can all be obtained by simple experiments involving the passage of gas through a tube. Just as GC has already taken a place alongside infrared spectroscopy as one of the most commonly used of all analytical techniques at the present time, it seems certain that within the next decade it will come to play a major role in many fields of physical measurement.

A. Nature of the Components of the System Studied

Characteristically, GC is particularly suited to studying systems of one volatile and one involatile component. While this fact limits the number of systems accessible to study, it is also an advantage in the sense that GC can complement existing techniques suitable for two involatile components. One example is the study of ion complexes by liquid–liquid extraction where difficulties are encountered if one of the components is volatile. In such cases GC opens up the possibility of new areas of study.

Kwantes and Rijnders (51) extended the technique to volatile solvents by presaturating the carrier gas with solvent at the column temperature and working with small column pressure gradients to minimize loss of solvent. The technique is, however, only partly satisfactory because solvent loss can never be wholly eliminated.

Frequently, although the two components differ greatly in volatility, bleeding of the solvent is significant at column temperature. If the column is to be used over a period of time with several solutes, the difficulty may be overcome by making several determinations of the retention of a reference solute at the outset, and subsequently including this solute in each mixed sample injected (58); or by remeasuring the retention of the reference solute at intervals. The procedure is of little use in extreme cases where a substantial length of packing near the column head is completely stripped of solvent.

An extension of the technique to multicomponent systems in which more than one volatile component is present has been effected by Koonce, Deans, and Kobayashi (92).

B. Influence of the Support

A second characteristic of GC is the large surface area of the stationary phase. In GSC this makes for adequately large retention and effective separation. In GLC, because of the small thickness of the liquid stationary phase and consequent rapid equilibration with solute, the technique inherently offers a more rapid means of investigating bulk properties than other equilibrium methods. Additionally, because of the high surface/volume ratio, liquid surface studies are possible. Against these advantages is the fact that the solid support could possibly influence the bulk properties of the liquid. Work published to date, however, provides no evidence to support the latter hypothesis. In particular, it has been demonstrated (29,93) that lowering of the vapor pressure of solvent is unlikely to be as much as 0.5%. It remains possible, nevertheless, that in certain limited cases the bulk properties of the liquid may be sufficiently altered for the effect to be detectable by GC.

Adsorption of solute on the support surface has been studied many times [a recent study is (94)], and the conclusions which may be drawn from such work concerning choice of support are summarized in

Section IV-F. When solutes are injected into columns containing an uncoated support of the diatomaceous earth type, the emergent peaks are frequently grossly asymmetrical and long retained. Solutes of a strongly polar nature, such as alcohols and ketones, may never be eluted at all. On the other hand, it is a common observation that addition of stationary phase to the support, particularly if the liquid is polar, very greatly reduces adsorption and peak tailing, presumably by covering and neutralizing the active adsorption sites. A number of studies of hydrocarbons dissolving in nonpolar and slightly polar solvents coated on diatomaceous earth supports have shown that at moderate liquid loadings (around 15%), adsorption of solute at the solid surface is undetectable within the precision of the measurements. When polar solutes are used in relatively nonpolar solvents adsorption on the support is definitely observed, as evidenced by peak tailing and decrease of retention volume with sample size. In such cases use of polymeric fluorocarbon supports (50) or even metal helices (51) may alleviate the difficulty.

The existence of support adsorption can be detected by varying the liquid loading. Some effect will almost always be observed at loadings below 1–5%, but if it is found that the retention volume is independent of liquid loading in the range of 10% upwards, it may be assumed that no adsorption effects are present in this case. Variation of retention with liquid loading can also be due to other causes (Sec. V-F).

A phenomenon sometimes observed is a change in retention volume while the column is in use, especially during the period immediately after the column is put into operation (95). This may indicate bleeding of the stationary phase, which can be corrected for as described in the preceding section. Less commonly it may indicate a support adsorption effect with redistribution of the stationary phase occurring on conditioning the column. A third possibility is decomposition of the stationary phase catalyzed by the support material. If this is the case, changing the nature of the support should solve the problem, unless the liquid is unstable in any event at the temperature used.

C. Accuracy and Reliability

Comparison of the results of gas chromatographic measurements with those obtained by other methods, in cases where other methods are available, has shown that GC is quite as reliable as other approaches. Except where certain anticipated vitiating effects, such as support adsorption or lack of complexing equilibrium are known to be present, GC measures the same quantity as determined by corresponding static methods, and not a hypothetical "dynamic" quantity peculiar to the technique.

The question as to whether complete equilibrium is achieved in the column as the peak or boundary progresses has been considered by Glueckauf (12) and answered in the positive (see Sec. III-B-1). Experimental confirmation is also available. Variation of gas flow rate, liquid loading, and column length has no effect on measured values of thermodynamic parameters (19,24,26,28,29,81). It is very likely that the discrepancies in the literature between GC measurements of activity coefficients in solution by different works are due in part to the use of different samples of stationary phase and application of different correction procedures for the effect of gas imperfection. Commercial samples of materials of high molecular weight may be far from pure, and extensive purification may be necessary for reproducible results. Further, experimental techniques have not always been adequate for the purpose of accurate measurement. In Table III are quoted measured values of the activity coefficient for one of the most intensively studied systems of all, n-hexane in squalane. The spread of the values is quite large, arising, at least in part, from varying experimental precision and differing methods of treating the data. Nevertheless, the absence of any systematic difference between the GC and statically determined values must be taken as evidence of the inherent reliability of GC.

The accuracy desirable in each of the types of measurement of which GC is capable varies widely. In some cases, such as determination of boiling points and latent heats, standard methods are capable of much greater accuracy, but GC provides a complementary technique suitable for rapid collection of large amounts of data. A less clear-cut case is that of solution and adsorption studies, where alternative static methods are capable of at least an order of magnitude greater precision than the 0.3–3% offered by GC. The greater precision, however, is offset by the greater time required for the experiments. In many cases the precision attainable by GC is quite adequate to distinguish between different models of solution behavior, and the main obstacle to further progress at the present time is paucity, rather than precision, of the data. Finally, in some areas, GC is not only competitive with existing methods but may well be the preferred method of approach. Examples are the determination of second virial coefficients in the gas phase and studies of weak charge-transfer complexes in solution.

TABLE III

Comparison of Determinations of the Activity Coefficient of *n*-Hexane
in Squalane at Infinite Dilution at 30 and 80°C

Authors	Method	γ 30°C	γ 80°C	Reference
GLC Determination:				
Desty, Goldup	Capillary column	0.61	0.54	96
Desty, Swanton	Packed column	0.63	0.62	97
Evered, Pollard	Packed column		0.65	98
Kwantes, Rijnders	Packed column		0.66	51
Porter, Deal, Stross	Packed column		0.62	26
Littlewood	Packed column		0.59	101
Conder	Packed column	0.640[a]		24
Cruickshank, Windsor, Young	Packed column	0.687[a]		29
Cruickshank, Everett, Westaway	Packed column	0.604[a]		19
	Packed column, from V_l[b]	0.646[a]		
Martire	Packed column, from V_l[b]		0.67	102
GC—Entrainment Method:				
Burnett	Bulk liquid		0.60	40
Static (Tensiometer) Method:				
Ashworth, Everett	Extrapolation linearly to $x = 0$	0.641[a]		30
	Extrapolation by Flory–Huggins fit	0.649[a]		
Martire, Pecsok, Purnell	Bulk liquid extrapolation to $x = 0$	0.658[a]		73

[a] Correct gas imperfection correction employed.
[b] See Section III-B-4.

D. Summary

In conclusion, we list some of the advantages offered by the GC approach to physical measurement:

1. The GC technique possesses inherent simplicity and is rapid in operation.

2. Apparatus is relatively easily constructed and does not normally require sophisticated fabrication techniques. For certain types of measurement, commercial analytical chromatographs are adequate.

3. Temperature is easily and precisely controlled.

4. Measurements over a range of composition can be made with no loss of precision at low concentrations of the more volatile component.

5. Rare solute materials can be used in trivial amounts at infinite dilution. Impure materials can be used without purification. By using mixtures it is possible to make many measurements in a single experiment.

6. The technique can be used for highly reactive solutes (99,100) when other methods would give false results through reaction over a period of time with the containing vessel or with traces of impurities.

References

1. D. H. James and C. S. G. Phillips, *J. Chem. Soc.*, **1954**, 1066.
2. A. B. Littlewood, C. S. G. Phillips, and D. T. Price, *J. Chem. Soc.*, **1955**, 1480.
3. M. R. Hoare and J. H. Purnell, *Trans. Faraday Soc.*, **52**, 222 (1956).
4. J. H. Purnell, *Endeavour*, **23**, 142 (1964).
5. C. N. Reilley, G. P. Hildebrand, and J. W. Ashley, *Anal. Chem.*, **34**, 1198 (1962).
6. J. R. Conder and J. H. Purnell, in press.
7. A. T. James and A. J. P. Martin, *Biochem. J.*, **50**, 679 (1952); cf. D. E. Martire and D. C. Locke, *Anal. Chem.*, **37**, 144 (1965).
8. J. N. Wilson, *J. Am. Chem. Soc.*, **62**, 1583 (1940).
9. J. Weiss, *J. Chem. Soc.*, **1943**, 297.
10. D. DeVault, *J. Am. Chem. Soc.*, **65**, 532 (1943).
11. E. Glueckauf, *J. Chem. Soc.*, **1947**, 1302.
12. E. Glueckauf, *Trans. Faraday Soc.*, **51**, 34 (1955).
13. S. J. Gregg and R. Stock, in *Gas Chromatography 1958*, D. H. Desty, Ed., Butterworths, London, 1958, p. 90.
14. C. H. Bosanquet and G. D. Morgan, in *Vapour Phase Chromatography*, D. H. Desty, Ed., Butterworths, London, 1957, p. 35.
15. C. H. Bosanquet, in *Gas Chromatography 1958*, D. H. Desty, Ed., Butterworths, London, 1958, p. 107.
16. G. Schay, *Theoretische Grundlagen der Gaschromatographie*, Deutscher Verlag der Wissenschaften, 1960.
17. P. Fejes, E. Fromm-Czaran, and G. Schay, *Acta Chim. Hung.*, **33**, 87 (1962).
18. D. L. Peterson and F. Helfferich, *J. Phys. Chem.*, **69**, 1283 (1965).
19. A. J. B. Cruickshank, D. H. Everett, and M. T. Westaway, *Trans. Faraday Soc.*, **61**, 235 (1965).
20. A. J. B. Cruickshank and D. H. Everett, *J. Chromatog.*, **11**, 289 (1963).
21. P. C. Haarhoff and H. J. van der Linde, *Anal. Chem.*, **38**, 573 (1966).
22. R. P. W. Scott, *Anal. Chem.*, **35**, 481 (1963).
23. P. C. Haarhoff and H. J. van der Linde, *Anal. Chem.*, **37**, 1742 (1965).

24. J. R. Conder, Ph.D. thesis, University of Cambridge, 1965.
25. F. H. Pollard and C. J. Hardy, in *Vapour Phase Chromatography*, D. H. Desty, Ed., Butterworths, London, 1957, p. 115.
26. P. E. Porter, C. H. Deal, and F. H. Stross, *J. Am. Chem. Soc.*, **78**, 2999 (1956).
27. J. H. Purnell, *Gas Chromatography*, Wiley, New York, 1962, p. 167.
28. D. H. Everett and C. T. H. Stoddart, *Trans. Faraday Soc.*, **57**, 746 (1961).
29. A. J. B. Cruickshank, M. L. Windsor, and C. L. Young, *Proc. Roy. Soc.*, (*London*) **A295**, 271 (1966).
30. A. J. Ashworth and D. H. Everett, *Trans. Faraday Soc.*, **56**, 1609 (1960).
31. E. Glueckauf, *Nature*, **156**, 748 (1945).
32. R. H. Perrett and J. H. Purnell, *J. Chromatog.*, **7**, 455 (1962).
33. F. I. Stalkup and R. Kobayashi, *Am. Inst. Chem. Eng. J.*, **9**, 121 (1963).
34. C. F. Chueh and W. T. Ziegler, *Am. Inst. Chem. Eng. J.*, **11**, 508 (1965).
35. E. Cremer, *Monatsh. Chem.*, **92**, 112 (1961); through E. Cremer and H. F. Huber, in *Gas Chromatography, Third International Symposium*, N. Brenner, J. E. Callen, and M. D. Weiss, Eds., Academic Press, New York, 1962, p. 169.
36. J. F. K. Huber and A. I. M. Keulemans, in *Gas Chromatography 1962*, M. van Swaay, Ed., Butterworths, London, 1962, p. 26.
37. L. Bachman, E. Bechtold, and E. Cremer, *J. Catalysis*, **1**, 113 (1962).
38. H. Knözinger and H. Spannheimer, *J. Chromatog.*, **16**, 1 (1964).
39. F. Helfferich, *J. Chem. Educ.*, **41**, 410 (1964).
40. M. G. Burnett, *Anal. Chem.*, **35**, 1567 (1963).
41. "Recommendations for the Publication of Retention Data by the Data Sub-Committee of the Institute of Petroleum Gas Chromatography Discussion Group," in *Gas Chromatography 1964*, A. Goldup, Ed., The Institute of Petroleum, London, 1965 (Overseas: Elsevier, Amsterdam, 1965), p. 348
42. J. H. Purnell, *Gas Chromatography*, Wiley, New York, 1962, p. 258.
43. R. P. W. Scott, in *Gas Chromatography 1958*, D. H. Desty, Ed., Butterworths, London, 1958, p. 189.
44. G. L. Pratt and J. H. Purnell, *Anal. Chem.*, **32**, 1213 (1960).
45. K. Amaya and K. Sasaki, *Bull. Chem. Soc. Japan*, **35**, 1507 (1962).
46. J. H. Purnell, *Gas Chromatography*, Wiley, New York, 1962; A. B. Littlewood, *Gas Chromatography*, Academic Press, London, 1962.
47. D. M. Ottenstein, *J. Gas Chromatog.*, **1**, 11 (1963).
48. R. G. Scholz and W. W. Brandt, in *Gas Chromatography, Third International Symposium*, N. Brenner, J. E. Callen, and M. D. Weiss, Eds., Academic Press, New York, 1962, p. 7.
49. J. H. Purnell, *Gas Chromatography*, Wiley, New York, 1962, pp. 235–240.
50. J. J. Kirkland, in *Gas Chromatography, Fourth International Symposium*, L. Fowler, Ed., Academic Press, New York, 1963, p. 77.
51. A. Kwantes and G. W. A. Rijnders, in *Gas Chromatography 1958*, D. H. Desty, Ed., Butterworths, London, 1958, p. 125.
52. D. H. Everett, *Discussions Faraday Soc.*, **15**, 126 (1953).
53. D. H. Desty, A. Goldup, G. R. Luckhurst, and W. T. Swanton, in *Gas Chromatography 1962*, M. van Swaay, Ed., Butterworths, London, 1962, p. 67.
54. D. H. Everett, *Trans. Faraday Soc.*, **61**, 1637 (1965).

55. E. A. Guggenheim, *Thermodynamics*, 4th ed., North-Holland, Amsterdam, 1959, ch. 5, 6.
56. E. A. Guggenheim, *Discussions Faraday Soc.*, **15**, 24 (1953).
57. D. E. Martire, in *Gas Chromatography, Fourth International Symposium*, L. Fowler, Ed., Academic Press, New York, 1963, p. 33.
58. S. H. Langer and J. H. Purnell, *J. Phys. Chem.*, **67**, 263 (1963).
59. S. H. Langer and J. H. Purnell, *J. Phys. Chem.*, **70**, 904 (1966).
60. R. K. Clark and H. H. Schmidt, *J. Phys. Chem.*, **69**, 3682 (1965).
61. M. J. S. Dewar and J. P. Schroeder, *J. Org. Chem.*, **30**, 3485 (1965).
62. H. Kelker, *Z. Anal. Chem.*, **198**, 254 (1963).
63. H. Kelker, paper presented at Liquid Crystal Conference, Kent State University, Ohio (August 1965).
64. M. J. S. Dewar and J. P. Schroeder, *J. Am. Chem. Soc.*, **86**, 5235 (1964).
65. E. M. Barrall, R. S. Porter, and J. F. Johnson, *J. Chromatog.*, **21**, 392 (1966).
66. G. W. Gray, *Molecular Structure and the Properties of Liquid Crystals*, Academic Press, London, 1962, p. 13.
67. R. S. Juvet and R. L. Fisher, *Anal. Chem.*, **38**, 1860 (1966).
68. J. A. Murphy, *Dissertation Abstr.*, **24**, 4008 (1964).
69. R. L. Martin, *Anal. Chem.*, **33**, 347 (1961).
70. R. L. Martin, *Anal. Chem.*, **35**, 116 (1963).
71. D. E. Martire, R. L. Pecsok, and J. H. Purnell, *Nature*, **203**, 1279 (1964).
72. R. L. Pecsok, A. de Yllana, and A. Abdul-Karim, *Anal. Chem.*, **36**, 452 (1963).
73. D. E. Martire, R. L. Pecsok, and J. H. Purnell, *Trans. Faraday Soc.*, **61**, 2496 (1965).
74. F. M. Nelsen and F. T. Eggertsen, *Anal. Chem.*, **30**, 1387 (1958).
75. H. Mackle, R. G. Mayrick, and J. J. Rooney, *Trans. Faraday Soc.*, **56**, 115 (1960).
76. H. Mackle and R. T. B. McClean, *Trans. Faraday Soc.*, **60**, 817 (1964).
77. J. H. Purnell, in *Vapour Phase Chromatography*, D. H. Desty, Ed., Butterworths, London, 1957, p. 52.
78. D. E. Martire and J. H. Purnell, *Trans. Faraday Soc.*, **62**, 710 (1966).
79. R. A. Hively, *Anal. Chem.*, **35**, 1921 (1963).
80. B. Halpern, J. W. Westley, and B. Weinstein, *Nature*, **210**, 837 (1966).
81. L. A. DuPlessis and A. H. Spong, *J. Chem. Soc.*, **1959**, 2027.
82. M. A. Muhs and F. T. Weiss, *J. Am. Chem. Soc.*, **84**, 4697 (1962).
83. R. J. Cvetanović, F. J. Duncan, W. E. Falconer, and R. S. Irwin, *J. Am. Chem. Soc.*, **87**, 1827 (1965).
84. E. Gil-Av and J. Herling, *J. Phys. Chem.*, **66**, 1208 (1962).
85. J. H. Purnell, in *Gas Chromatography 1966*, A. B. Littlewood, Ed., The Institute of Petroleum, London, 1967 (Elsevier, New York, 1967) p. 3.
86. A. B. Littlewood and F. W. Willmott, *Anal. Chem.*, **38**, 1031 (1966).
87. S. H. Langer, C. Zahn, and G. Pantazoplos, *Chem. Ind. (London)*, **1958**, 1145.
88. S. H. Langer, C. Zahn, and G. Pantazoplos, *J. Chromatog.*, **3**, 154 (1960).
89. G. P. Cartoni, R. S. Lowrie, C. S. G. Phillips, and L. M. Venanzi, in *Gas Chromatography 1960*, R. P. W. Scott, Ed., Butterworths, London, 1960, p. 273.

270   J. R. CONDER

90. A. J. B. Cruickshank, M. L. Windsor, and C. L. Young, *Proc. Roy. Soc.*, **A295**, 259 (1966).
91. J. R. Conder and S. H. Langer, *Anal. Chem.*, **39**, 1461 (1967).
92. K. T. Koonce, H. A. Deans, and R. Kobayashi, *Am. Inst. Chem. Eng. J.*, **11**, 259 (1965).
93. S. J. Hawkes and J. C. Giddings, *Anal. Chem.*, **36**, 2229 (1964).
94. P. Urone and J. F. Parcher, *Anal. Chem.*, **38**, 270 (1966).
95. R. A. Keller, R. Bate, B. Costa, and P. Forman, *J. Chromatog.*, **8**, 157 (1962).
96. D. H. Desty and A. Goldup, in *Gas Chromatography 1960*, R. P. W. Scott, Ed., Butterworths, London, 1960, p. 162.
97. D. H. Desty and W. T. Swanton, *J. Phys. Chem.*, **65**, 766 (1961).
98. S. Evered and F. H. Pollard, *J. Chromatog.*, **4**, 451 (1960).
99. D. R. Owens, A. G. Hamlin, and T. R. Phillips, *Nature*, **201**, 901 (1964).
100. R. S. Juvet and R. L. Fisher, *Anal. Chem.*, **38**, 1860 (1966).
101. A. B. Littlewood, *J. Gas Chromatog.*, **1**, 6 (1963).
102. D. E. Martire, Ph.D. dissertation, Stevens Institute of Technology, Hoboken, N.J., 1963.
103. D. O. Hayward and B. M. W. Trapnell, *Chemisorption*, 2nd ed., Butterworths, London, 1964, ch. 6, 9.

Flow Programming

R. P. W. Scott, *Unilever Research Laboratory, Colworth House, Sharnbrook, Bedford, England*

I. INTRODUCTION

Flow programming is the term given to the method of chromatographic development in which the carrier gas flow rate is continually increased during the elution process. Stepwise changes in carrier gas flow rate have been used for some time by many workers who wished to speed the elution of later peaks after the early peaks of interest had been developed isorheically. Lipsky, Landowne, and Lovelock (1) were the first to describe the use of this technique, but the first use of true flow programming was described by Morgantini (2). Morgantini used a simple system that involved splitting the carrier gas flow upstream of the chromatograph. The flow restriction in the side stream was continuously increased hydrostatically, which resulted in an almost linear increase in column flow with time. This apparatus had a very limited flow range, however, and little further was published until 1962 when Purnell (3) again emphasized that considerable advantages could be obtained if the carrier gas were programmed during chromatographic development. In 1963–64 Scott (4,5) described a simple pneumatic flow programming system with wide flow limits and program rates, and he gave an account of its application to the use of analytical columns for handling large charges and for chromatographing thermally labile materials. Since 1964 several workers have published applications

271

of the use of flow programming and, in particular, Zlatkis and Ettre (6) demonstrated its use with capillary columns.

Flow programming is a complementary technique to temperature programming, where the column temperature is continually raised during the development of the chromatogram. The effects of the two programming techniques on retention time, however, are somewhat different. The retention time of a solute is linearly related to the distribution coefficient which increases exponentially with the reciprocal of the absolute temperature. Thus, as the retention time of a homologous series of solutes is exponentially related to the carbon number, under linear temperature programming conditions the retention time will be linearly related to the carbon number of the solute. In flow programming, however, retention times are linearly related to column flow rate, and thus to obtain a linear relationship between carbon number and retention time from a homologous series of solutes, the column flow must be exponentially programmed. In practice, exponential flow programming is not normally used, as it necessitates the use of inordinately high column-inlet pressures if solutes of a reasonable boiling range are to be chromatographed. Further, if exponential flow programming is employed, the very high flow rates that result cause serious band spreading due to the increase in resistance to mass transfer in both the mobile and stationary phases. Linear or logarithmic flow programs are usually employed, as these forms of program are more easily obtained using simple pneumatic systems.

A. The Simple Flow Programmer

The simplest type of flow programmer to construct is the pneumatic analog of the resistance-capacity network used in electronics for introducing a time constant into an amplifier. A diagram of the pneumatic form is shown in Figure 1. A vessel of volume V is introduced

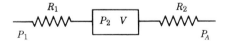

Fig. 1. Diagram of a simple flow programmer.

between two pneumatic resistances which have an inlet pressure P_1 and an outlet pressure P_A. The pressure of the gas in the vessel will be considered as P_2.

Assuming Newtonian flow, then the volume of gas entering the vessel from the first resistance in unit time is given by the equation:

$$Q_2 P_2 = (\pi a^4 / 16 N l)(P_1^2 - P_2^2)$$

where a and l are the effective radius and length of the restriction, respectively, and N is the viscosity of the gas.

Since N is independent of pressure, the equation can be put in the form:

$$Q_2 = (R_1 / P_2)(P_1^2 - P_2^2)$$

and the volume of gas leaving the vessel Q_2' is given by:

$$Q_2' = (R_2 / P_2)(P_2^2 - P_A^2)$$

thus:

$$Q_2 - Q_2' = \frac{1}{P_2}(R_1 P_1^2 - R_1 P_2^2 - R_2 P_2^2 + R_2 P_A^2) = \frac{\partial V}{\partial t} - \frac{\partial V'}{\partial t} \quad (1)$$

where V is the volume of gas in cc's and $Q_2 = \partial V / \partial t$ and $Q_2' = \partial V' / \partial t$.

From Boyle's law, the pressure increase in the vessel will be proportional to the net volume of gas entering it. Thus:

$$\left(\frac{\partial V}{\partial t} - \frac{\partial V'}{\partial t} \right) \frac{P_2}{V} = \frac{\partial P_2}{\partial t}$$

Substituting for $\partial V / \partial t$ and $\partial V' / \partial t$ from eq. (1), i.e.,

$$\frac{\partial P_2}{\partial t} = \frac{1}{V} [R_1 P_1^2 + R_2 P_A^2 - P_2^2 (R_1 + R_2)]$$

or:

$$\frac{\partial P_2}{\partial t} = \frac{1}{V}(c - a P_2^2)$$

where $c = R_1 P_1^2 + R_2 P_2^2$ and $a = (R_1 + R_2)$. Rearranging:

$$\frac{\partial P_2}{c - a P_2^2} = \frac{\partial t}{V} \quad (2)$$

Equation (2) is a standard integral and thus, integrating:

$$\frac{1}{2\sqrt{ac}} \log \frac{\sqrt{c} + P_2 \sqrt{a}}{\sqrt{c} - P_2 \sqrt{a}} = \frac{t}{V} + K$$

the limiting conditions are when $t = 0$, $P_2 = P_A$. Substituting to eliminate K and rearranging,

$$P_2 = \sqrt{\frac{c}{a}} \left[\frac{\sqrt{\frac{c}{a}} + P_A - \left(\sqrt{\frac{c}{a}} - P_A\right) \exp \frac{-2t\sqrt{ac}}{V}}{\sqrt{\frac{c}{a}} + P_A + \left(\sqrt{\frac{c}{a}} - P_A\right) \exp \frac{-2t\sqrt{ac}}{V}} \right] \tag{3}$$

Now:

$$Q_3 P_A = R_2(P_2^2 - P_A^2) \tag{4}$$

Substituting from eq. (3) for P_2 in eq. (4) leads to

$$Q_3 = \frac{R_2}{P_A} \left[\frac{c}{a} \left[\frac{\sqrt{\frac{c}{a}} + P_A - \left(\sqrt{\frac{c}{a}} - P_A\right) \exp \frac{-2t\sqrt{ac}}{V}}{\sqrt{\frac{c}{a}} + P_A + \left(\sqrt{\frac{c}{a}} - P_A\right) \exp \frac{-2t\sqrt{ac}}{V}} \right]^2 - P_A^2 \right] \tag{5}$$

when c and a have the values previously defined.

Equation (5) gives the relationship between outlet flow and time, which can be calculated by assuming values for P_1, V, R_2, and R_1. In practice, this system lends itself readily to use with dual column chromatographs and was used with the Pye 104 chromatograph. The values of R_1 and R_2 were determined experimentally for the separate columns (8 ft in length) and found to be 11.3 ml/atm minute and 11.4 ml/atm minute, respectively; V was made 1820 ml. The inlet pressure was applied to the end of the first column, the injection systems of the two columns were connected to the buffer vessel by capillary connections, and the detector was situated at the end of the second column. The theoretical and experimental curves obtained from this system are shown in Figure 2.

It can be seen that this simple system produces a very effective flow programmer and can be used to demonstrate the value of flow programming relative to isorheic operations with isothermal or temperature programming operations. The sample chosen was a mixture of C_6, C_8, C_{10}, C_{12}, C_{14}, and C_{16} hydrocarbons and was placed on the second column through its particular injection system. This column was 5 ft long, 4 mm in diameter, carrying 10% Apiezon Grease on 180–200 brick dust. Figure 3a is a chromatogram obtained under isothermal and isorheic conditions at 200°C. Figure 3b shows the same separation under isorheic conditions but temperature programmed from

50 to 200°C at 12°/min. The analysis time has been increased from about 50 to 62 minutes but the separation of the C_6 isomers is improved. Figure 3c is again the same separation under isothermal conditions but flow programmed from 20 to 600 ml/min. The analysis time has

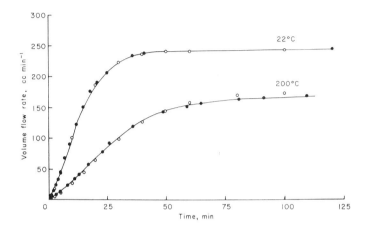

Fig. 2. Theoretical and experimental curves for the simple flow programmer. (●) Experimental points. (○) Theoretical points.

been reduced to 35 min, but the separation of the C_6 isomer is completely lost. In Figure 3d the separation obtained by a temperature program from 50 to 200°C at 12°/min and simultaneous flow program has taken 40 min to develop and the separation of the C_6 isomer maintained clearly indicating the effect of the two programming techniques on resolutions and analysis time.

B. Pressure Programmer

A more versatile type of flow programmer is shown in Figure 4. It consists of a downstream pressure controller A similar to the type manufactured by A.E.I. Ltd., Catalog No. 63 BDL. This controller has to be slightly modified to operate satisfactorily as a pressure programmer. The normal seating of the valve is metal, which is replaced with a rubber seal by inserting a rubber O ring over the control cone (Fig. 5). As the control is entirely pneumatic, the control springs are also removed.

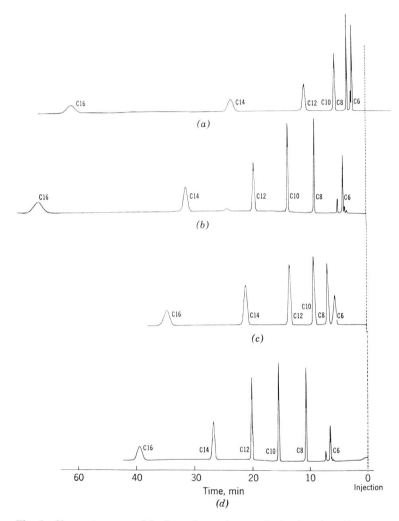

Fig. 3. Chromatograms of hydrocarbon mixture obtained under different programming conditions.

The inlet of the controller is connected to the carrier gas supply and
the outlet leads to the column via the injection system. A needle valve
E which is adjusted to give the lower program limit is connected between
the inlet and the outlet of the controller. The controller port is connected via a good quality needle valve C to the gas supply line and a
buffer vessel B of 1–2 liter capacity is situated between the controller and

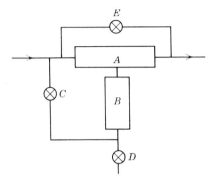

Fig. 4. Pressure programmer: (A) downstream controller; (B) ballast vessel, 1-2 liters; (C, E) needle valves; (D) on-off valve.

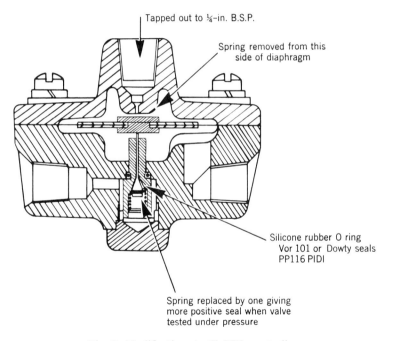

Fig. 5. Modifications to 63-BDL controller.

the needle valve. The buffer vessel has to be capable of withstanding the maximum pressure to be used by the flow programmer. Between the buffer vessel and the needle valve, a T junction leads to a simple on–off valve D.

The upper limit of the program is set by the pressure controller on the gas supply cylinder and the lower limit is obtained by the appropriate setting of the needle valve E. The program rate is adjusted by means of needle valve C which can be calibrated for a series of program times. If precise reproducibility is required, the program rate can be checked against the leak flow measured through the on–off valve D. The buffer vessel B allows slow program rates to be obtained without using the limiting settings of the needle valve which may be rather coarse. After the program is complete the pressure is released by venting through the on–off valve D.

During a long program, the leak through the needle valve is very small and therefore it is essential to keep the system completely gas tight. The curve relating gas flow to time for three different program rates using this type of flow programmer is shown in Figure 6. The curve is for isothermal operation and the glass column used was 20 ft long,

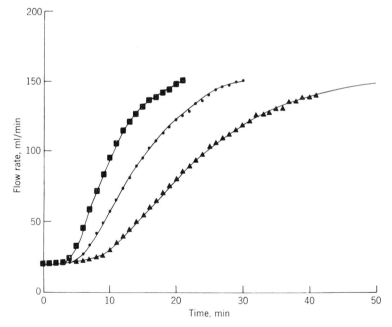

Fig. 6. Performance of pressure programmer at different program rates.

4 mm in diameter, packed with 7.5% w/w P.E.G. 20M on 100–120 Celite operating at maximum final pressure of 60 psi. The initial flow of 20 ml/min was set by needle valve E and the different program rates set by needle valve C. If temperature programming is also used, the viscosity of the carrier gas changes with the temperature and thus affects the flow rate. Therefore, as the system is a pressure-controlling device, the flow program obtained with temperature-programmed operation will not be the same as that obtained under isothermal conditions.

II. PROGRAM FORMS OTHER THAN LOGARITHMIC

It has been pointed out by Kreusen (7) that a downstream controller can be connected in such a way as to give program forms other than logarithmic. Two examples are shown in Figure 7. In Figure 7a, the needle valve controlling the leak to the pressure programmer is connected to the column side of the downstream controller. This means that the leak controlling the flow increases as the downstream pressure increases and this results in an exponential form of the flow program. Theoretically, however, the system described in Figure 7a cannot be self-initiated unless some pressure is built up at the column side. This pressure is produced by the needle valve E which also controls the lower program flow rate. The pneumatic arrangement shown in Figure 7b is a combination of the two systems previously described.

The leaks to the programmer which will control the column flow are derived from two needle valves, one from the inlet pressure and the other from the outlet pressure. The needle valve C will produce a logarithmic program, whereas needle valve F produces an exponential

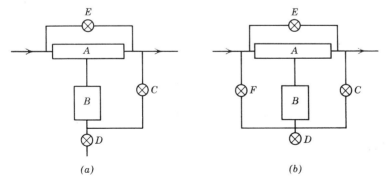

(a) (b)

Fig. 7. Different forms of pressure programmer. (A) Downstream pressure controller, (B) ballast vessel, (C, E, F) needle valves, (D) on–off valves.

program. Using various settings of C and F it can be seen that quite involved programs can be obtained between that of a logarithmic and that of an exponential function.

A truly linear form of a pneumatic flow programmer was suggested by Hurrel (8). The system used is similar to that shown in Figure 4. The leak through needle valve C, however, is supplied by a mass flow controller similar to that used for carrier gas control. Since the flow of gas into the buffer vessel B would then be constant, the pressure in the buffer vessel and consequently the column flow would increase linearly with time.

III. APPLICATION OF FLOW PROGRAMMING

Flow programming can be used in exactly the same way as temperature programming and, in many instances, more effectively. It can shorten analysis times for wide boiling-range mixtures while allowing the column to be operated at a significantly lower temperature. As the separation ratios of components generally increase at lower operating temperatures, the use of flow programming can give better resolution without increasing the analysis time. The limiting volatility of a substance that can be chromatographed on a given column is set by the maximum operating temperature, which in turn is set by the vapor pressure of the stationary phase. If, when the maximum operating temperature has been reached by the temperature programmer, the column is flow programmed, the lower limits of volatility for the substances being chromatographed will be extended. Higher boiling substances which would normally be held in the column for many hours will be eluted in a few minutes. The high column inlet pressures, necessitated by the high gas flows at the end of the program, present no problem if the chromatograph is designed correctly. The loading of the column is carried out at the beginning of the program at low inlet pressures.

Flow programming can be used to particular advantage when separating thermally labile materials. Figure 8 shows the separation of lemon grass oil by temperature programming and also by flow programming. Lemon grass oil contains citral, which on the column commences to decompose at temperatures above 125°C. However, if the column is operated isothermally at 125°C after an initial temperature program, the higher boiling components take many hours to elute. The

analysis time can be reduced to a reasonable period, however, if the
column is flow programmed during the isothermal operation at 125°C.
In Figure 8 it is seen that with temperature programming only, thermal
decomposition of the citral results in a changing base line, and the subsequent contamination of many peaks by pyrolysis products. The same

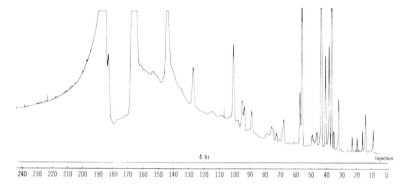

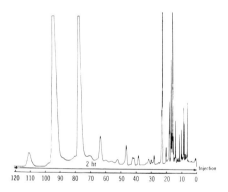

Fig. 8. (Upper) chromatogram of lemon grass oil. Isorheic operation at
100 psi giving a flow rate of 60 ml/min. Temperature program: 125–200°C at
½°/min. Charge: 2 μl. (Lower) chromatogram of lemon grass oil. Isothermal
operation at 125°C. Flow program: 40–450 ml/min. Charge: 2 μl.

separation carried out isothermally at a lower temperature with the use
of flow programming gives an improved separation with no thermal
decomposition and a stable base line.

Flow programming can also be used in the semi-preparative
operation of analytical columns. Two major problems are encountered

when using large samples in gas chromatographic separations. First, the charge has to be placed on the column in such a manner that serious band broadening does not occur due to slow volatilization of the sample. Secondly, the column should be operated so that peak asymmetry, resulting from the nonlinear nature of the adsorption isotherm at high levels of concentration, is eliminated or counteracted. This first problem can be overcome by placing the charge on the column and allowing a period of five minutes to elapse before the commencement of elution. This procedure is similar to that used by Daniel (9) who used the delayed elution technique to improve the performance of analytical columns. The second problem, that of counteracting or eliminating the peak asymmetry resulting from solute overload, can be overcome for reasonable charges by the use of flow programming, usually in conjunction with temperature programming. In order to explain the method, it is necessary to describe briefly the thermal changes that occur in a column when a solute passes through it (10).

As a solute enters a theoretical plate, the heat of solution is evolved and the temperature rises and reaches a maximum near the point of maximum solute concentration. As the solute is eluted from the plate, the heat of solution is absorbed and cooling takes place. For charges of a few milligrams, the temperature change can be as great as 5°C. This thermal effect will cause the higher concentrations in the peak, where the temperature is greatest, to move more rapidly through the column than the lower concentrations; this relative movement of the different concentrations in the peak results in an asymmetric elution curve opposite in form to that due to column overload. From the equation of the temperature curve of a theoretical plate during the passage of a solute through it, it was shown that the temperature increases proportionally with increasing flow rate, producing greater peak asymmetry at higher gas flows. The overloading effect on a column increases with the solubility of the solute in the liquid phase and thus with the retention time or partition coefficient of the substance chromatographed. By the selection of a suitable program for increasing the flow rate as elution proceeds, the peak asymmetry caused by the two nonideal effects, thermal changes and column overload, can be made to counteract one another to give a symmetrical peak. The increasing flow rate, however, will cause bandbroadening as well as rendering the peak symmetrical. Some loss of resolution would therefore occur which would have to be counteracted by reducing the mean operating temperature or comparative program rate.

An example of the use of temperature and flow programming to separate large charges on an analytical column is given in Figure 9. The sample was 120 μl of peppermint oil on a 40 ft column, 3.5 mm in diameter, packed with 60–80 brick dust carrying 5% w/w of P.E.G. 20M as stationary phase. The temperature and flow programs are shown and, although the larger components present still contain some trace material, an excellent separation is obtained.

The technique of flow programming can be used with any column system and, in fact, with any form of chromatography. Zlatkis, Ettre, and their co-workers were some of the first to use programming with capillary columns (6). These workers demonstrated the use of flow programming in the analysis of Menhaden oil. Menhaden oil is a complex fish oil with substances present up to the C_{18} range. The later peaks are particularly important as they correspond to highly unsaturated fatty acids. Zlatkis and Ettre ran the mixture under three conditions, first isothermal and isorheic, secondly isorheic but with temperature program operation, and finally with temperature programmed and flow programmed operation. The chromatogram of the oil obtained under isothermal and isorheic conditions is shown in Figure 10a; the analysis took about 60 min. Figure 10b shows a chromatogram of the same sample separated with temperature programming. Due to the instability of the stationary phase used, 205°C was the maximum temperature at which the column could be operated. The chromatogram shows a sinusoidal movement of the base line subsequent to 205°C which was due to stationary phase deterioration. The analysis time under these conditions was about 35 min. Figure 10c shows the chromatogram obtained by separating the mixture with a combination of both temperature and flow-programming operation and it is seen that good resolution is obtained and the analysis time has been further reduced to about 26 min. Moreover, the instability of the base line due to sustained heating of the stationary phase at 205°C is not present.

IV. QUANTITATIVE ANALYSIS WITH FLOW PROGRAMMING

The most common detectors used for quantitative analysis are the catharometer and the flame ionization detector. It is well known that the catharometer is extremely sensitive to flow rate, and Sternberg and Dewar have shown that the response of the flame ionization detector

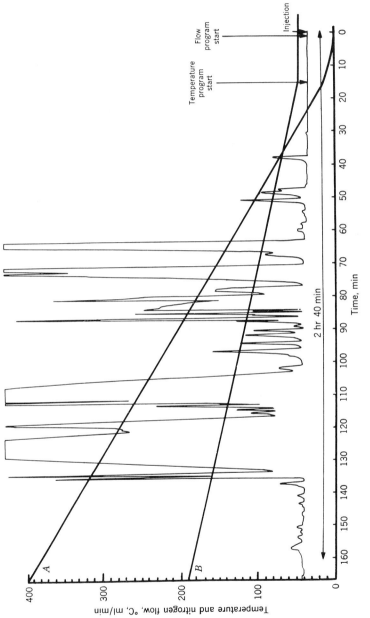

Fig. 9. Semipreparative scale chromatogram of peppermint oil. Charge: 120 µl. Temperature program: 50–225°C at 1°/min. Flow program: 0–400 ml/min N₂.

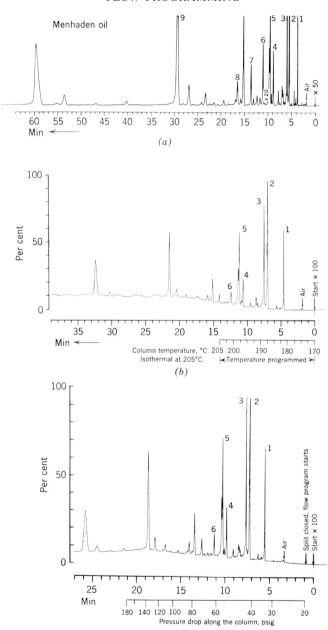

Fig. 10. Menhaden oil analysis.

varies both with column flow rate and temperature. The effect of temperature on the response of the flame ionization detector can be eliminated by thermostatting the detector in a separate oven. However, at first sight it would appear difficult to compensate for changes in flow rate. A possible method for permitting quantitative analysis while at the same time carrying out flow programming was suggested by Kreusen (7) as shown in Figure 11. Two controllers are used; the normal flow program controller A made from a downstream controller with its ballast capacity B and needle valves E and C operates in the manner previously described; a second upstream controller F with its needle

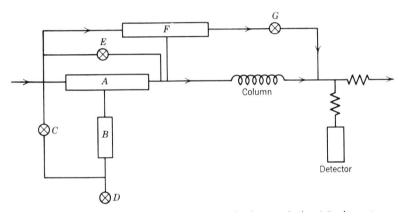

Fig. 11. Pressure programmer for quantitative analysis. (A) downstream controller, (B) ballast vessel, (C, E, G) needle valves, (D) on–off valve, (F) upstream controller.

valve G is controlled by the inlet column pressure and supplies a flow to the end of the column where it mixes with the column flow and passes through a stream splitter to the detector and out to vent. As controller F is an upstream controller, however, the outlet pressure and thus the outlet flow will decrease with increased column inlet pressure. Thus as the column flow increases the flow through F to the end of the column decreases. If G is suitably adjusted, the flow past the detector to vent remains constant throughout the flow program. Under these circumstances, the detector can operate under constant sample flow and give accurate quantitative results.

Simple flow programming can only be used with detectors that are flow insensitive, providing that maximum sensitivity is not being employed. For this reason, simple flow programming is best used in conjunction with the flame ionization detector. However, the use of the system described above would permit flow programming to be used with most types of detecting systems. It should be pointed out that with a little modification the system could also be effectively used for determining the effect of carrier gas flow rate on detector response.

The main applications of flow programming in gas chromatography can be summarized as follows:

1. The extension of the boiling range of substances that can be chromatographed above the limit previously set by the maximum operating temperatures of the stationary phase.

2. The reduction of analysis time.

3. The gas chromatographic separations of thermally labile compounds.

4. The increase of sample size that can be chromatographed on analytical and preparative scale columns.

Acknowledgments

The author would like to thank the Institute of Petroleum for permission to reproduce Figures 8 and 9, the *Journal of Gas Chromatography* for permission to reproduce Figures 10*a*, 10*b*, and 10*c*, and Mr. J. R. Ravenhill for providing the data on the simple flow programmer.

References

1. S. R. Lipsky, R. A. Landowne, and J. E. Lovelock, *Anal. Chem.*, **31**, 852 (1959).
2. M. Morgantini, *Boll. Sub. Chim. Provinciali (Bologna)*, **13**, 545 (1962).
3. H. Purnell, *Gas Chromatography*, Wiley, New York, 1962, p. 387.
4. R. P. W. Scott, *Nature*, **198**, 782 (1963).
5. R. P. W. Scott, in *Gas Chromatography 1964*, A. Goldup, Ed., Institute of Petroleum, p. 25.
6. A. Zlatkis, D. C. Fenimore, L. S. Ettre, and J. E. Purall, *J. Gas Chromatog.* **3**, No. 3, 75 (1965).
7. A. Kreusen, Unilever Research Laboratory, Vlaardingen, private communication.
8. R. Hurrel, Philips Chromatography Ltd., private communication.
9. N. W. R. Daniel and J. W. Richmond, *Chem. Ind. (London)*, **1961**, 1441.
10. R. P. W. Scott, *Anal. Chem.*, **35**, 481 (1963).

Theory and Principles for Choosing and Designing Selective Stationary Phases*

STANLEY H. LANGER and RICHARD J. SHEEHAN, *Department of Chemical Engineering, University of Wisconsin, Madison, Wisconsin*

I. INTRODUCTION

Selective stationary phases are of interest in gas–liquid chromatography, not only because they ease the separation of intractable mixtures, but because through their action they also give information for qualitative identification and characterization of unknown compounds. The use of selective phases, in turn, continues to give increased information about molecular interactions in solution.

Although the original developers of gas–liquid chromatography demonstrated early awareness of the role of chemical interaction in separation through their choice of selective liquid phases (1–6),

* Supported in part by the National Science Foundation (fellowship for R.J.S.), the Petroleum Research Fund, and the Wisconsin Alumni Research Foundation.

289

subsequent stationary phase selection and development frequently has been based on chance and empiricism alone. Consequently, many discussions of selectivity are in the general language of polar and nonpolar stationary phases and/or based on phenomenological rules and observations. This is understandable if one considers the following: (a) gas–liquid chromatography is such a powerful and effective separation technique that intimate knowledge of selective interactions involved is seldom needed; (b) the critical selective interaction involved may be unknown, unidentified, or is the result of a number of interactions which cannot be individually evaluated; or (c) the detailed or even general composition of a number of selective liquid phases, especially polymeric materials, is not known. This is especially true of a number of stable high-temperature materials.

However, the desire for faster analysis, the need to separate closely similar isomers, and the interest in preparative gas–liquid chromatography all portend greater future interest in the principles of stationary phase selectivity and interaction. Recent publication frequency and discussion in this area already are indicative of increased inquiry into the mode of action of stationary phases. Fortunately, solution theory combined with qualitative knowledge of molecular interactions provides a basis for extending the rules for design and choice of selective stationary phases. While the theoretical picture may be oversimplified and somewhat inaccurate, the mode of approach is apparent and can be systematic. Indeed, the range of interactions and combination of interactions that can be invoked is so great that the approach can only be illustrated here. Furthermore, in order to focus on principles, discussion will be limited to interactions within the liquid phase and to gas–liquid chromatography. Interactions with the solid support will be discussed only to the extent that they interfere, in a few outstanding instances, with liquid-phase interaction with the solute.

The general rules and considerations for stationary phase selection which have existed heretofore are summarized in Keulemans (7) and the three most recent texts to appear in English (8–10).

II. SELECTIVITY

For mixtures of close-boiling materials of different chemical classes, separation is relatively easy and the general principle that "like dissolves like" is applicable. Thus, benzyldiphenyl will hold benzene preferentially over cyclohexane, and aliphatic-type hydrocarbon liquid phases will reverse the elution order and preferentially hold cyclohexane (1,2). An alcohol–hydrocarbon mixture of components of the same vapor pressure would be separated similarly.

Evaluation of selectivity for mixtures of similar compounds or isomers is best done in terms of the separation factor, $\alpha_{1,2}$, which is equal to the ratio of retention volumes (measured from the air peak) for compounds 1 and 2 or their partition coefficients. *Selective* liquid phases, then, are characterized by high separation factors for the compounds or classes of compounds in question. From the simplest relationship between retention volume per gram of solvent, V_g, and activity coefficient (7–14)

$$V_g{}^T = RT/(Mp^\circ \gamma^\infty) \qquad (1a)$$

it can be shown that

$$\alpha_{1,2} = (\gamma_2{}^\infty p_2{}^\circ)/(\gamma_1{}^\infty p_1{}^\circ) \qquad (1)$$

where γ^∞ is the activity coefficient of the solutes at infinite dilution and p° is the saturation vapor pressure of these solutes, the compounds of interest, at the temperature of chromatographic operation. If the vapor pressures of two compounds are equal, then it can be seen that separation is dependent on the ratio of their activity coefficients in the stationary phase or solvent. Under some conditions it is most convenient to chemically alter solutes of interest (15–18) in order to change γ or p° or both and thus achieve separation with a given selective stationary phase. However, the most desirable approach is a judicious choice or synthesis of a stationary phase so that the activity coefficient for one material is relatively low and this material is selectively held in the column.

III. SOLUTION INTERACTIONS AND THEIR EFFECT

Solvent interaction with a solute, and therefore the activity coefficient of the solute in the solvent is complex, but is mainly influenced by varying operative solution forces through control of the chemical composition of the solvent molecules and to a lesser but significant extent their molecular size and shape. The three types of forces generally thought to be operative in solution are (7,19,20):

(1) *London or Dispersion Forces.* These are attractive forces which are best treated quantum mechanically. They are due to transient dipoles set up because of the "looseness" and mobility of the electron

cloud relative to the positive charge of atomic nuclei. The time averaged net dipole is zero, but the net effect of dipole interaction between molecules is attractive interaction. The smaller atoms with shorter atomic radii tend to hold outer electronic clouds "tighter" (less polarizable) and to contribute least to dispersion forces. Nevertheless, dispersion forces contribute 80 to almost 100% of the attractive energy between molecules which do not have large dipoles and are not unusually polarizable. Unfortunately for the molecular architect, these forces, because of their complexity, are not easily predicted for building into molecules, and therefore they cannot be readily utilized for separation.

(2) *Dipole–Dipole Interactions or Orientation Forces.* These attractive forces result from the net attraction between molecules or portions of molecules possessing a permanent dipole moment. A Boltzmann distribution treatment shows a higher probability for attractive low-potential interactions than the repulsive high-energy interactions. However, the dipole interaction energy varies inversely with temperature, and at higher temperatures random thermal molecular motion competes with the tendency for favorable orientations and the effect of dipole–dipole attraction is diminished.

(3) *Induction or Dipole-Induced Dipole Interactions.* These are attractive forces resulting from the interaction between a permanent dipole and the dipole induced in a neighboring molecule or a portion of that molecule because of the polarizability of the electron cloud in the neighboring molecule. Again, this is a function of atomic radii (sulfur is more polarizable than the smaller oxygen) and the nature of the electron cloud, e.g., benzene with its π electron cloud is more polarizable than cyclohexane. Dipole-induced dipole interactions are not the same in all directions and are dependent on relative molecular orientation.

In a sense, we utilize our knowledge of these interactions when we use a stationary phase resembling one member of a dissimilar mixture since this solute interacts in the solvent in a manner similar to another solvent molecule. The appendage of an extra group, such as a long alkyl chain in a nonaliphatic solvent, changes the validity of this generalization.

In addition to the solution forces which are listed above, there are also special chemical bonding interactions such as coordination forces between metal ions and olefins, e.g., silver ions in solution to separate olefins (21,22), charge transfer forces to separate aromatics (24,25), and hydrogen bonding involving the interaction between polar H in —OH or —NH with unshared electron pairs in nitrogen, oxygen, or sulfur (3).

Recently, Pearson has proposed a new general principle (26,27) which may be of special assistance in utilizing and classifying molecular interactions. The principle is that of "hard and soft acids and bases" (HSAB principle). Essentially all interactions are viewed in the Lewis sense, where acids are electron acceptors and bases are electron donors. Thus in the hydrogen bonded $—OH:O(R)_2$, hydrogen is acting as a Lewis acid and the oxygen in ether as a Lewis base. Similarly, in a silver–olefin complex, the silver ion is viewed as an acid and the electron-rich double bond as a donor. The HSAB principle states that "hard acids prefer to coordinate to hard bases and soft acids prefer to coordinate to soft bases." Terms are defined as follows. A *soft base* is a donor center which is highly polarizable, easily oxidized, and associated with empty, low-lying orbitals; it has low electronegativity. A *hard base* is a donor center which has low polarizability, high electronegativity, and is hard to oxidize; it is associated with empty orbitals of high energy, and hence is inaccessible. A *soft acid* is the acceptor center which has low positive charge, large size, and easily excited outer electrons. A *hard acid* is the acceptor center which has high positive charge, small size, and does not have easily excited outer electrons.

Tables I and II, classifying acids and bases of particular interest from the viewpoint of solute–solvent interactions, follow (26,27).

TABLE I
Classification of Some Bases

Hard	Soft
H_2O, F^-	R_2S, RSH, RS^-
$CH_3CO_2^-$, ClO_4^-, NO_3^-	I^-, Br^-, R_3P, R_3As
ROH, RO^-, R_2O	$(RO)_3P$, RNC, CO
NH_3, RNH_2, N_2H_4	C_2H_4, C_6H_6
	Borderline
$C_6H_5NH_2$, C_5H_5N, Cl^-	

Despite the simplicity of the hard and soft classifications of interactions, it must be remembered that the most commonplace gas–liquid separation can involve a combination of interactions. For instance, with a polyglycol, $HO—(CH_2—CH_2O)_nCH_2CH_2OH$, solvent and amine solutes, there are several interactions; in addition to dispersion and dipole-induced dipole interactions, there are the hard interactions between the amine hydrogens and ether oxygens and between terminal hydroxyl groups and the nitrogen electron pair of the solutes. The latter

TABLE II
Classification of Some Lewis Acids

Hard	Soft
H^+, K^+	Cu^+, Ag^+, Au^+
Cr^{3+}, Co^{3+}, Fe^{3+}, As^{3+}, Ce^{3+}	Pd^{2+}, Cd^{2+}, Pt^{2+}
Si^{4+}, Ti^{4+}	$Tl(CH_3)_3$, BH_3, $CO(CN)_5^{2-}$
UO_2^{2+}, $(CH_3)_2Sn^{2+}$	I_2, Br_2, ICN, etc.
$BeMe_2$, BF_3, BCl_3, $B(OR)_3$	Trinitrobenzene, etc.
$Al(CH_3)_3$, $Ga(CH_3)_3$, AlH_3	Chloranil, quinones, etc.
RSO_2^+, $ROSO_2^+$, SO_3	Tetracyanoethylene, etc.
RCO^+, CO_2, NC^+	
HX, hydrogen bonding molecules	
Borderline	
Fe^{2+}, Cu^{2+}, Bi^{3+}, Rh^{3+}, $B(CH_3)_3$, SO_2	

becomes less important as the molecular weight of the polyglycol (that is, n) increases (3,4). The simplest amines are eluted in the order trimethylamine, bp 3.5°C, methylamine, bp −6.5°C, dimethylamine, bp 7.4°C, indicating that amine hydrogen bonding is significant but not predominant. (Vapor pressure is also important, otherwise methylamine would have maximum retention in the column.) The "hardest" amine hydrogen–oxygen interaction can be made dominant by using triethanolamine as a liquid phase (28) so that relative retentions are trimethylamine: 1.0, dimethylamine: 2.61, and methylamine: 3.6, in the order of amine–hydrogen availability. Hydrogen bonding from solvent to the amine–nitrogen is minimized by stronger competition from oxygen in the solvent hydroxyl environment. From an aliphatic solvent (3,4), the methylamines are simply eluted in order of boiling point without specific bonding interaction.

A simple example of a selective "soft" coordination interaction is the separation of 1- and 3-methylcyclohexene with silver ion in ethylene glycol (22). 1-Methylcyclohexene (bp 110°C) emerges in only one quarter of the time necessary to elute 3-methylcyclohexene (bp 102.7°C) because of the interference with coordination by the 1-methyl group on the olefinic carbon atom. This is an orientational or entropy effect. Seldom is a simple specific interaction available such as oxygen–hemoglobin which enables the separation of oxygen and nitrogen to be made with mammal blood on a suitable support (29). Therefore, discussion of selectivity is generally only semiquantitative, *vide infra*, and empirical. Many excellent examples and specific directions for separations are summarized by Burchfield and Storrs (30).

IV. THERMODYNAMIC APPROACH TO SELECTIVITY

A. General Principles

Additional principles of selectivity can be developed, using solution theory, by considering excess partial molar thermodynamic functions (14,31). We may define the excess partial molar free energy of mixing at infinite dilution per mole of solute, $\Delta \bar{G}_e^{\infty}$, as

$$\Delta \bar{G}_e^{\infty} = RT \ln \gamma^{\infty} \qquad (2)$$

The (excess) partial molar enthalpy (temperature-sensitive contribution to $\Delta \bar{G}_e^{\infty}$), $\Delta \bar{H}_e^{\infty}$, becomes

$$R \frac{\partial \ln \gamma^{\infty}}{\partial (1/T)} \qquad (3)$$

and $\Delta \bar{S}_e^{\infty}$, the excess partial molar entropy, may be calculated from

$$\Delta \bar{G}_e^{\infty} = \Delta \bar{H}_e^{\infty} - T \Delta \bar{S}_e^{\infty} \qquad (4)$$

Negative $\Delta \bar{G}_e^{\infty}$, negative $\Delta \bar{H}_e^{\infty}$, and positive $\Delta \bar{S}_e^{\infty}$ all favor the solution process for the solute from the gas phase.

From the definitions of logarithms and eqs. (2)–(4), eq. (1) becomes

$$\alpha_{1,2} = \frac{e^{\Delta \bar{G}_{e,2}^{\infty}/RT} p_2^{\circ}}{e^{\Delta \bar{G}_{e,1}^{\infty}/RT} p_1^{\circ}} = \frac{e^{\Delta \bar{H}_{e,2}^{\infty}/RT} e^{-\Delta \bar{S}_{e,2}^{\infty}/R} p_2^{\circ}}{e^{\Delta \bar{H}_{e,1}^{\infty}/RT} e^{-\Delta \bar{S}_{e,1}^{\infty}/R} p_1^{\circ}} \qquad (5)$$

To maximize the separation factor then, it is desirable to achieve the greatest possible difference between $\Delta \bar{G}_e^{\infty}$ values for compounds 1 and 2. Now, one may consider $\Delta \bar{G}_e^{\infty}$ to be the result of a number of interactions between solute and solvent involving all permutations of solvent and solute functional groups. On this basis, $\Delta \bar{G}_e^{\infty}$ is the sum of the free energy for a number of interactions for solute 1 of G_{11}–G_{1x}, where x is the total number of interactions involved between solute and stationary phase. This group interaction approach with modification is used successfully with eq. (2) in predicting activity coefficients for a number of solute families in conventional solvents (7,9,32–35). However, the approach can be refined to take into account interactions and solution theories in addition to conventional group interactions (31). Considering, then, that the total interaction between each solute and the solvent is the sum of a number of interactions, x, each interaction having an associated heat, H, and entropy, S, eq. (5) becomes

$$\alpha_{1,2} = \frac{[e^{H_{21}/RT} e^{H_{22}/RT} \cdots e^{H_{2x}/RT}] [e^{-S_{21}/R} e^{-S_{22}/R} \cdots e^{-S_{2x}/R}] p_2^{\circ}}{[e^{H_{11}/RT} e^{H_{12}/RT} \cdots e^{H_{1x}/RT}] [e^{-S_{11}/R} e^{-S_{12}/R} \cdots e^{-S_{1x}/R}] p_1^{\circ}} \qquad (6)$$

B. Implications of General Principles

For closely similar isomers, at infinite dilution, it would be expected that solute–solute interactions and solvent–solvent interactions, included in some group interaction treatments, would each cancel. From eq. (6) it can be seen that favorable selective interactions will reinforce each other and are desirable. Some of the interactions may involve positive heats (unfavorable to solution) and may outweigh the sum of negative heats to give a resultant positive heat or deceptively small heat of solution. If such effects operate equally on both solutes 1 and 2, this is desirable since it means higher activity coefficients and consequently more rapid elution from the column. In theory, and as we have seen in considering various forces, entropy (orientational) effects may be either positive or negative or they may possibly interact with heat effects (14,31,36). Thus if it is desired to utilize a specific interaction for selective separation, it is appropriate to minimize other solvating (attractive) interactions which may act counter to the desired separation and simply increase the time for separation and time of column residence if nonselective. The effect of "selective" interactions is enhanced by increasing the concentration of selective interacting groups in the solvent, provided unfavorable entropy factors do not appear and adsorption on solvent (37,38) does not complicate the separation.

Inspection of eqs. (5) and (6) leads to the conclusion that differences between activity coefficients due to net heats of solution of two solutes are greatest when operating at the lowest possible temperature. This is most feasible when overall activity coefficients tend to be high, i.e., where net heats of solution are small or positive and entropies are negative. The liquid phase must be chosen accordingly.

Of course, where net heats act counter to the desired separation, operation at elevated temperatures is appropriate.

V. UTILIZATION OF SPECIFIC INTERACTIONS

Stationary phases such as the dipropionitriles (oxy, thio, and imino), glycerol, and triethanolamine are examples of solvents with high concentrations of selective interacting groups. At a given boiling point, dioxypropionitrile retains alkylbenzenes 20 times longer than paraffins because of interaction between the strong polar $—\overline{C}\!\equiv\!N^{+}$ nitrile groups and the soft polarizable aromatic π electrons (39). The small interaction energy with paraffins is evident from the low specific retention volume of pentane in dioxypropionitrile, 8 ml/g at 25°C. However, the interaction with alkylbenzenes, though strong, is not particularly selective for separation of aromatic isomers such as m- and p-xylene; evidently the interaction energies are nearly equal and not specific. For this latter separation and similar ones, nonselective strong polar interactions should be avoided or minimized.

One effect of specific group interaction may be illustrated by triethylene glycol with and without silver nitrate (39); for the group paraffins, olefins, and alkylbenzenes, addition of silver ion to the glycol increases relative retention volumes of the type-1 olefins (CH_2=CHR) by a factor of 2 but not type-3 olefins (CH_2=CRR) or alkylbenzenes. Solvation interaction between silver ion and the glycol group is sufficient to reduce the absolute retention volume of pentane, the reference solute ("squeezing out"), by a factor of three to only 4 ml on a 1-m column.

The effect of counterselective interactions is illustrated by the data of Table III, for the m-/p-xylene separation on tetrahalophthalates. The *para* isomer, which has the higher vapor pressure, is held selectively in

TABLE III

Separation Factors for m-/p-Xylenes on Tetrahalophthalate Esters

Liquid phase	Temperature, °C	Separation factor, p-/m-	V_g, Toluene, ml/g
Methyl propyl tetrachlorophthalate	100	1.044	187
Di-n-propyl tetrachlorophthalate	100	1.043	204
	90	1.045	
Di-n-butyl tetrachlorophthalate	100	1.037	217
Di-n-propyl tetrabromophthalate	100	1.035	134

the column because it has a lower ionization potential than the *meta* isomer, though both have electron-rich aromatic rings. The interaction involved is soft charge transfer with the electron-poor tetrahalophthalate ring (24,25).

For the first three tetrachlorophthalate esters of Table III, the p-/m-xylene separation factor diminishes as ester alkyl groups increase in length. The alkyl groups result in greater solubility, but from similar long-chain aliphatic substrates p-xylene emerges prior to m-xylene; thus the interaction between the xylenes and the alkyl portion of the ester acts counter to the interaction between the tetrachlorophthalate ring and the xylenes. The increase in solubility is reflected by the tabulated V_g values of toluene. While the substitution of a tetrabromophthalate for the chlorinated ring results in a lower retention volume for the alkylbenzenes, the separation factor for the xylenes is diminished further. This is because bromine is less electronegative than chlorine and the charge-transfer interaction energy is diminished because the liquid phase aromatic ring is less electron poor. Unfortunately, as the alkyl ester groups are decreased in size in the tetrachlorophthalate ester series the ester melting point and volatility increase so that the lower members of the series are not suited for use as liquid phases.

In discussing the xylene separation, it must be noted that the p-xylene/m-xylene vapor pressure ratio is of the order of 1.03 and that the charge-transfer interaction has to be strong and specific to counter this factor. For a specific interaction which favors retention of m-xylene in a column [from eq. (1)] it can be seen that the separation factor needs to be reinforced by only a small amount to make gas chromatographic separation practical. More about this will be discussed later.

Another example of specific interaction is provided by Littlewood (40), who studied primary alcohols in 1-dodecanol and 2-dodecanol, respectively. At 80°C, for primary alcohols such as n-butanol, V_g (1-dodecanol)/V_g (2-dodecanol) is approximately one, whereas for a secondary alcohol, such as 2-butanol, the ratio is close to 1.1, indicating the higher specific interaction energy of the solvent secondary hydroxyl group with solute primary hydroxyl groups as compared to such secondary groups.

The effect of dispersion energy on solution for a variety of compounds in a truly nonpolar solvent (expected not to have a specific interaction) such as squalane is summarized by Littlewood (41). He shows that for an alkane, alkene, nitroalkane, thiophene, aromatic compound, and ester

$$\text{Log } V_g \cong [M(n^2 - 1)]/(n^2 + 2) \tag{7}$$

where M is the solute molecular weight and n is the refractive index of the solute. This is principally (42) because the dispersion energy can be expressed as a function of the polarizability of solute and solvent (constant) and the polarizability of the solute is expressed to a large extent as a function of $[M(n^2 - 1)]/(n^2 + 2)$. Again, it can be noted that these forces are not readily predicted, therefore specific interactions, if they can be made operable in solution, are preferable.

Perhaps at this point the importance of a small change in separation factor should be noticed. A reasonable basis for predicting the number of chromatographic plates necessary for a given separation can be obtained from a plot by Gluekauf (43) which is reproduced in most gas chromatographic texts. If peaks are gaussian and a separation of four standard deviations is considered adequate for analysis from peak heights, then the number of column plates necessary for separation factors of 1.02, 1.04, 1.06, and 1.10 are approximately 4×10^4, 10^4, 4×10^3, and 1.5×10^3, respectively. It is apparent then that, if the separation factor is close to unity (in the range of 1.02–1.05), a very small favorable change which can be implemented through improved design of the stationary phase will reduce considerably the number of plates necessary for separation. In fact, such a change may determine whether or not separation by gas chromatography is truly practical.

VI. SOLUBILITY PARAMETERS AND THEIR IMPLICATIONS

For solutes where no functional group interactions with the solvent are involved, such as with aliphatic and aromatic solutes, the Hildebrand-Scatchard equation (19) for a regular dilute solution affords an interesting approach. Here

$$\gamma_{\text{solute}} = e^{V_2(\delta_1 - \delta_2)^2/RT} \cong e^{\Sigma H/RT} \cong e^{\Delta H_m/RT} \qquad (8)$$

where δ_1 is the solubility parameter of the solvent and δ_2 is the solubility parameter of the solute. V_2 is the solute molar volume. The term ΣH represents a combination of the general solution interactions which were discussed at the beginning of this chapter and indicated in eq. (6), and is approximately the heat of mixing. We should cautiously note the Hildebrand definition of a regular solution as being "one involving no entropy change when a small amount of one of its components is transferred to it from an ideal solution of the same composition." In other words, from a rigorous viewpoint, specific orienting and chemical effects are not present, and for solutes, distribution and orientation are random in the solvent.

The parameter δ is taken as $(\Delta E^v/V)^{1/2}$, where ΔE^v is the molar energy of vaporization and V is the molar volume of the compound under consideration. The quantity in parentheses can be taken as approximately the cohesive energy density. Actually, given one or two values of δ for certain spherical reference solvents, values of δ for other solvents may be calculated from the heats of mixing and solubility which are more applicable than those obtained from energies of vaporization. Though eq. (8) was derived with a number of restrictions for spherical nonpolar molecules, it is surprisingly valid for a number of mixtures involving polyatomic moderately polar molecules, but without specific interactions of any considerable energy. Thus δ is a qualitative measure of the general solution forces present in pure materials, solvent or solute.

For polymers and nonvolatile compounds, δ may be evaluated in a number of ways, including an additive group contribution method (44), swelling, solubility, and viscosity (45–47).

Some time ago, Burrell extended the application of solubility parameters to a variety of polymer solutions, and compiled an extensive list of these parameters (45). Some of these, and some from other sources (19,46,47) of interest from the standpoint of gas chromatography, are collected in Tables IV and V.

Since the entropy increase of solution of small molecules in large ones is generally large and favorable to solution, a large heat of solution (heat of mixing from the Hildebrand–Scatchard equation is always positive) can counterbalance this and give a positive free energy of solution and high activity coefficient for a material being eluted from a column.

Ignoring the entropy term for the present, from eqs. (5) and (8) it can be seen that the effect of any small differences between Hildebrand parameters of two solutes is enhanced by using a solvent of very different δ value so that the ratio of heats of mixing of the solutes in the solvents is greatest, and the separation factor $\alpha_{1,2}$ is larger. A high activity coefficient or positive value of $\Delta \bar{G}_e^{\infty}$ also permits the use of lower operating temperatures. As already mentioned, this may be advantageous since it means an increased difference in $\Delta \bar{G}_e^{\infty}$ terms and a large activity coefficient.

Table IV includes a number of stationary phases and related compounds. In view of the argument above and the low δ value of many of the aliphatic and aromatic compounds of Table V, it seems reasonable that so many of the popular polar stationary phases are those with high δ values. Where there are specific selective interactions desired, it still seems desirable to pick solutes or solvents with appending groups which tend to give the greatest difference in δ values between the solvent and solutes. This approach gives the greatest difference in excess partial molar free energy and permits the desired operation at a lower temperature with a corresponding tendency to increase $\alpha_{1,2}$ when vapor

TABLE IV

Solubility Parameters of Molecules Used as or Similar to Stationary Phases at 25°C

δ, cal$^{0.5}$/cm$^{1.5}$	Compound	$\Delta\mu$
10.5	Acrylonitrile	0.08
15.4	Polyacrylonitrile	
10.6	α-Bromonaphthalene	Low
9.3	Dibutyl phthalate	Medium
12.1	Dimethylformamide	High
14.7	Ethylene carbonate	Medium
13.3	Propylene carbonate	
16.5	Glycerol	High
15.7	Ethylene glycol	
10.0	Nitrobenzene	0.04
10.7	Polyglycol terephthalate	Medium
7.3	Silicones, dimethyl	See discussion
6.2	Teflon	
8.9	Dihexyl phthalate	Medium
7.9	Polyethylene	
9.8	Phenanthrene	
8.0	Hexadecane	Low
9.1	Diethylene glycol	
10.9	"Epon" 1004	

TABLE V

Solubility Parameters of Some Small Molecules at 25°C

δ, cal$^{0.5}$/cm$^{1.5}$	Compound	$\Delta\mu$
7.05	Pentane	
7.3	Hexane	Low
6.75	2-Methylbutane	
7.55	Octane	Low
8.2	Cyclohexane	
7.85	Methylcyclohexane	
8.80	m-Xylene	
8.75	p-Xylene	
7.4	Ethyl ether	0.19
9.2	Benzene	Low
10.0	o-Dichlorobenzene	Low
10.4	Tetrachloroethane	
5.8	Perfluoroheptane	
6.0	Perfluoromethylcyclohexane	
10.0	Acetone	0.14
11.9	Propyl alcohol	High
10.7	Hexyl alcohol	High

pressure ratios of pure solutes act in the same direction to reinforce separation.

While the approach outlined above is greatly simplified and not always applicable, the model indicates how to accentuate differences. Most important, it contradicts considerably the frequent recommendation to "use a stationary phase of similar nature to the solutes being separated." It is consistent with the common use of stationary phases containing fluorinated groups, cyano groups, aromatic rings, and a siloxane backbone. Where selective interactions between functional polar groups of the solute and solvent are involved, it is helpful not to have attractive interactions between appended groups on either (48) since random heats or associated entropies of interactions may interfere with the desired interaction. Nonselective strong polar interactions also should be avoided, if possible.

Gordy (49) has studied mixtures of some hydrogen bonding materials with heavy methanol (CH_3OD) and noted the shift in OD infrared adsorption, $\Delta\mu$. $\Delta\mu$ is approximately proportional to hydrogen bond strength and a few values are given in Tables IV and V. Some of Burrell's qualitative hydrogen bonding classifications are also included. Generally the relationship $\Delta\mu$ of alcohols > ethers > ketones > aldehydes > esters is helpful as a guide to hydrogen bonding where it is desired to employ this interaction in assisting specific separation. Of course where hydrogen bonding occurs it may still interfere with conclusions based on consideration of δ values only (45–47).

The values given in Tables IV and V are 25°C. While rules for correcting δ values for temperature change to 50 or 100°C have been given (19,45), a compilation of δ values at some such temperature directed to gas chromatographic properties would probably be most helpful and desirable. The establishment of some standard δ values would also permit future expansion of such compilations.

For those attempting to use δ values extensively and perhaps more precisely, there are several additional considerations. The first of these has to do with the solute molar volume, V_2, used in eq. (8). Martire (50) has treated this as an adjustable parameter for separating energy (ΣH) and size effects in gas–liquid chromatography. V_2 then becomes V_2^*, an effective molar volume. There is precedent for this (51,52). V_2^* can be related to the effective surface interface area between molecules of different shapes. Thus, the basic principles of using stationary phases with δ as different as possible from the δ of the isomers still seems valid. However, differences created might be less than expected because of the dependence of the heat of mixing on respective $V_2{}^*$ values for solutes.

A second consideration has to do with the fact that δ^2, the cohesive energy density, is related to the total solution interaction due to dipole–dipole, induced dipole, and London forces. Gardon (46,47) has suggested a method of correcting eq. (8) in order to more accurately calculate the heat of mixing. This takes into account dipole–dipole interactions and deviations caused by differences between dipole–dipole interactions in pure solute and pure solvent (stationary phase) other than hydrogen bonding. Equation (8) would be most applicable for solutes and solvents in which dipole–dipole interactions are similar. One also must be wary of using solvents with δ varying in the extreme from the δ of the solutes. Under these conditions, solubility in the stationary phase is so limited that separation due to solution effects may not occur because there is essentially no solution. Under these conditions also, surface effects can become very important (37).

Another effect which must be considered is a result of the fact that the geometric mean rule, assumed in the Hildebrand–Scatchard treatment, does not hold very well for fluorocarbon–hydrocarbon mixtures. For more precise treatment of such mixtures it may be advisable to consider the modification of eq. (8) suggested and discussed by Reed (53,54). Much of the deviation is caused by the difference between hydrocarbons and fluorocarbons. The large size of the fluorine atoms tends to shield potentially interacting carbon centers. The situation is different for hydrocarbons where small hydrogen atoms produce a smaller shielding effect, allowing carbon centers to interact attractively with polar centers of adjacent molecules.

Finally, it must be recognized again that many specific solution interactions are probably still unidentified or not treated theoretically; one should therefore be alert to systematic deviations from eq. (6).

In considering eq. (6), it should be remembered that if a heat or an entropy contribution for a specific interaction does not exist or exists singularly without the other effect, then the absent effect has a value of zero and e^0 is unity; thus, the absent effect does not alter the separation factor α. However, there frequently is a linear relationship between $\Delta \bar{H}_e$ and $\Delta \bar{S}_e$ for a specific interaction (14,36,55). This is most likely to occur when the total interaction, entropy and energy, may be expressible as a function of a single variable (36). This is true for many gas chromatographic situations involving weak interactions; the solvent may be considered as constituting a fixed atmosphere in which the small solute molecule moves without appreciably disturbing solvent molecular configuration.

VII. EFFECT OF SIZE OF SOLUTES

There is reason to expect that solutions will deviate from ideality simply on the basis of difference in size between the solute and solvent molecules. This is most conveniently treated in terms of molar volumes and volume fractions (14,31,50,56). In gas chromatography, these effects may be important because so many solutions involve small solute molecules dissolved in larger solvent molecules. These effects may be considered simply in terms of either the Flory–Huggins or Miller–Guggenheim treatment. [Clark and Schmidt (57) have elegantly treated aromatics in polyaromatic liquid phases from the more complex Prigogine viewpoint.] The difference in size is expected to cause an appreciable deviation from ideality which may be expressed in terms of an athermal or entropy contribution to the activity coefficient. With the Flory–Huggins treatment, this athermal contribution, γ_a^∞, at infinite dilution may be expressed (14) as

$$\gamma_a^\infty = e^{-\Delta S/R} = (1/m)\, e^{(1-1/m)} \tag{9}$$

where m is the size ratio of solvent molecules to solute molecules, approximated as the ratio of molar volumes. The effect of a difference in molar ratios is easily inserted as an entropy term in eq. (6). The calculated effect on the athermal activity coefficient term is shown in Figure 1. The term, γ_a^∞, is seen to have a maximum at $m = 1$; at all other ratios a negative deviation from Raoult's law is predicted on the basis of size alone. Except for very polar solvents, the gas chromatographic situation will generally involve values of $m > 1$ if the stationary phase is to be relatively involatile.

Pertinent here is the predicted effect of the difference between molar volumes of two isomers of slightly different density. In Figure 2, the calculated effect on the ratios of $e^{-\Delta S/R}$ or γ_a^∞ terms is plotted against m, the size ratio of the solvent for two hypothetical solutes having molar volumes of 150 and 155 ml, respectively. The maximum change of a single activity coefficient with m occurs at $m = 1.7$. Here, about 40% of the total effect of the size ratio difference is achieved; at $m = 5$, 80% of the final ratio difference is achieved. Thus when $m > 1$ and the difference in molar volumes of solutes tends to reinforce separation, it

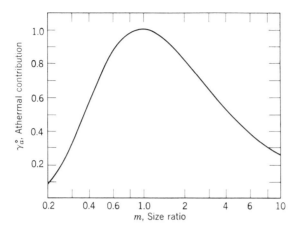

Fig. 1. Athermal contribution to activity coefficient (at infinite dilution) versus
size ratio based on the Flory–Huggins treatment. m = molar volume solvent/molar
volume solute.

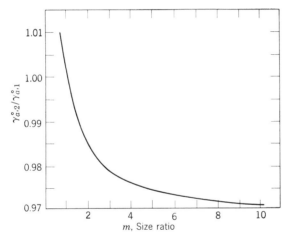

Fig. 2. Athermal activity contribution to separation factor (at infinite dilution)
for two solutes of molar volumes 150 and 155.

is desirable to use higher molecular weight solvents where $m \simeq 5\text{--}10$;
where this effect does not reinforce the separation lower molar volumes
are desirable. About 90% of the size effect apparently occurs before
$m > 10$ so that extraordinarily high molecular weight stationary phases
are not necessary to emphasize size differences. The limiting ratio of

S. H. LANGER AND R. J. SHEEHAN

306

the size contribution to the activity coefficient at $m > 1$ is the ratio of the molar volumes of the two solutes.

At $m < 1$ the effect of the size difference would be predicted to be reversed, but the problem of stationary phase volatility prevents its use in most cases. One might attempt to use this effect to assist a separation in some exceptional situations such as with the relatively polar dimethylformamide.

TABLE VI

Effect of Solute Size Difference

Solutes	Stationary phases, °C		γ_A/γ_B experimental[a]	$\gamma_{a,A}/\gamma_{a,B}$ calculated
2-Methylhexane(A)	Hexadecane, C_{16}	22	1.039	1.007
3-Methylhexane(B)	Squalane, C_{30}	20	1.041	1.009
Molar volume ratio 1.012	Difference		0.002	0.002
2-Methylpentane(A)	Hexadecane	22	1.036	1.008
3-Methylpentane(B)	Squalane	22	1.045	1.012
Molar volume ratio 1.016	Difference		0.009	0.004
2,4-Dimethylpentane(A)	Hexadecane	22	1.068	1.016
2,3-Dimethylpentane(B)	Squalane	20	1.077	1.025
Molar volume ratio 1.033	Difference		0.009	0.009

[a] Experimental values based on data from Lewis (99).

The data of Table VI tend to support the arguments above on the effect of size. The stationary phases and solutes are saturated hydrocarbons so that solution forces are of equal and similar nature. There is a variety of solution interactions involved, and size effects do not predict the ratio of activity coefficients for the closely similar isomeric solutes in the solvent hydrocarbons. However, because of the similarity of the C_{30} squalane stationary phase to the C_{16} hydrocarbon, differences in the ratio of the activity coefficients for the solutes in the two phases should be due to differences in size alone. It can be seen that this is approximately true and that the size effect reinforces the separation effect in going to the higher molecular weight solvent. Admittedly, the effects are small and we are using the data at the limits of credibility. However, the data indicate the nature of the trend and justify the consideration of effects due to differences in size. The difference in activity coefficient ratio increases as the molar volume ratio of the solutes deviates from unity, indicating that the effect becomes of increasing importance as solute molar volume ratios increase.

In the study of solute–solvent interactions, it is often of interest to attempt to evaluate the effect of systematically varying substituents on the solute structure (32,33). For example, an attempt might be made to correlate the logarithm of the measured activity coefficient (or retention volume) of a solute containing a benzene ring with the substituent on the ring. This could be a correlation with a Hammett substituent constant or one derived from a similar type of linear free energy relationship. The effect should be basically on the thermal portion of the activity coefficient, γ_t^∞, where

$$\gamma^\infty = \gamma_t^\infty \gamma_a^\infty \tag{10}$$

Equation (10) follows from eqs. (2), (4), (5), and (9), and is discussed in greater detail elsewhere (14,31,50,56).

For gas chromatographic solute–solvent interactions, it should be remembered that, with smaller solutes, substituents may materially alter molar volumes as well as electron distribution. (For example, this would be true in the series: benzene, fluorobenzene, chlorobenzene, bromobenzene, iodobenzene.) As a first approximation, γ_t^∞ may be calculated from the measured activity coefficient, γ^∞, eq. (10), and eq. (9). At small values of $m(<10)$, γ_a^∞ may be obtained directly from the plot of Figure 1. Other methods of calculating size correction might also be used. It would appear (and is our experience) that it is γ_t^∞ which would be best correlated with a substituent constant. Of course, with larger molecules the molar volume effect of a single substituent would be minor, and it is reasonable to correlate directly with the measured activity coefficient.

VIII. LIQUID CRYSTALS

It is appealing to attempt to utilize other entropy effects in addition to size to enhance the separation factor represented in eq. (6). The most obvious approach is to utilize an oriented liquid phase such as a liquid crystalline material as a stationary phase. Fortunately, some liquid crystals already have been investigated as liquid phases and there is some benefit from reviewing the results (58–63). The properties of these materials are described in the foregoing references, by Gray (64), and others (65). Generally, these compounds initially melt to give oriented mesophases which may be smectic, nematic, or cholesteric; these crystalline phases lose orientation at a transition temperature to give isotropic liquids. A single compound may exist in one or all of the mesocrystalline forms before assuming a conventional organic liquid form.

Smectic phases possess two-dimensional orientation in which rod-like molecules are arranged in parallel to give a structure with layers having a thickness approximately the length of the molecules comprising the layer. In the nematic phase, parallel orientation is maintained, but layered structure does not exist and liquid molecules are free to move within the limits of parallel configuration. The cholesteric transition phase is one exhibited by cholesteryl derivatives and similar compounds in which some molecular rotation is permitted in the plane of each layer in a layered two-dimensional structure.

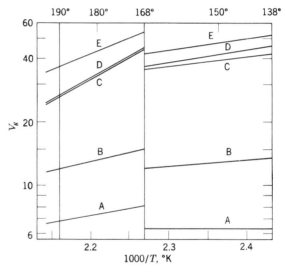

Fig. 3. Specific retention volumes of hydrocarbons as a function of temperature in the liquid crystal p,p'-azoxyphenetole. (A) cyclohexane, (B) benzene, (C) m-xylene, (D) p-xylene, (E) o-xylene.

Gas chromatographic investigations of liquid crystals have been carried out for isomers of a variety of compounds, including aliphatic and aromatic hydrocarbons, halogenated hydrocarbons, phenols, etc. (58–63). All phases show special selective features, and any discussion of individual features is complex and specialized. However, much of the nature of the action of mesophases can be illustrated again by reference to the m-/p-xylene separation and other data as reported by Kelker (58) and illustrated in Figure 3 for p,p'-azoxyphenetole (1). The data are reported in terms of V_g, but could be transformed to activity coefficients by use of eq. (1a) and vapor-pressure data. Most of the results are in agreement with the principles discussed earlier.

$$C_2H_5O-\langle \ \rangle-N{=}NO-\langle \ \rangle-OC_2H_5$$

(1)

The data of Figure 3 cover the range of 138°C (initial melting point) through the nematic phase region to 168°, where the change to an isotropic liquid takes place, and somewhat higher to 185°. For each of the compounds studied, including cyclohexane, toluene, and *meta*-, *para*-, and *ortho*-xylenes, there is a uniform decrease in retention volume to the nematic → liquid transition temperature. At the transition temperature of 168° there is an abrupt increase in retention volume and solubility (despite the fact that solute vapor pressure continues to increase and retention volume would decrease if activity coefficient were constant). Some of this undoubtedly corresponds to an increase in entropy of solution consistent with formation of a complex, less-ordered phase capable of a variety of interactions. The decrease in liquid phase orientation would result in a loss of local molecular selectivity and therefore afford a greater volume of solvent stationary phase wherein solubility can take place. If the volumes available for the solute were of equivalent energy, the entropy difference, ΔS, would be approximated by

$$\Delta S = R \ln (V_i/V_n) \qquad (11)$$

where V_i is the volume available for solute in the isotropic phase and V_n is the volume available for solute in the nematic phase.

At the nematic → liquid transition temperature, activity coefficients for the aromatic compounds are decreased about 25%. The change in ΔH_e^{∞} is about 3 kcal less positive and ΔS_e^{∞} about 7 or 8 eu more positive. For both nematic and isotropic phases the net heat is positive. The most striking feature is the loss of selectivity for the *m*-/*p*-xylene separation at the nematic–liquid transition temperature. Below this temperature, the selective interaction causes *p*-xylene to be held selectively in the column despite a vapor pressure higher than *m*-xylene. The interaction apparently is similar to that described for the tetrahalophthalates (24,25) earlier in this chapter. The mesophase here, then, has some of the characteristics already deduced for a selective phase; a selective interaction (with a definite entropy requirement) accompanied by nonsolubilizing interactions so that net heat is positive and activity coefficient is relatively high. (For the xylenes, γ^∞ is in the range of 2.5–3.) The relatively nonselective isotropic liquid phase is characterized by higher solute solubility and general interaction and lower entropy requirements. One approach to improving selectivity in the liquid crystal, then, is to attempt to reinforce the selective interaction (as yet, not specifically identified) while maintaining the ordered nonsolubilizing appended liquid crystal structure.

IX. SILICONES AND SILICON CHEMISTRY

Silicones frequently are used as liquid phases because they are the most common and notable class of high temperature-stable organic liquids. Their effective utilization is complicated by the fact that, as commercial materials from several sources, little is known specifically about their exact composition and molecular weight. Furthermore, silicones are generally utilized at low loading for samples of low volatility so that surface effects from the solid support may make the solute-stationary phase interaction more complex. Some time ago, we showed that many surface adsorption effects could be virtually eliminated by treatment of the silica type supports with hexamethyldisilazane (2) (66). Others (67,68,69) have used dimethyldichlorosilane (3). The sequence of reactions for both treatments is represented opposite.

The essence of both treatments is the removal of hydrogen bonding —OH groups from the surface as well as any residual water. These groups hydrogen bond to ketones, aromatics, and apparently even interact with cyclohexane as judged by tailing (66). Stronger interactions and tailing occur with alcohols. Experimentally, it appears that with proper pretreatment and organosilicon treatment many surface interaction complications involving the surface hydrogen can be eliminated. Nevertheless, our experience with alcohols (unpublished) and that of others indicates some hydrogen bonding to the organosilicon surface still occurs with some alcohols and polyhydroxy compounds. This is due to bonding to the $Si—O—Si(CH_3)_3$ surface bond in 4 and 5 and possibly the $Si—O—C$ bond in 5.

The tendency to hydrogen bond to $Si—O$ linkages is indicated somewhat by the data of Table VII taken from the work of West and his collaborators (70). The frequency shift for phenol upon hydrogen bonding to various bases is shown in Table VII. This shift is an indication of the proton base strength of the oxygen in the listed compounds

$$\underset{(2)}{\overset{\displaystyle \begin{matrix} H & H \\ O & O \\ | & | \end{matrix}}{-O-Si-O-Si-O-}} + (CH_3)_3SiNHSi(CH_3)_3 \rightarrow \underset{(4)}{\overset{\displaystyle \begin{matrix} CH_3 & CH_3 \\ H_3CSiCH_3 & H_3CSiCH_3 \\ O & O \\ | & | \end{matrix}}{-Si-O-Si-}} + NH_3 \quad (12)$$

$$\underset{(3)}{\overset{\displaystyle \begin{matrix} H & H \\ O & O \\ | & | \end{matrix}}{-O-Si-O-Si-O-}} + (CH_3)_2SiCl_2 \rightarrow \underset{}{\overset{\displaystyle \begin{matrix} CH_3 \quad CH_3 \\ \diagdown \diagup \\ Si \\ \diagup \diagdown \\ O \quad O \\ | \quad\quad | \end{matrix}}{-Si-O-Si-}} + HCl \quad (13)$$

$$\searrow \text{or} \\ + CH_3OH$$

$$\underset{(5)}{\overset{\displaystyle \begin{matrix} CH_3 & CH_3 \\ H_3CSiOCH_3 & H_3CSiOCH_3 \\ O & O \\ | & | \end{matrix}}{-Si-O-Si-}} \quad (13a)$$

TABLE VII
IR Frequency Shift of Phenol Hydroxyl Band Upon Hydrogen Bonding

Base	$\Delta\nu$, cm^{-1}
Me$_3$SiOEt	271
Me$_3$COEt	300
Me$_2$Si(OEt)$_2$	257
Me$_2$C(OEt)$_2$	256
(Me)$_3$SiOSi(Me)$_3$	168
Polysiloxanes	130–150
Ethers and polyethers	250–300

(71). There is some loss in base strength (electron availability) due to $d_\pi - p_\pi$ bonding in silicon–oxygen compounds as shown:

$$[R_3Si-\overset{..}{\underset{..}{O}}- \longleftrightarrow R_3Si=\overset{..}{O}-] \quad (14)$$

However, it is to be noted that some base strength is apparently retained, and this may be greater for an oxygen bridge between an organosilicon atom and a silicon atom attached to three oxygens (as on the surface). Much of the surface interaction effect may be masked by using larger amounts of polar type stationary phases which themselves interact at the support surface. Except where specifically invoked, surface interactions should be minimized because they sometimes cause decomposition or isomerization of sensitive organic materials.

Since silica (untreated) is often used to fill silicone greases, it is reasonable that it should be removed where these greases are to be used as stationary phases, particularly for solutes which can participate in hydrogen bonding (72).

Hydroxyl isomers can exist in either an unhindered axial or equatorial conformation (as on a cyclohexane ring or a similar fused structure). Often, such a conformation may be used to advantage for separation with a hydrogen bonding solvent since the unhindered equatorial hydroxyl group will have the strongest tendency to hydrogen bond and would be expected to increase retention time to an extent greater than would result from an axial hydroxyl group. Hindrance at a site adjacent to a hydroxyl group, as with o-cresol, interferes with hydrogen bonding and solvent interaction. This is discussed in a general manner for steroids by Bush (73), but generally o-isomers present no separation problem because steric interference detracts from or prevents a specific interaction with stationary phases.

While specific knowledge of the composition of common silicone liquid phases is not generally available, they have been characterized in general terms. Since this information could be of help in choosing a silicone liquid phase, we have presented as much of it as possible (to the extent of our knowledge) in Table VIII.

Some of the information of Table VIII may be in error. In order to gain some insight into the mode of functioning of specific stationary phases in anticipation of gathering new experimental information, it should help to briefly survey industrial silicone practice (74,75).

The dimethyl polysiloxanes have the lowest intermolecular attraction, high compressibility, and low heats of fusion. Phenyl groups are added to improve oxidation stability, lubricating properties, and, sometimes, to lower freezing points. There may be a very small proportion of trifunctional methyl-Si$\equiv$O$_3\equiv$ in some silicone fluids to increase chain-branching and lower melting points and viscosities. Phenyl silicone fluids are among the most heat resistant. Chlorophenyl groups improve lubricity and also apparently induce some dipole interaction between chains (76). Cyanoalkyl groups and fluorinated alkyl groups in minor amounts impart better low-temperature properties to silicone rubbers, while in larger amounts they improve resistance to solvents. Fluorosilicone rubber resists fuels, oils, and hydraulic fluids as well as aliphatic, aromatic, and chlorinated nonpolar solvents; cyanoalkyl rubbers have similar resistance to fuels and oils.

Gums are frequently high molecular weight linear polysiloxanes; dimethylsiloxanes may be modified or cross-linked by treatment with peroxides. Vinyl groups are also incorporated for ease of cross-linking via peroxide treatment.

Dimethylsilicones can generally be regarded as liquids with low solubility parameters, little tendency for specific interaction, and hard in the Pearson classification. SE-30 gum, a popular phase, is evidently a very high molecular weight material. It can be used for simulated distillation of hydrocarbons because the lack of selectivity gives elution properties which can be compared to the distillation process (77). As expected from solubility parameter considerations, aromatics are eluted somewhat sooner than aliphatics with comparable boiling points. Nonspecific sensitivity to functional groups and high temperature stability make the SE-30 phase useful for general steroid separation. However, both cholesteryl methyl ether and cholestanyl methyl ether have retention volumes of about 0.9 relative to the retention volumes of parent cholesterol and cholestanol (78), despite the higher molecular

TABLE VIII

Silicone Stationary Phases

Commercial designation [a]	Composition
DC 200, GE SF-96, UC L-45	Polydimethylsiloxane fluids
DC 550	Phenylmethyl polysiloxane fluid
DC 710	Polyphenyl polysiloxane fluid
GE Versilube F-50	Chlorophenylmethyl polysiloxane fluids
GE 560, formerly F-60	
GE XF-1105, XF-1150	5 and 50% cyanoethylmethyl polysiloxane fluids, respectively
DC QF-1 (FS-1256)	Trifluoropropylmethyl polysiloxane fluid
GE SE-30, JXR	Dimethyl polysiloxane gums
GE SE-31, GE SE-33	Methyl vinyl polysiloxane gums
UC W-98, UC W-96	
GE SE-52	Methylphenyl polysiloxane gum
GE SE-54	Methylphenyl vinyl polysiloxane gum
GE XE-60	Cyanoethylmethyl and dimethyl polysiloxane gum
DC LSX-3-0295	Trifluoropropylmethyl and vinyl polysiloxane gum
DC-11 (Hi Vac)	Silica-filled methyl polysiloxane grease

[a] DC, Dow Corning; UC, Union Carbide; GE, General Electric

weight of the former. (The latter have approximately equal retention volumes.) This might be attributed to either a molar volume effect, discussed earlier, or a slight amount of hydrogen bonding by the parent sterols; most likely, the major part of this effect is a result of the higher vapor pressure of the pure ethers. Janak and Komers find the phenols to be eluted from a polydimethylsilicone phase in the order of boiling point with the lowest boiling compound emerging first (79).

While silicones are frequently used in combination with acids and bases under a variety of conditions, more caution in their use under these conditions is necessary. Strong acids and bases are used in the equilibration process to rupture $\equiv$Si—O—Si$\equiv$ bonds. Treatment of these materials with some of the stronger volatile acids at elevated temperatures could result in the loss of portions of the lower molecular-weight silicones. Phenyl–silicon bonds are also susceptible to cleavage with hydrochloric acid to give benzene and a silicon–chlorine bond.

Substitution of phenyl groups into methyl silicones would be expected to increase the solubility parameter to something approaching that of benzene. A value of 9.0 is reported for phenylmethyl silicones (46,47). Phenylmethylpolysiloxanes also would be expected to be more polarizable than the dimethyl compounds, and to have some of the solvating properties of a benzenelike solvent without the accompanying volatility. Furthermore, there is the possibility of weak hydrogen bonding to the π electrons of the phenyl ring (80,81). Thus, DC 550 would be expected to be a good general-purpose stationary phase for a variety of compounds, including phenols and natural oils (82–84), but not very specific or sensitive to functional groups. Diphenyl silicones would be expected to be of more aromatic nature, tending to reject aliphatic hydrocarbons and separating aromatic compounds by boiling point. The diphenylsiloxanes might be moderately selective in terms of groups which might or might not interact with the benzene π electrons.

The incorporation of a chlorophenyl group into silicone polymers as in F60 would be expected to yield a high-temperature stationary phase with solvent properties resembling those of chlorobenzene. The presence of a slight dipole is also evident from electrical properties (76). Only moderate to slight selectivity to functional groups might be expected here. However, interaction between methylene groups adjacent to an ester group and chlorobenzene has been reported and studied (85).

Crosslinking (to a slight degree) might be expected to decrease solubility without affecting selectivity greatly. Where interactions are involved, the decrease in overall solute solubility and decrease in retention time would permit operation at a low temperature; as we already have seen, this would be advantageous.

In view of the small intermolecular attraction in pure fluorocarbons (53,54), it does not seem probable that the incorporation of a trifluoropropyl group into a methyl polysiloxane, as in QF-1, produces a "polar" stationary phase in the sense of inducing a large dipole moment. The adjacent methylene group might be polarized somewhat by the strong electronegative trifluoromethyl group so that some positive charge is induced there. However, the localized effect should be to add a group which has a positive heat of interaction with hydrocarbon groups and thus tend to decrease the solubility of this type of compound in a manner similar to that described earlier; this correlates with the oil resistance of the related elastomer. However, at the same time the silicone becomes more heterogeneous and perhaps somewhat segregated on a molecular scale (trifluoropropyl groups tending to cluster), a greater variety of specific interactions with a relatively poor solvent would be possible; this presents a desirable solvent atmosphere for selectivity, especially to group variation.

Evidently, the QF-1 solvent has an unusual affinity for the $C=O$ group. Some evidence for this comes from the swelling data for a similar rubber (Dow Corning LS-53), in volume percent; isooctane: $+15$; xylenes: $+19$; carbon tetrachloride: $+21$; ethyl alcohol: $+5$; and acetone: $+180\%$. The results of Ziebinski and Fishbein (86) for substituted 3,4-methylenedioxyphenyl (6) compounds on QF-1 illustrate functional effects more specifically:

(6)

R=	Relative retention volume
H	0.081
$CH_2CH_2CH_3$	0.31
$CH_2CH=CH_2$	0.29
$CH=C-CH_3$	0.55
CHO	1.00
CCH_3 $\parallel$ O	1.7
OH	0.54
COOH	1.7
$CH_2CH(CH_3)\overset{\displaystyle O}{\overset{\parallel}{S}}C_8H_{17}$	0.53

The cyanoethyl methyl silicones would be expected to have definite polar properties similar to propionitrile derivatives discussed earlier. The oil resistance is probably a result of a "squeezing out" process due to strong interaction between the cyano groups. This strong dipolar group would interact selectively, depending on the dipole moment and polarizability of materials being separated on the column. Hydrocarbon solutes of the aliphatic type would have little solubility in the liquid phase. However, polarizable aromatics would be held selectively. Tenney's results (39) on nitriles would suggest strong retention of ketones, alcohols, and esters and rapid elution of ethers and olefins. In comparing the nitrile-substituted silicones with the trifluoropropyl silicones, the relatively high value of the cohesive energy density for aliphatic nitriles relative to the low value of δ for fluorocarbons should be noted. The properties of these materials as stationary phases are generally consistent with their cohesive energy density and specific polar interaction tendencies.

For interesting and more quantitative studies on the dimerization of nitrile groups and the consequent effect on gas chromatographic solute–solvent interactions, the work of Saum (87) and Genkin, et al. (88) should be consulted. Of course, in silicone polymers, cyano dipole-pair bonding would result in some crosslinking effects.

X. THE CHOICE OF DERIVATIVES AND STATIONARY PHASE

The advent of gas chromatography has shifted considerable analytical interest in derivatives from the solid crystalline materials of classical organic chemistry to more rapidly eluted low melting type compounds (16,17). While volatile derivatives such as trimethylsilyl ethers previously were recognized as being of obvious utility for separation and identification purposes (89,90,91), it has been the range of available interactions with different stationary phases which has made them most useful. Because the choice of liquid derivative and liquid phase is frequently interrelated (and much of the foregoing material is relevant), some discussion here seems appropriate.

Liquid derivatives are used with gas chromatography as an aid in separation and identification, and because through "derivatization" an unstable or nonvolatile material may be made volatile. Unfortunately, it is not always appreciated that derivative formation is effective from the viewpoint of eq. (1) for two reasons: solute–liquid phase interaction, or

γ^∞, is altered; and the vapor pressure, p°, or vapor pressure ratio of solutes is changed. In addition, derivative formation may be used to avoid solid support–solute interaction, to prepare a more stable molecule than the parent compound in the vapor phase, and for "peak shift" identification (17,18,91,92). However, it is the first two effects

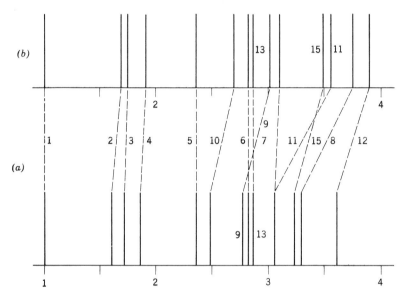

Fig. 4. Relative retention volumes of trimethylsilyl ethers in a nonselective (a) (DC Silicone 550) and (b) a selective (di-n-butyl tetrachlorophthalate) stationary phase. (1) Phenol (relative retention volume = 1); (2) o-cresol; (3) m-cresol; (4) p-cresol; (5) o-ethylphenol; (6) m-ethylphenol; (7) p-ethylphenol; (8) 2,3-dimethylphenol; (9) 2,4-dimethylphenol; (10) 2,5-dimethylphenol; (11) 2,6-dimethylphenol; (12) 3,4-dimethylphenol; (13) 3,5-dimethylphenol; (15) 1-hydroxy-2-methoxybenzene.

which are pertinent here. Since vapor pressures of pure parent compounds as well as of the derivatives are frequently unknown, derivative formation and choice has often been an art, and success is attributed to a change in volatility.

Some of the potential of derivative formation can be illustrated by reference to the problem of phenol separations and the skeletal chromatograms of Figure 4. While m-cresol (bp 202.8°) and p-cresol (bp 202.5°) can be separated on a phosphate ester (93), their separation on most other phases is virtually impossible. This is also true for DC Silicone 550;

it can be concluded that the same or similar molecular interactions to those which give these cresols virtually identical boiling points also operate with the phenylmethyl silicone liquid to give closely similar retention volumes. The major nonselective solubilizing interaction appears to be hydrogen bonding, which has been discussed earlier in connection with silicones. Conversion of the phenols to trimethylsilyl ether derivatives, $(CH_3)_3Si$—OR, eliminates the possibility of hydrogen bonding and makes separation possible (16). A skeletal chromatogram of the separation on DC 550 is shown in Figure 4a. DC Silicone 550 is not selective here and the trimethylsilyl ethers of the cresols are eluted at 125°C in the order of vapor pressure and boiling point: o-derivative 195°, m- 197°, and p- 199°. The conversion in this instance essentially produces a change in the ratio of $p°$ values of the m- and p-isomers.

Conversion to trimethylsilyl ethers of the phenols still produces a complication in that the trimethylsilyl derivatives of 2,4-dimethyl-, m-ethyl-, and 3,5-dimethyl-phenol are eluted over a narrow time range. The relative elution time of the 2,4-dimethylphenyl trimethylsilyl ether can be shifted considerably and helpfully by using the solvent di-n-butyl tetrachlorophthalate which acts selectively through "charge transfer" interaction as illustrated in Figure 4b. The relative retention volumes of the 2,6- and 2,3-dimethylphenol derivatives are also greatly changed. The tetrachlorophthalate solvent is not particularly effective in separating the parent phenols. In terms of eq. (6), this is presumably so because the strong nonselective hydrogen bonding interactions with the solvent override the weaker selective charge-transfer interaction and associated effects. Thus, conversion to derivatives may help to eliminate nonspecific interactions, and may enable one to produce large changes in activity coefficient ratios of derivatives through selective interaction with the stationary phase.

The suggestions put forth earlier still hold, and exploration of phases very different from selected derivatives would seem appropriate. Thus, fluoro- and cyano-substituted compounds, especially silicones, would seem useful for hydrocarbon type derivatives, and hydrocarbon-type liquid phases would seem useful for trifluoroacetoxy derivatives (94). Shulgin's successful use of trifluoroacetoxy derivatives of phenols with a liquid phase consisting mainly of DC Silicone 710 would support this type of argument (95).

The separation of diastereoisomers by gas chromatography is notable (96–98) and serves to illustrate and further support the suggestion above. For acetylated diastereoisomeric esters of lactic acid

(7), separation factors from stationary phases are in the following order—squalane < polypropylene glycol < DC Silicone 710 < 1,2,3-tris(2 cyanoethoxy)-propane. While exact vapor pressure values are not known, they do differ for the isomeric pairs, with the D-s-alcohol D-lactic acid esters (or the L-L isomers) having lower vapor pressures than the mixed D-L esters. Specifically interacting liquid phases can enhance the vapor pressure difference.

$$\underset{\text{(7)}}{\overset{\displaystyle \text{CH}_3\text{C}\!-\!\text{O}\!-\!\underset{\underset{\text{CH}_3}{|}}{\text{C}}\!-\!\overset{\overset{\text{O}}{\|}}{\text{C}}\!-\!\underset{\underset{\text{CH}_3}{|}}{\text{OC}}\!-\!\text{R}}{}}$$

Gil-Av and co-workers (96,97) and Rose, Stern, and Karger (98) find enhanced separation with increase in size of R (methyl → ethyl → propyl, etc.) in compounds such as 7. This apparently is a concerted vapor pressure and activity coefficient effect. Important here is the fact that an appended group in the derivative does assist in the separation. Furthermore, such an appended group in a derivative can facilitate separation via the created difference between vapor pressures of stereo-isomeric compounds even without a selective stationary phase.

The choice of derivative should be guided by the liquid phases available, and selection of a derivative which has a chemical character considerably different from at least one available solvent would seem appropriate. It might be expected that retention volumes would be shortened, permitting lower temperature operation with the advantages this may afford, and selective interactions might be more effective in a stationary phase in which the activity coefficient of the solute tends to be high.

XI. CONCLUSION

Simple solution theory and our present knowledge of molecular interactions allow the construction of a qualitative "model" for choosing and designing selective gas chromatographic liquid phases to separate close boiling isomers and similar mixtures. While many relevant parameters are unknown, and there is a need for better theory, the approach is indicated. In addition to rules previously set forth, the following generally seem to apply.

1. Desirable features are high molar concentration of selectively interacting groups, minimal concentration of groups which interact counter to the desired separation, and minimal concentration of solvating nonselective interacting groups to allow low-temperature operation.

2. A single strong selective interaction is preferred. Under some conditions, inclusion of groups which contribute positive heats of solution or negative entropies will make possible a practical separation. Thus, a stationary phase of different chemical nature from solutes should be seriously considered.

3. The molar volume of the stationary phase may differentially affect the activity coefficient of isomers or closely similar compounds. Under these conditions, the molecular weight of the stationary phase should be selected to reinforce the desired interaction.

The general classification of stationary phases as polar or nonpolar often can be eliminated in favor of more specific designations in terms of group interactions, solvent properties, and sometimes the thermodynamics of interaction. All of these assist in choosing and designing selective stationary phases. Specific molecular interactions should also be considered. Complications may result from the relationship between excess enthalpies and entropies of interaction.

Liquid crystal mesophases sometimes meet the general criteria developed for selective liquid phases. Appreciable selectivity in these phases seem to be associated with specific relatively strong interactions.

The interaction of silicones with solutes may be considered using the concepts developed here and knowledge of the general chemistry of these unique materials. Their high temperature stability makes them desirable stationary phases, and they are available with properties and compositions which give a range of selectivity.

Derivative formation may ease the separation of related compounds by altering relative vapor pressures, by eliminating dominant undesired interactions, or by allowing the utilization of favorable solution interactions. However, available stationary phases should influence the choice of derivative.

Finally, it should be recognized that refinement and improvement of our understanding of the action of liquid phases should permit the eventual synthesis of some materials which can interact to mimic naturally occurring and physiologically important interactions. Under such conditions, gas chromatographic action might be used to screen large numbers of volatile compounds for physiological activity, e.g., carcinogenic hydrocarbons.

References

1. A. T. James, *Research* (*London*), **8**, 8 (1955).
2. A. T. James and A. J. P. Martin, *J. Appl. Chem.* (*London*), **6**, 105 (1956).
3. A. T. James, A. J. P. Martin, and G. H. Smith, *Biochem. J.*, **52**, 238 (1952).
4. A. T. James, *Biochem. J.*, **52**, 252 (1952).
5. A. T. James and A. J. P. Martin, *Biochem. J.*, **50**, 679 (1952).
6. A. T. James and A. J. P. Martin, *Analyst*, **77**, 915 (1952).
7. A. I. M. Keulemans, *Gas Chromatography*, 2nd ed., Reinhold, New York, 1959.
8. S. Dal Nogare and R. S. Juvet, *Gas Chromatography*, Interscience, New York, 1962.
9. A. B. Littlewood, *Gas Chromatography*, Academic Press, New York, 1962.
10. H. Purnell, *Gas Chromatography*, Interscience, New York, 1962.
11. A. B. Littlewood, C. S. G. Phillips, and D. T. Price, *J. Chem. Soc.*, **1955**, 1480.
12. M. R. Hoare and J. H. Purnell, *Trans. Faraday Soc.*, **52**, 222 (1956).
13. P. E. Porter, C. H. Deal, and F. Stross, *J. Am. Chem. Soc.*, **78**, 2999 (1956).
14. S. H. Langer and J. H. Purnell, *J. Phys. Chem.*, **67**, 263 (1963).
15. S. H. Langer, S. Connell, and I. Wender, *J. Org. Chem.*, **23**, 50 (1958).
16. S. H. Langer, P. Pantages, and I. Wender, *Chem. Ind.* (*London*), **1958**, 1664.
17. S. H. Langer and P. Pantages, *Nature*, **191**, 141 (1961).
18. M. W. Anders and G. J. Mannering, *Anal. Chem.*, **34**, 730 (1962).
19. J. H. Hildebrand and R. L. Scott, *The Solubility of Nonelectrolytes*, Reinhold, New York, 1950.
20. A. I. M. Keulemans, A. Kwantes, and P. Zaal, *Anal. Chim. Acta*, **13**, 357 (1956).
21. B. W. Bradford, D. Harvey, and D. E. Chalkley, *J. Inst. Petrol*, **41**, 80 (1955).
22. E. Gil-Av, J. Herling, and J. Shabtai, *Chem. Ind.* (*London*), **45**, 1483 (1957).
23. R. J. Cvetanović, F. J. Duncan, W. E. Falconer, and R. S. Irwin, *J. Am. Chem. Soc.*, **87**, 1927 (1965).
24. S. H. Langer, C. Zahn, and G. Pantazopolos, *Chem. Ind.* (*London*), **1958**, 1145.
25. S. H. Langer, C. Zahn, and G. Pantazopolos, *J. Chromatog.*, **3**, 154 (1960).
26. R. G. Pearson, *Science*, **151**, 172 (1966).
27. R. G. Pearson and J. Songstad, *J. Am. Chem. Soc.*, **89**, 1827 (1967).
28. R. E. Burks, Jr., E. B. Baker, P. Clark, J. Esslinger, and J. C. Lacey, Jr., *J. Agr. Food Chem.*, **7**, 778 (1959).
29. E. Gil-Av and Y. Herzberg-Minzly, *J. Am. Chem. Soc.*, **81**, 4749 (1959).
30. H. P. Burchfield and E. E. Storrs, *Biochemical Applications of Gas Chromatography*, Academic Press, New York, 1962.
31. S. H. Langer and H. Purnell, *J. Phys. Chem.*, **70**, 904 (1966).
32. G. J. Pierotti, C. H. Deal, E. L. Derr, and P. E. Porter, *J. Am. Chem. Soc.*, **78**, 2989 (1956).
33. L. R. Snyder, *J. Phys. Chem.*, **65**, 247 (1961).
34. E. A. Molwyn-Hughes, *Physical Chemistry*, Pergamon, London, 1961, p. 702.
35. J. N. Bronsted and J. Koefoed, *Kgl. Danske Videnskab. Selskab, Biol. Medd.*, **22**, 1 (1946).
36. R. P. Bell, *Trans. Faraday Soc.*, **33**, 496 (1937).
37. R. L. Martin, *Anal. Chem.*, **33**, 347 (1961); **35**, 116 (1963).

38. D. E. Martire, R. L. Pecsok, and J. H. Purnell, *Nature*, **203**, 1279 (1964).
39. H. M. Tenney, *Anal. Chem.*, **30**, 2 (1958).
40. A. B. Littlewood, *Anal. Chem.*, **38**, 1076 (1966).
41. A. B. Littlewood, *J. Gas Chromatog.*, **1**, No. 5, 6 (1963).
42. K. S. Pitzer, *Advances in Chemical Physics*, Vol. 2, 1. Prigogine, Ed., Interscience, Wiley, 1959, 59.
43. E. Gluekauf, *Trans. Faraday Soc.*, **51**, 34 (1955).
44. P. A. Small, *J. Appl. Chem.*, **3**, 71 (1953).
45. H. Burrell, *Offic. Dig.*, **1955**, 726.
46. J. L. Gardon, *J. Paint Tech.*, **38**, 43 (1966).
47. J. L. Gardon, in *Encyclopedia of Polymer Science and Technology*, H. F. Mark, N. G. Gaylord, and N. Bikales, Eds., Interscience, New York, 1966, pp. 833–862.
48. H. Tompa, *Polymer Solutions*, Butterworths, London, 1956, pp. 56–122.
49. W. Gordy, *J. Chem. Phys.*, **8**, 170 (1940); **9**, 204 (1941).
50. D. E. Martire, in *Fourth International Symposium on Gas Chromatography*, L. Fowler, Ed., Academic Press, New York, 1963, pp. 33–54.
51. Ref. 19, p. 133.
52. H. G. Drickamer, G. G. Brown, and R. R. White, *Trans. Am. Inst. Chem. Engrs.*, **41**, 555 (1945).
53. T. M. Reed III, *J. Phys. Chem.*, **59**, 425 (1955); **63**, 1798 (1959).
54. T. M. Reed III, in *Fluorine Chemistry*, Vol. 5, J. H. Simon, Ed., Academic Press, New York, 1964, pp. 197–218.
55. J. A. V. Butler, *Trans. Faraday Soc.*, **33**, 171, 229 (1937).
56. D. H. Everett and C. T. H. Stoddard, *Trans. Faraday Soc.*, **57**, 746 (1961).
57. R. K. Clark and H. H. Schmidt, *J. Phys. Chem.*, **69**, 3682 (1965).
58. H. Kelker, *Z. Anal. Chem.*, **198**, 254 (1963).
59. H. Kelker, *Ber. Bunsenges. Physik. Chem.*, **67**, 698 (1963).
60. H. Kelker and H. Winterscheidt, *Z. Anal. Chem.*, **220**, 1 (1966).
61. M. J. S. Dewar and J. P. Schroeder, *J. Am. Chem. Soc.*, **86**, 5235 (1964).
62. M. J. S. Dewar and J. P. Schroeder, *J. Org. Chem.*, **30**, 3485 (1965).
63. E. M. Barrall, R. S. Porter, and J. E. Johnson, *J. Chromatog.*, **21**, 392 (1966).
64. G. W. Gray, *Molecular Structure and the Properties of Liquid Crystals*, Academic Press, New York, 1962.
65. G. H. Brown and W. G. Shaw, *Chem. Rev.*, **57**, 1049 (1957).
66. J. Bohemen, S. H. Langer, R. H. Perrett, and J. H. Purnell, *J. Chem. Soc.*, **1960**, 2444.
67. A. Kwantes and G. W. A. Rijnders, in *Gas Chromatography 1958*, D. H. Desty, Ed., Butterworths, London, 1958, pp. 125–135.
68. E. C. Horning, E. A. Moscatelli, and C. C. Sweeley, *Chem. Ind. (London)*, **1959**, 751.
69. W. R. Supina, R. S. Henly, and R. F. Kruppa, *J. Am. Oil Chemists' Soc.*, **43**, 202A (1966).
70. R. H. Baney, K. J. Lake, R. West, and L. S. Whatley, *Chem. Ind. (London)*, **1959**, 1129.
71. R. F. Badger, *J. Chem. Phys.*, **8**, 288 (1940).
72. J. Nelson and A. Milun, *Chem. Ind. (London)*, **1960**, 663.

73. I. E. Bush, *The Chromatography of Steroids*, Pergamon, Oxford, 1961, pp. 117–131.
74. C. Eaborn, *Organosilicon Compounds*, Butterworths, London, 1960, pp. 454–477.
75. G. G. Freeman, *Silicones*, Iliffe, London, 1962.
76. K. A. Andrianov, *Metalorganic Polymers*, Interscience, New York, 1964, ch. II.
77. L. E. Green, L. J. Schmauch, and J. C. Worman, *Anal. Chem.*, **36**, 1512 (1964).
78. W. J. A. VandenHeuvel, C. C. Sweeley, and E. C. Horning, *J. Am. Chem. Soc.*, **82**, 3481 (1960).
79. J. Janak and R. Komers, in *Gas Chromatography 1958*, D. H. Desty, Ed., Butterworths, London, 1958.
80. S. Wada, *Bull. Chem. Soc. Japan*, **35**, 707 (1962).
81. Z. Yoshida and E. Osawa, *J. Am. Chem. Soc.*, **88**, 4019 (1966).
82. A. Liberti, *Ann. Chim.* (*Rome*), **48**, 40 (1958).
83. Y. R. Naves, *J. Soc. Cosmetic Chemists*, **9**, No. 2, 101 (1958).
84. K. J. Bombaugh, *Anal. Chem.*, **33**, 29 (1961).
85. C. H. Giles and S. N. Nakhwa, *J. Appl. Chem.*, **11**, 197 (1966).
86. W. L. Zielinski, Jr., and L. Fishbein, *Anal. Chem.*, **38**, 41 (1966).
87. A. M. Saum, *J. Polymer Sci.*, **42**, 57 (1960).
88. A. N. Genkin, B. I. Boguslavskaya, L. S. Bresler, and M. S. Nemtsov, *Dokl. Akad. Nauk SSSR* (*English Transl.*), **164**, 1089 (1965).
89. R. W. Martin, *J. Am. Chem. Soc.*, **74** 3024 (1952).
90. C. A. Burkhard, J. V. Schmitz, and R. E. Burnett, *J. Am. Chem. Soc.*, **75**, 5957 (1953).
91. S. H. Langer, R. A. Friedel, I. Wender, and A. G. Sharkey, Jr., *Anal. Chem.*, **30**, 1353 (1958).
92. J. K. Haken, *J. Gas Chromatog.*, **1**, No. 10, 30 (1963).
93. V. T. Brooks, *Chem. Ind.* (*London*), **1959**, 1317.
94. T. M. Reed III, *J. Chromatog.*, **9**, 419 (1962).
95. A. T. Shulgin, *Anal. Chem.*, **36**, 921 (1964).
96. E. Gil-Av and D. Nurok, *Proc. Chem. Soc.*, **1962**, 146.
97. R. Charles, G. Fisher, and E. Gil-Av, *Israel J. Chem.*, **1**, 234 (1963).
98. H. C. Rose, R. L. Stern, and B. L. Karger, *Anal. Chem.*, **38**, 469 (1966).
99. J. S. Lewis, Ed., *Compilation of Gas Chromatographic Data*, ASTM, Philadelphia, 1963.

Preparative Gas Chromatography*

DONALD T. SAWYER and GARRARD L. HARGROVE, *Department of Chemistry, University of California, Riverside, California*

I. INTRODUCTION

A. Goals for Preparative Separations

With the discovery of gas chromatography in 1952, scientists almost immediately saw the possibility of extending this important analytical technique to preparative separations. In preparative gas chromatography, the primary consideration relative to analytical gas

* This work was supported in part by the United States Atomic Energy Commission under contract AT(11-1)-34, Project No. 45.

chromatography is sample size and sample through-put. The high efficiencies of analytical gas chromatography are dependent to a significant extent upon the minute sample required. Direct scale-up of analytical systems to handle preparative-size samples, although common, always results in a significant deterioration of the quality of separation, leading to impure fractions and negating many of the apparent advantages assumed for gas chromatography *vis-à-vis* other separation methods. The basic attractiveness of gas chromatography as a preparative method is its very high separation efficiency and its high speed.

Because gas chromatography is basically a gas-phase system, partitioning processes are a hundred times or more faster than are possible in liquid–liquid and liquid–solid systems such as countercurrent extraction and column chromatography. Likewise the high surface area relative to liquid volume that is common with gas chromatographic packings provides much shorter equilibration times than are possible in preparative distillation. Furthermore, distillation is inherently limited in terms of high quality separations to two-component systems. Another limitation of distillation is the large sample volume required for highly efficient columns.

However, there is an important factor which is frequently overlooked in comparing the quality of separations possible with preparative-scale gas chromatography versus efficient distillation columns. The high number of theoretical plates commonly associated with gas chromatographic systems (3000–40,000 theoretical plates) cause many to believe that gas chromatography is in a separate class from distillation. Comparison is placed in perspective when the fact is recognized that gas chromatographic plates are of less utility in separation efficiency than are distillation plates. This is true because the gas chromatographic plate is used only once (on average) by a given component as it passes down the column, whereas a distillation plate is used many times (approximately N times, where N is the number of theoretical plates in the distillation column). Thus, a more realistic comparison between gas chromatographic separations and distillation separations is the approximate relation that $N_{\text{dist}} = N_{\text{gc}}^{1/2}$. Hence, a 10,000-plate gas chromatographic column has approximately the separating ability of a 100-plate distillation column.

For gas chromatography to offer real advantages for preparative separations, its inherent high speed and high efficiency must be maintained while increasing the through-put. If the separation efficiency is sacrificed in the scale-up, many alternative separation methods may actually be preferable in both through-put and cost.

B. Review of Basic Types of Gas Chromatography

Although virtually all analytical gas chromatographic equipment is based on the elution method, the frontal and displacement methods are worthy of consideration in the area of preparative gas chromatography. The elution technique assumes that the sample pulse is essentially a line pulse relative to the overall eluted bandwidth. This places a severe limitation on the sample size and requires that the majority of the column length be unoccupied by the solute system. The quantitative discussion of this limitation is presented in a later section. The frontal method involves continuous introduction of the sample system; analysis is based on the time of emergence of the various components of the mixture. Obviously, the entire length of the column is occupied by solute soon after the sample is introduced and much larger through-puts are possible. However, only the first segment of a mixture separated by the frontal method is pure. A discontinuation of sample introduction results in the last component eluted from the column also being pure. Hence, for two-component mixtures the discontinuous frontal approach provides the possibility of large through-puts of highly purified components. A detailed consideration of this method also is discussed in a later section.

The displacement method is based on the principle of introducing the sample at the head of the column and subsequently pushing the components down the column with a more strongly absorbed material. The pure components of the mixture are displaced with rectangular profiles. The major problem is the necessity of removing the displacer from the column before another sample can be introduced; a second problem is the overlap of adjacent components which causes some contamination of the pure fraction. For specialized situations, however, the displacement method offers many advantages for preparative separation. Some examples are discussed in a later section.

II. SUMMARY OF APPROACHES TO PREPARATIVE
GAS CHROMATOGRAPHY

A. Increased Column Diameter

The primary approach to preparative gas chromatography has been the scale-up of analytical columns to accommodate larger and larger samples, mainly through increased column diameter. This approach is based on the assumption that the sample size, as a minimum, can be increased proportionately to the cross sectional area of the column. Evans and co-workers (1,2) have discussed the use of columns up to 75 mm in diameter and cite examples of preparative separations using such systems; another early discussion (3) describes the use of preparative columns up to 30 mm in diameter. Purnell (4) cited the basic problem of large-diameter columns; namely, that efficient lateral mixing becomes less likely as the diameter of the column is increased.

A detailed study (5) of the lateral mixing problem for large-diameter columns has been made. This has resulted in the suggestion that rings be placed in the column at 10-cm intervals (for a 10-cm i.d. column) to serve as a baffle system and cause the carrier gas near the wall to be forced to the center of the column and thus improve lateral mixing. By this approach it is possible to reduce theoretical plate heights below 0.2 cm.

An alternative approach has been suggested by Giddings (6) to accomplish the same improvement of lateral mixing. He recommends that preparative columns be constructed by using two concentric tubes with the packing between the walls; this would eliminate the center portion of the column packing to provide a more uniform flow pattern of the carrier gas.

B. Long, Narrow Columns with Sample Overloading

Verzele and co-workers (7–9) have studied the use of very long and relatively narrow-bore columns, of sufficient length that severe overloading is possible without precluding quality separations. By using a 75-m column, 9 mm in diameter and packed with 10% by weight SE-30 on 10–20 mesh Chromasorb A, this group has been able to separate 10-ml mixtures of benzene, toluene, ethylbenzene, and cumene. With this same column, resolution of the four isomeric butanols has been possible using 1-ml samples.

Although this approach does permit useful separations with

relatively large sample sizes, there is a distinct deterioration in the separation efficiency of such columns. For example, a 0.1-ml sample in a 20 m × 9 mm column, using 30–60 mesh Chromasorb W coated with 25% by weight SE-30, gives an efficiency of only 40 plates/ft (about ten times less efficient than a standard analytical column).

The argument for the long, narrow-bore column is that with preparative-size samples capacity is proportional to the amount of solid support and stationary phase, regardless of the mesh size of the packing and of the column dimensions. The emerging bandwidth is determined by the overloading alone and is essentially independent of flow rate, carrier gas, and support particle size. Hence, when using large samples the usual parameters that determine column efficiency are no longer operative; long, narrow columns with the same amount of packing as contained in short, fat columns are possible and would have much greater separating power. Thus, for a situation where severe overloading gives a column efficiency of 100 plates/ft for a total volume of packing of 10 liters, use of a 4-cm diameter column would yield about 2400 plates. Conversely, by using a column with a diameter of 1 cm the same volume of packing would provide 38,000 plates. The first column would be 8 m long while the latter would be about 127 m long. However, if the carrier gas velocity is the same for the two example columns, then the long narrow column will require 16 times as long to elute a given sample as would the short, fat column.

C. Repetitive Automatic Injection

One of the simplest and most obvious approaches to obtain preparative quantities of pure materials is to use an analytical column and manually inject analytical-size samples repetitively. With enough patience and perseverance the very high separating efficiencies inherent in analytical columns can be maintained while acquiring useful quantities of pure materials. An obvious improvement is to automate repetitive injections such that samples are collected by a mechanized system, thereby freeing the operator. Such an approach has been discussed along with proposals for obtaining the greatest through-put per unit time for long, narrow analytical columns (10).

D. Multicolumn Arrays

An alternative approach to increasing the diameter of a column is to increase the number of columns and thereby have a group of parallel and identical columns with a manifold system, such that a large sample is disbursed to flow down the set of parallel columns. This approach (11) maintains the inherent efficiencies of small-diameter columns while increasing the total cross-sectional area such that much larger samples may be injected. The major problems are the development of an efficient manifold system and the matching of the group of columns such that they each have the same retention characteristics for the sample system. With extremely careful adjustment theoretical plate heights as small as 0.06 cm are possible for an array with a cross-section diameter equivalent to 1 in.

E. Continuous Sample Introduction by Use of Rotating Parallel Columns

An ingenious modification of the parallel column system is an arrangement whereby sample is continuously introduced into a set of columns which move transversely to the carrier gas flow and the point of sample injection (12). Using this approach 100 parallel columns (each 1.2 m by 6 mm i.d.) have been arranged on a cylindrical surface; these are rotated at a controlled frequency while keeping the sample introduction point and the collection system fixed.

With such a system the point of elution on the cylindrical base, x_i, of component i in terms of t_{R_i}, its retention time, is given by

$$x_i = 2\pi r a t_{R_i} \qquad (1)$$

where a is the number of revolutions of the cylinder per unit time and r is the radius of the cylinder. The position x_i is referred to the fixed point of injection of the entire array. The condition for maximum efficiency is obtained when the nth component (retention time, t_{R_n}) of an n-component separation is eluted adjacent to the first component (retention time, t_{R_1}). To achieve a $2\pi r$ difference in position between the first and nth component, the frequency of revolution must be

$$a = 1/(t_{R_n} - t_{R_1}) \qquad (2)$$

A practical example of the separating ability of this system is the separation of benzene and cyclohexane at 80°C on a tricresyl phosphate column, using a feed rate of 200 ml/hr. The reported purity of the separated components is 99.9%. Table I summarizes some other values for the separation of n-heptane and toluene at various feed rates.

Even at feed rates of 1 liter/hr recovery of 95% of the total amount introduced is possible at a purity of at least 98.5%.

TABLE I
Purity of Central Cut versus Feed Rate

Feed rate,	*n*-Heptane		Toluene	
ml/hr	Purity	% Volume of fraction	Purity	% Volume of fraction
200	99.99	92.9	99.96	97.9
400	99.90	96.7	99.96	97.1
1000	98.50	94.9	99.60	94.7

Although this 100-column system in theory should have the efficiency of a single column constructed in the same manner, such efficiencies are not realized because of column-to-column variations and excess feed volumes. In spite of these qualifications the through-put and separating efficiencies for this system are impressive. The theory of parallel rotating columns has been further developed in a later study (13).

F. Sample Recirculation

Martin (14,15) has proposed that the solute mixture be recirculated from one column into a second column and back again until the degree of separation necessary is obtained. This approach provides a relatively large number of theoretical plates from a pair of short columns. A similar approach has been suggested using a single column in the shape of a loop with a pumping system and a valve arrangement (16). However, both recirculating approaches are of limited general use and have as their major potential the separation of two neighboring components. Components significantly far removed from the difficultly separable pair will complicate matters unless rejected from the system.

Golay, Hill, and Norem (17) have taken note of this problem and have described a chromatographic system whereby a narrow cut of closely similar materials is selected from the faster and slower components of a complex sample mixture. The selected components are recirculated through a set of columns until a sufficient number of theoretical plates is achieved to provide separation. As an example, a 50-ml mixture of iso-butane, *n*-butane, and propane has been separated completely using a three-column arrangement with appropriate valving (each column was 2 m long × 6 mm in diameter). The separation required approximately 15 min. For a single pass the maximum sample size had been determined to be 1 ml for the separation of iso- and *n*-butane; the time for a single pass was slightly longer than 3 min.

Hence the recirculation approach increased the through-put per unit time by a factor of ten.

G. Frontal Analysis

Reilley and co-workers (18) have approached preparative gas chromatographic separations by determining the emergent profiles resulting from different types of input profiles. Assuming that the processes in a column are based on linear independent chromatography, the response to a complex set of inputs can be expressed as the sum of the responses to each element of the input. Thus, the response to a step input (frontal chromatography) can be calculated by summing together the responses of an infinite series of successive line impulses. This approach, in conjunction with the use of Laplace transformations, has permitted mathematical solutions for the response functions resulting from impulse, single-step, and double-step inputs associated with gas chromatography. These functions are summarized by eqs. (3)–(5):

    (1) *Impulse*

$$R(t) = \sum_j \frac{C_j'}{\sqrt{2\pi}\,\sigma_j} \exp -\left(\frac{t - t_{R_j}}{\sqrt{2}\,\sigma_j}\right)^2 \tag{3}$$

where $R(t)$ is the response, C_j' is $\int C_j\,dt$, C_j is the concentration of component j in the input, t is the time after injection, t_{R_j} is the retention time (at peak maximum) for component j, and σ_j is one-fourth the distance between the intersections of the t axis by the tangents to the inflection points of the response (gaussian).

    (2) *Single Step*

$$R(t) = \sum_j \frac{C_j}{2} + \sum_j \frac{C_j}{2} \operatorname{erf}\left(\frac{t - t_{R_j}}{\sqrt{2}\,\sigma_j}\right) \tag{4}$$

where erf $([(t - t_{R_j})/2^{1/2}\sigma_j])$ represents the error function associated with the normal curve, t_{R_j} is the retention time of component j (measured from point of injection to point of inflection of the step response for the jth component), σ_j equals $w_j/(2\pi)^{1/2}$, and w_j is the ratio of the value of $R(t)$ at large t (which approaches C_j) to the slope at the inflection point of the step response for the jth component.

    (3) *Double Step* (Second Step Occurring at $t = t_2$)

$$R(r, j) = \sum_j \frac{C_j}{2} \operatorname{erf}\left(\frac{t - t_{R_j}}{\sqrt{2}\,\sigma_j}\right) - \sum_j \frac{C_j}{2} \operatorname{erf}\left(\frac{t - t_2 - t_{R_1}}{\sqrt{2}\,\sigma_j}\right) \tag{5}$$

where $\sum_j C_j$ and $-\sum_j C_j$ are the two-step inputs for the jth component.

With eqs. (3) and (4) the bulk separation possible using the ideal impulse and the single-step input approaches can be compared for three hypothetical sample pairs of varying levels of separation difficulty. The three pairs $(A,B_1; A,B_2;$ and $A,B_3)$ have been chosen to represent separations between the two components of σ, 2σ, and 3σ, respectively. The comparison is made easier by assuming that the mixture compositions are $1:1$ and that the input concentrations are the same for both the impulse and the single-step inputs.

Using these assumptions the total accumulated quantity of each component that can be collected versus the number of plate volumes of mobile phase introduced can be calculated. This is graphically presented by Figure $1a$ for the impulse method and by Figure $1c$ for the step input. Figure $1a$ indicates that the maximum amount of material that can be obtained by the ideal impulse input is limited to one unit whereas the amount obtainable by the step input is not limited on any theoretical grounds. The advantage of the step input versus the impulse technique is further emphasized by Figure $1b$ which presents the impurity ratio, B/A, as a function of carrier gas volume. Only in the case of a $1 - \sigma$ separation does the impulse technique, at any volume of carrier gas, yield a lower impurity ratio than the step-input technique. However, even in this case the greater amount of a component acquired by the step-input procedure permits termination of the collection at a lower number of plate volumes to offset the increase in impurity. Table II

TABLE II

Total Amount of A Recovered at a 5% Impurity Level (Arbitrary Units)

Pair	Step input	Impulse input
A,B_1	0.60	0.05
A,B_2	12.0	0.58
A,B_3	30.0	0.90

summarizes the amount of A recovered for the three different pairs, assuming a 5% impurity level. Even for the A,B_1 separation the step-input technique yields more than ten times the amount of A relative to the impulse technique.

By using a back-step response it is possible to obtain B free of A based on the previous arguments. This is seen if one interchanges

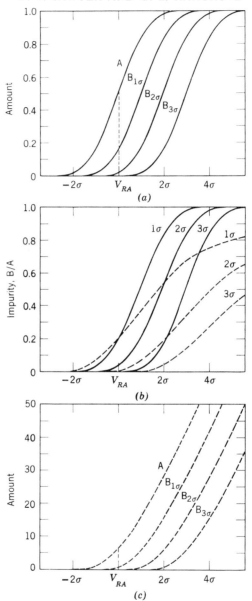

Fig. 1. Comparison of impulse (———) and step (- - -) techniques in terms of through-put and purity. (a) and (c) represent the amount of each component collected as a function of carrier-gas volume. (b) represents the impurity ratio, B/A, as a function of carrier-gas volume. Courtesy C. N. Reilley, G. P. Hildebrand, and J. W. Ashley, Jr., and *Analytical Chemistry*.

components A and B and reverses the sign of the σ values in Figure 1. This symmetry of the back to the front step implies that the back-step method also is superior to ideal impulse chromatography for the separation of the second of a two-component system. This argument also applies to the last component of a polycomponent mixture.

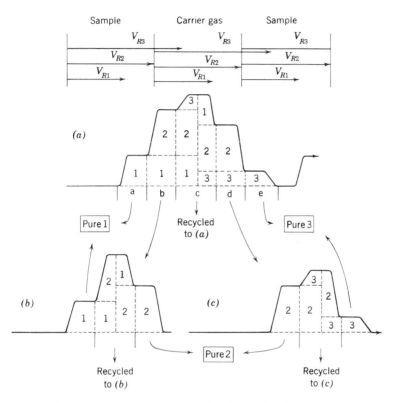

Fig. 2. Separation scheme for a polycomponent mixture using the step technique. Courtesy C. N. Reilley, G. P. Hildebrand, and J. W. Ashley, Jr., and *Analytical Chemistry*.

Figure 2 illustrates the separation of a three-component mixture by the use of the step-impulse technique with three columns used in an integrated fashion. By appropriate selection of column parameters, temperature, programming of sample and carrier gas inputs, and sample selection, this arrangement permits almost complete recovery of the three components in the original mixture.

H. Mechanical Counter-Current Separation

The oldest and most successful plant-scale separation system based on principles of chromatography is that developed by Benedek and co-workers (19–21). This system, which has been summarized in some detail by Purnell (22), uses a counter-current technique whereby the gaseous sample is introduced at the bottom of the tower while the partitioning agent (charcoal in this case) falls down the length of the tower by gravitational force. Thus, in a two-component mixture such as methane and acetylene the methane is carried to the top of the tower while the acetylene is adsorbed by the charcoal and carried to the bottom of the tower. The latter is removed from the charcoal by heating and then collected as a pure fraction. Although this type of mechanical approach lends itself only to two-fraction separations, it does provide for large through-put. The problems of handling solid packing in a cyclic fashion are overcome to a major extent by modern fluid bed systems.

I. Displacement Separations

Scott and Phillips (23) have used gas–solid displacement chromatography for the preparation of extremely pure alkanes, alkenes, aromatics, and esters. They have developed small preparative-scale units for separating 1–5 g samples as well as scaled-up systems capable of 50-g separations. The basic instrument consists of a saturator for the introduction of the displacer into the mobile phase, the separation column which is constructed from successively smaller-diameter glass tubes filled with adsorbent retained by flat sintered disks, a detection system, and a collection system. Some of the actual separations accomplished with this method are discussed in a later section.

A specialized version of the displacement approach is the Skarstrom "Drier" (24). This system consists of a pair of identical columns containing either alumina or silica gel, which are used to purify a gas stream or air itself. By passing air through one of the columns impurities are continuously removed until the column is completely saturated with them. To regenerate such a column would require a volume of pure air equal to that which has been purified; hence, this approach in itself is self-defeating. However, a useful system is possible if the air to be purified is passed through the first column at a high pressure (for example 10 atm); after this column is loaded with impurities the stream is switched to the second column. The effluent from the second column now is pressurized at 2 rather than 10 atm, and only 20% of the effluent stream is required to back flush out the impurities. Thus, this two-column system is capable of an 80% yield of purified air.

III. LIMITING FACTORS IN PREPARATIVE GAS CHROMATOGRAPHY

A. Feed-Volume and Solution Limitations

A preponderance of preparative gas chromatography is based on conventional elution chromatography employing an impulse injection. Because elution chromatography assumes an impulse for the sample input, the effect upon efficiency of the large samples desired in preparative separations must be considered. Two considerations are relevant, (a) excess feed volume and (b) solute concentrations in the solvent phase such that the distribution constant (K) is no longer a constant. Although a detailed discussion of feed-volume limits and solution limits has been presented (25), a review of these arguments is appropriate in view of the extreme importance of these factors if the utmost is to be attained in preparative gas chromatographic separations. If the inherent speed and efficiency of gas chromatography are to be effectively applied to preparative separations, realistic limits for the feed volume and the concentration of the sample in the solvent phase must be established.

The maximum feed volume which is permissible if the intrinsic theoretical plate height (H) of the column is not to be affected adversely is given by the expression

$$V_{fg} \leqslant \frac{V_R{}'}{2\sqrt{N}} = \frac{V_d(1 + k')}{2\sqrt{N}} \tag{6}$$

where $V_R{}'$ is the total retention volume which includes the free gas volume, V_d, k' is the capacity factor, and N is the intrinsic number of plates. The feed volume, V_{fg}, represents the volume of the vaporized solutes plus any dilution by the carrier gas. As a minimum this quantity would be the vaporized volume of the solute at the temperature and pressure at the head of the column.

The number of plates required to exactly separate a pair of components in a mixture is given in terms of k' and the corrected retention volume ratio, α, by the expression

$$N'_{\text{req}} = 36[\alpha/(\alpha - 1)]^2[(1 + k')/k']^2 \tag{7}$$

This equation may be used to calculate the number of plates required to exactly separate the most difficult pair. By assuming no dilution by the carrier gas and that the solute acts as an ideal gas, the upper limit for the sample volume as a liquid can be expressed in terms of column parameters.

$$V_{fl} \leq [F_g p_i k' L_{\mathrm{req}}/12RT(\alpha/\alpha - 1)][(\pi r^2 M_s)/\rho_s] \qquad (8)$$

where F_g is the fractional free gas space, p_i is the inlet pressure at which it is assumed the vaporized sample exists, L_{req} is the column length corresponding to N_{req}, r is the column radius, and M_s and ρ_s are the average molecular weight and density of the sample, respectively; R and T have their usual meaning. If there is sample dilution by the carrier gas, p_i becomes the average partial pressure of the sample and thus is reduced linearly with dilution.

Table III summarizes the maximum sample size for feed-volume controlled column performance, based on realistic column parameters. Reference to this table indicates that when a separation of a relatively small sample is to be accomplished by a single injection, columns with high capacity factors, k', should be used. However, Table III indicates that the permitted sample size increases only as $k'^{1/2}$, whereas retention time increases directly proportional to the increase in k'. Thus the through-put of sample per unit time is clearly smaller at high k'.

For a fixed value of k' the data in Table III superficially appear to indicate that systems with larger α values require smaller sample sizes. This implies that it would be better to use the column system that gives

TABLE III

Calculated Maximum Sample Size for Condition of Feed-Volume Controlled Column Performance[a]

	$k' = 1$	$k' = 10$
$\alpha = 1.15$ N_{req}	8400	2500
L_{req}, cm	420	125
V_{fl}, ml	0.071	0.212
$\alpha = 1.50$ N_{req}	1300	390
L_{req}, cm	65	20
V_{fl}, ml	0.029	0.088
$\alpha = \infty$ N_{req}	144	43
L_{req}	7.2	2.2
V_{fl}, ml	0.010	0.029

[a] $r = 1.25$ cm, $H = 0.05$ cm, $T = 373°$K, $p_i = 2$ atm, $F_g = 0.5$, $M_s = 100$, $\rho_s = 1$.

low α values. However, this conclusion is fallacious because Table III indicates that L_{req} at $\alpha = 1.5$ is about six times smaller than that for $\alpha = 1.15$. Thus, if a column 125 cm long were used at $\alpha = 1.5$ and $k' = 10$, a six-fold increase in sample would be permitted, i.e., approximately 0.5 ml, and at this length N_{req} would be so exceeded that the peaks would be clearly separated and some overloading could be tolerated. Thus something close to 1 ml of liquid could be processed in each run. Reference to the literature indicates that most preparative columns currently are operated in this condition of excessive length and some overloading.

While small single sample processing is likely to be the main aim of many laboratory chemists, the economic future of preparative columns lies in their ability to achieve high rates of sample separation for complex mixtures. Thus, a large number of small samples, each separated in a short period of time, may well be superior to the separation of one large sample in a much longer time.

The basic elution time equation for the condition of exact separation of a pair of components is

$$t_{req} = [L_{req}(1 + k')]/u_o f \cong 36[\alpha/(\alpha - 1)]^2[(1 + k')^3/(k')^2]C \quad (9)$$

where u_o is the outlet carrier gas velocity, f is the James–Martin compressibility factor, and C is the mass-transfer term for both gas and liquid phases. Some examples of minimum separation times are summarized in Table IV.

TABLE IV
Minimum Separation Times from eq. (9) with $C = 1.5 \times 10^{-3}$ sec

	Time, sec		
k'	$\alpha = 1.15$	$\alpha = 1.50$	$\alpha = \infty$
1	25.4	3.9	0.43
2	21.4	3.3	0.37
10	42.2	6.5	0.72

The maximum rate of sample separation fixed by feed-volume restrictions can be derived by dividing eq. (8) by eq. (9) to give

$$V_{fl}/\text{unit time} = \frac{F_{gi}p}{12RT[\alpha/(\alpha - 1)](1 + k')} \frac{k'}{} \left[\frac{\pi r^2 M_s u_o f}{\rho_s}\right] \quad (10)$$

This expression is valid and exact only for the specific condition that the column is of length L_{req}, which must be calculated from eq. (7) and a knowledge of H. Equation (10) specifies that the rate of separation is independent of carrier gas and of L_{req}. This latter result, which might appear surprising, derives from the fact that at fixed k', for example, a reduction in α demands an increase in L_{req}, which in turn allows a proportionate increase in the feed volume. Thus, mixtures of widely different degrees of difficulty of separation can be processed at about the same rate. According to eq. (10) the rate of separation tends to a maximum as $k' \to \infty$. However, at $k' = 10$, the rate is 90% of its maximum value and there is little advantage in working at higher values.

Equation (10) may be used to calculate the rates of sample separation attainable at a carrier-gas velocity of 100 cm sec^{-1}, but otherwise for conditions identical with those used to construct Table III. These data are given in Table V and show that the maximum rate is achieved with a maximum α and a k' close to 10 for the most difficultly separable pair.

TABLE V

Maximum Rates of Sample Separation, Feed-Volume Limited [a]

	Rate, ml liquid/sec		
k'	$\alpha = 1.15$	$\alpha = 1.50$	$\alpha = \infty$
1	0.0055	0.014	0.042
2	0.0073	0.019	0.057
10	0.0100	0.026	0.078

[a] $r = 1.25$ cm, $T = 373°K$, $u_o = 100$ cm sec^{-1}, $p_i = 2$ atm, $F_q = 0.5$, $M_s = 100$, $\rho_s = 1$.

Even though a sample may be injected so as to meet feed-volume restrictions it may still be so large that, on condensing into the solvent at the head of the column, its concentration may exceed that at which anything approaching a linear partition isotherm exists. In general a linear isotherm cannot be expected for solute concentrations above 10 mole %, and in many instances the limit will be considerably lower (< 1 mole %). In the region where a linear isotherm pertains, column efficiency, in terms of solution limitations, is independent of sample size, i.e., K is a constant.

The volume of injected sample, expressed as liquid, V_{sl}, can be written in terms of column parameters as

$$V_{sl} = \frac{X}{(1 - X)} \left(\frac{L_f}{L} \right) \frac{\rho_p w_l}{M_l} \left[\frac{\pi r^2 L M_s}{\rho_s} \right] \tag{11}$$

Where X is the mole fraction of solute in the solvent, L_f/L is the fractional length of column into which injection is made, ρ_p is the density of the composite packing, w_l is the fraction of the total weight of packing which is solvent, and M_l is the molecular weight of the solvent.

In the situation that feed-volume restrictions are to be met, $L_f/L \leqslant 1/2N^{1/2}$, the restriction on V_{sl}, for a given column, then derives entirely from $[X/(1 - X)]$.

Some feeling for the limitations imposed by eq. (11) can be gained by assuming X equals 0.1 and by considering a preparative column of 250×2.5 cm filled with packing of $\rho_p = 0.5$, $w_l = 0.5$ with $M_l = 600$. The column will then contain 310 ml of solvent and can accommodate a liquid sample size up to 0.040 ml for a 5000-plate separation (assuming $M_s = 100$ and $\rho_s = 1.0$); when this column only has an efficiency of 100 plates then it can accommodate a sample size up to 0.28 ml of liquid. The latter result would seem to represent an absolute upper limit in almost any circumstances for a column of the assumed dimensions. Obviously, these sample limits are much smaller than are commonly used for preparative columns of 1-in. diameter. This, in itself, would account for the poor efficiencies frequently observed in practice.

Substitution of eq. (7) for N in eq. (11) plus combination of eq. (9) leads to the result

$$V_{sl}/\text{unit time} = \frac{(X/1 - X)k'\rho_p w_l}{12[\alpha/(\alpha - 1)](1 + k')^2 M_l} \left[\frac{\pi r^2 M_s u_o f}{\rho_s} \right] \quad (12)$$

This equation, which shows that V_{sl}/unit time does not depend on column length or carrier gas, indicates that, in contrast with feed-volume restricted systems, the maximum rate of separation occurs when k' is unity. Thus, to use this equation, it is necessary to ascertain the value of k' for the second member of the most difficultly separable pair in the sample for the conditions of the column, to ascertain the value of α for this pair, to determine the number of plates necessary to separate this pair, to determine the theoretical plate height from the rate equation using the velocity that is to be used in eq. (12), and to calculate the length of column necessary to give the required number of plates. For example, a 2.5-cm diameter column with $w_l = 0.5$, $\rho_p = 0.5$, $M_l = 600$, $\rho_l = 1.0$, $M_s = 100$, and $\rho_s = 1.0$ can separate samples, as an upper limit, at the rates tabulated in Table VI, assuming that the flow rate is 100 cm/sec and the inlet pressure is 2 atm ($f = 0.64$).

Comparison of eqs. (10) and (12) permits a number of unequivocal recommendations to be made, and these are valid whether the rate of sample separation is feed-volume or solution limited. Thus, (a) provided there is no significant loss of column efficiency with increasing diameter,

TABLE VI

Maximum Rates of Sample Separation in Terms of Solution Limitations[a]

	Rate, ml liquid/sec		
k'	$\alpha = 1.15$	$\alpha = 1.50$	$\alpha = \infty$
1	0.0040	0.0102	0.031
2	0.0035	0.0090	0.027
10	0.0013	0.0033	0.010

[a] $r = 1.25$ cm. Operated at a flow of 100 cm/sec.

through-put increases with cross-sectional area; (b) the conditions leading to the largest possible value of α for the most difficultly separable pair should be employed. This demands a search for a selective solvent; (c) high carrier-gas velocity is advantageous; (d) the through-put, in terms of weight, increases as the molecular weight of sample increases and as the inverse of the sample density; and (e) there is no justification for operating a column such that k' for the most difficultly separable pair exceeds 10.

These conclusions are, for the most part, intuitively evident but nevertheless should be kept in mind. Less obvious general conclusions which may be drawn from this treatment are: (f) when the sample mixture is of high volatility, such that $p_i \geqslant 1$ atm is readily attained without decomposition, then the rate of separation can most probably be made solution-limited by use of high injection-block temperatures and elimination of dilution of feed by carrier gas. The ratio p_i/T in eq. (10) increases approximately logarithmically with temperature. In this circumstance, low values of k' (ca. 1) should be used to attain high through-put; (g) when the sample mixture is of low volatility, that is, of high molecular weight and low thermal stability, the low partial pressure attainable before decomposition occurs in the injection chamber means that the system is likely to be feed-volume limited. For example, at a maximum attainable $p_i = 10$ mm Hg the through-puts quoted in Table V would all be reduced by a factor of 150 whereas the upper limit for linearity of the solution isotherm is still likely to be $X = 0.01$–0.1. In this situation, a high value of k' (~ 10) is advisable. In addition, of course, the highest possible injection temperature should be used; (h) when sample volatility lies between the extremes of (f) and (g), each case must be evaluated on its merits by use of eqs. (10) and (12).

The retention volume ratio, α, is dependent only upon column temperature, T_c, and the solvent. Its dependence on T_c is relatively small, and so attainment of high values of α is primarily a matter of solvent selection. On the other hand, the capacity factor, k', depends upon T_c, the solvent, and the amount of solvent. With a solvent chosen on the basis of a favorable α, k' can be adjusted only through change of T_c or amount of solvent.

In summary, when through-put is limited by feed volume, low T_c and high solvent-support ratio is indicated by eq. (10). When through-put is solution limited, however, while a high solvent-support ratio (w_l) is still desirable, a low partition coefficient, K, is advantageous; one way of achieving this is to increase T_c.

These limitations apply regardless of column dimensions or efficiencies and must be met in practice before worthwhile studies of column performance can be made. Whether or not large-diameter, batch-operated columns ultimately represent the best approach to preparative work, the examples quoted in Tables V and VI indicate that through-puts in the order of 40 ml/hr should be attainable readily for mixtures which might require a distillation unit of 100 plates or more. Because, in chromatography, all components are recovered essentially simultaneously, the significance of this for costly and complex mixtures may well be considerable.

B. Thermal Effects

Two temperature effects arise in preparative gas chromatography that cause significant deterioration in column efficiency. The first of these arises from the heat of solution attendant with the large samples characteristic of preparative gas chromatography. The second arises from poor heat transfer from the oven system across large-diameter preparative columns.

Scott (26) has presented a detailed discussion of the temperature changes occurring with the passage of a solute through a theoretical plate. He has derived an equation yielding the excess temperature of the theoretical plate above its surroundings as a function of carrier-gas flow rate, partition coefficient, and heat of solution for the solute. This relationship takes into account the specific heats of the support material and of the stationary liquid phase. In addition, the temperature of a point in a column has been measured during the course of the passage of a solute through the column. The variation of the temperature with respect to the mean column temperature has been studied as a function of flow rate, sample size, and partition coefficient. The data indicate that the excess plate temperature increases with (a) increasing flow rate, (*b*) increasing sample size, and (*c*) decreasing values of the partition coefficient for a series of solutes eluted under the same experimental conditions; i.e., earlier peaks are more distorted than those eluted later in the gas chromatograms.

An increase in excess plate temperature has the effect of increasing the peak asymmetry for a given solute. This is to be expected because the speed with which a solute band passes through a column is inversely proportional to the partition coefficient which, in turn, decreases exponentially with temperature. For a given peak the higher concentrations within the solute band will be at a higher temperature than the lower-concentration portions. Thus, a phenomenon similar to the self-sharpening frequently observed for solutes in gas–solid chromatography can be expected from temperature effects in preparative gas chromatography. Experiments with preparative columns indicate that the solute peaks generally possess sharp fronts and sloping tails and that this effect is more pronounced when the excess plate temperature is higher. Scott suggests that this problem can be minimized by designing preparative scale columns which provide for rapid heat exchange between the interior of the column and its surroundings.

The temperature variations associated with heat transfer across large-diameter columns are entirely different from the heat-of-solution problems and are caused by the poor heat-transfer characteristics of support materials. Hence, the excess plate temperatures generated by the passage of the solute will be dissipated more rapidly at the edge of the column than they will be at the center. This will result in a radial temperature gradient. Such an effect has been studied by placing thermocouples across the diameter of a 1-in. preparative column (27). Using a flow rate of 100 ml/min and a 1.5-ml sample of *n*-hexane with a 20% SE-30 column (60–80 mesh Chromosorb P), the temperature excursion about the mean (80°C) for the center of the column when the solute peak passed was approximately $\pm 6°C$. When the thermocouple was $\frac{1}{4}$ in. from the column wall these excursions were only $\pm 3°C$ and with a thermocouple $\frac{1}{32}$ in. from the wall they were reduced to $\pm 2.5°C$.

A related problem results when preparative separations are attempted using programmed temperature operation. Not only are temperature gradients frequently observed that amount to several degrees centigrade across the column, but the temperature in the center of a 1-in. column will lag behind the wall temperature by one minute or more in a programming operation.

Thus, if large-diameter columns are to be used for preparative separations cognizance must be taken of the heat-transfer problem. Specialized column configurations that provide for good thermal conductors to be inserted across the column profile are essential if gross peak distortion is not to result.

C. Deterioration of Efficiency Due to Increased Column Diameter

Because large-diameter columns are by far the most common approach in the application of analytical gas chromatography to preparative quantities of material, a review of some of the factors that lead to a decreased separation efficiency from expansion of column diameter is useful. An early, but detailed, study of the efficiency of large-diameter columns with respect to injection systems, mode of packing, column length, and velocity profiles across the diameter of the column has provided important background data for the intelligent design of efficient preparative columns (28). A major consideration has been a study of the velocity profiles resulting in a 3-in. diameter column, 1 m in length. These were determined by using ammonia vapor diluted by inert carrier-gas and having an end section on the column containing phosphoric acid. By titrating the unreacted phosphoric acid a quantitative measure of the radial distribution of the ammonia could be determined, and thereby the effect of the mode of packing could be established. The results of such studies are summarized in Table VII and indicate that the packing mode has a profound effect on column efficiency and velocity profile.

The various contributions to plate height can be expressed as a summation

$$H = A + (B_o/u_o) + (C_{g_{tc}} + C_{g_1} + C_{g_2} + C_{g_3})u_o + C_l\bar{u} \quad (13)$$

TABLE VII
Effect of Packing Mode Upon Velocity Profile [a]

Packing mode	Packed density, g/cm³	Plates	Velocity ratio, $V_{outside}/V_{inside}$	Plate height ratio, H_{wall}/H_{center}
Pouring followed by gentle beating	0.51	150	1.2	10
Vibration	—	250	1.3	2.5
Beating; filling velocity 20 g/min	0.54	480	1.5	—

[a] Column, 1 m × 3 in., 30% silicone oil (MC 200/200) on Silocel (C22), 30–40 mesh; temperature: 22°C; carrier: N_2 (385 liters/hr); sample: 1 ml n-pentane.

where A, B_o, and C_l have their usual meaning, and where $C_{g_{tc}}$ is the contribution due to the velocity variation across the column, C_{g_1} is the contribution due to diffusion into and out of pores, C_{g_2} is the contribution due to interaction between unequal flow channels (the main contribution to the total C_g in analytical columns), and C_{g_3} is the Golay type contribution. All of the terms in eq. (13) except B_o, C_{g_1}, and C_{g_3} depend to some extent upon the mode of packing used for preparing the column. Thus, the better performance of the column with the largest variation of velocity from center to outside is not necessarily surprising because, although the largest mass-transfer contribution comes from $C_{g_{tc}}$ in large-diameter columns, the other terms make substantial contributions in badly packed columns. Therefore in the most densely packed column, the other contributions have been minimized and the performance is better, although still substandard in comparison to an analytical column because of the contribution from $C_{g_{tc}}$.

In this same study (28) theoretical plate heights were measured at various distances from the center of the column; in one case the plate height at the wall was more than ten times as great as at the center of the column. The ratio of the plate height at the wall relative to that at the center is tabulated in Table VII for two modes of packing.

Consideration of the data indicates that tapping or beating the column while filling yields the highest number of plates, but also results in the greatest velocity maldistribution. This approach to column packing also yields lower plate heights in the center of the column relative to those at the wall. To minimize velocity profile and wall effects the authors suggest that preparative columns should be constructed from short lengths of wide-diameter tubing connected by narrow-diameter tubing. A further suggestion is that sample collection should be separate for the center portion of the column as opposed to the wall portion; the latter material should be recirculated if higher efficiencies and greater purity are sought. By collecting only 50% of the outlet flow through the use of concentric outlet cones, efficiencies of 275 plates/ft have been achieved for a 10-cm diameter column. A final observation from these experiments is that the mode of packing has a significant effect upon the rate of lateral mass transfer of the solute.

Giddings (29,30) has considered, from a theoretical standpoint, the additional plate height contribution due to flow-velocity variations

across the column and has developed an expression for this extra contribution to the plate height, H_p

$$H_p = (C_g)_p u_o = \left[\left(\frac{G}{1 + G/2}\right)^2 \frac{r_o{}^2}{96\gamma D_g}\right] u_o \qquad (14)$$

where G is fractional velocity non-uniformity $(\Delta u/u)$, γ is the obstruc-
tion factor associated with the longitudinal diffusion term (B), r_o is the
radius of the column, and u_o is the average outlet velocity.

For a 2-in. diameter column with butane as the solute in hydrogen
carrier gas, a value of 0.75 has been calculated for G (30). When this is
inserted in eq. (14) the gas-phase mass transfer term due to large-
diameter columns $(C_g)_p$ has a value of 0.066 sec. This is approximately
110 times as large as the gas phase mass transfer term observed for the
same solute-carrier gas system with an analytical column.

Hargrove and Sawyer (31) have made a careful experimental comparison between analytical and preparative gas chromatographic columns in terms of their efficiencies. The results are discussed in relation
to the band broadening predicted by Giddings in terms of eq. (14). The
liquid-phase mass transfer terms are identical for the two types of
columns. Conversely, the gas-phase mass transfer term is approximately 10 times as large for a 1-in. preparative column as for a $\frac{1}{4}$-in.
analytical column. Thus, the major band-broadening factor with
increasing column diameter is the inhomogeneity of the carrier-gas
velocity within the column cross section. Whereas the gas-phase mass
transfer term, C_g, for an analytical column is 0.5×10^{-3} sec, for a
preparative column the same term has a value of 5.9×10^{-3} sec. Assuming a reasonable value for G in eq. (14), values similar to the experimental results for the two types of columns are calculated from the equation.
Hence there seems to be good experimental support for the validity
of Giddings' theory for the band-broadening contributions of column
inhomogeneity.

In this same study (31) the effect of geometry and mode of sample
injection upon preparative column efficiencies was investigated. Figure 3
indicates that truncated cone caps provide significantly better flow
geometries with resultant improvement in column efficiency. Similarly,
injection of the solute with a sample valve rather than a syringe provides improved column efficiency. This minor change in the mode of
injection indicates the major consequences that result when one attempts
to vaporize instantaneously from 1 to 100 ml of liquid sample such that
it is placed at the head of the column in the first few plates. Considering

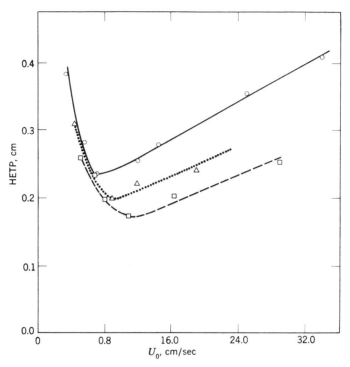

Fig. 3. Theoretical plate heights as function of helium carrier-gas velocity for two preparative columns using two modes of injection. (○) Syringe injection of vapor; flat caps. (△) Valve injection of vapor; flat caps. (□) Valve injection of vapor; empty cone caps. $T_{col} = 25.0 \pm 0.5°C$.

that a 10-ml liquid sample may require from 3 to 30 liters of gas space to accommodate its vapor at the temperature and pressure at the head of the column, many commercial preparative instruments physically preclude instantaneous vaporization and injection of the solute.

D. Effect of Column Length

Giddings and Jensen (30) have considered the effect of column length on the efficiency of large-diameter columns. In the case of analytical columns there is no dependence of column efficiency upon length, assuming that a column has a uniform permeability and packed density. However, for large diameter columns, flow inhomogeneities across the column are significantly greater than in the case of analytical columns.

Furthermore, the velocity gradient across the diameter of a preparative column will tend to increase as the column length increases. Hence the plate height for preparative scale columns tends to increase linearly with column length; this effect is represented by $H = (G^2L)/16$. However, lateral diffusion tends to promote exchange between solute molecules near the wall and near the center of the column, and this counteracts the plate-height contribution resulting from flow inhomogeneities. By using a coupled formulation to relate these two contributions for large-diameter columns, the plate height is given by

$$H_{large\ diam.} = 1/\{(16/G^2L) + [D_g/(\alpha G^2 u_o r_o^2)]\} \quad (15)$$

where α is a parameter related to the flow profile in the column.

This expression implies that the plate height of a preparative column will increase with length up to a certain point and then become independent of column length. The larger the diameter of the column the longer the distance down the column before plate height becomes independent of column length. For example, these authors compute that the plate height does not become independent of column length for a 4-in. column until it is 400 cm long.

E. Column Packing Techniques

The earlier work (28) on velocity profiles for preparative columns led Giddings and Fuller (32) to determine the particle-size distribution in a packed column 4.69 cm in diameter. Using 80–100 mesh packing with light tapping on the walls, the average particle diameter (d_p) in the center of the column was 0.154 and 0.172 mm at the wall. Using the same packing material without tapping, the particle diameter at the center of the column was 0.145 and 0.174 mm at the wall. If the flow velocity of the gas within a section is roughly proportional to $(d_p)^2$, then the outside-to-inside velocity ratio for such a particle distribution should be about 1.2–1.4. This is in agreement with velocity profile measurements (28) and adds further support to the conclusion that the flow velocity variation in large-diameter columns is due to the particle size distribution across the column. A proposed solution to this problem is to design preparative columns using two concentric cylinders and to fill the annular space between them. This arrangement gives better packing distribution and should provide more uniform velocity profiles while maintaining a large volume of packing (6).

To obtain a more uniform distribution of particle diameters in wide-diameter columns, a filling arrangement has been developed using a rocking table with a frequency of 50 cps (5). This system, with an amplitude of 1.5–5 mm, has been applied to the filling of columns ranging in diameter from 0.4 to 10 cm. The advantage of this approach is that reproducible efficiencies for a series of columns can be obtained. The reproducibility for a group of 1-cm columns was better than $\pm 3\%$. A 4-in. column packed by this procedure had a plate height of 3 mm when a 10-g sample of pentane was used as a solute.

The results obtained using the standing wave method of packing indicate that the decrease in efficiency of large-diameter columns is due to a porosity gradient across the diameter from particle size maldistribution. Studies of packed beds in analytical reactors (33) permit equations to be developed for the velocity profile across a column under a range of conditions. For particles with 0.25-mm diameters the added contribution to the plate height resulting from the porosity gradient is given by the expression

$$H = 2.83 D^{0.58}/u^{1.886} \qquad (16)$$

where D is the column diameter and u is the average carrier-gas velocity. Equation (16) indicates that for a 10-cm i.d. column the insertion of mixing rings every 10 cm down the length of the column should minimize the porosity effect. Using this approach, plate heights of less than 0.2 cm have been achieved for such columns. Better packed columns have also been obtained through the use of a fluidized packing technique (34). This approach has provided an efficiency of 110 plates/ft for a 6-cm i.d. column.

F. Sample Introduction and Collection

A major problem in preparative gas chromatography is the instantaneous injection of large volumes of liquid sample to the head of the column. Two approaches have been used; one is the rapid vaporization of the sample with subsequent introduction as a vapor at the head of the column. The alternative to this is to introduce the liquid directly onto the head of the packing of the column. The latter obviously presents problems in terms of physically washing the stationary liquid phase from the packing. However, the problem of rapidly vaporizing from 10 to 100 ml of liquid is formidable and requires extremely careful engineering of injector volumes and of heat-transfer systems. Many workers have concluded that the problems of effectively injecting large, single samples of solute are sufficiently formidable to warrant the time and effort required by the alternative of injecting a number of small samples. The tedium of multiple injections and collection has been circumvented by the design of systems for automatic injection and collection of gas chromatographic samples; a number of effective designs have been discussed (35–39).

A major problem, whether large samples or multiple small samples are used, is the efficient collection of the separated fractions at the end of the column. A number of specialized designs have been developed to overcome fog and aerosol formation (the cause of serious collection losses). One approach has been to use a multiple temperature-gradient trap (40); a related design is the use of a gradient cooling principle for the collection of high boiling long-chain fatty acids (41). For the latter system efficiencies approaching 90–95% are claimed. A metal precipitator with an electric field between 5000 and 12,000 V operated at radio frequencies has been used to condense fogs that appear in column effluents; this approach has provided collection efficiencies as high as 98% (42). A system for overcoming aerosol formation (43) is based on the use of a Volman trap (44); the latter employs a large temperature gradient ($-80 \rightarrow 150$–$200°C$). A specialized collector for small quantities of high boiling compounds also has been described with a high collection efficiency (45).

IV. EXAMPLES OF PREPARATIVE SEPARATIONS

Although the literature contains numerous examples of preparative separations using gas chromatography, a comprehensive review here would be of little benefit and would be overly repetitious. Representative examples are cited, however, to give some introduction to the range and type of separations that have been carried out successfully.

Without question the most impressive plant-scale application of preparative chromatography to date is the mechanical counter-current separation of acetylene from methane discussed in an earlier section (19–22). This gas–solid system is used in commercial plants to process thousands of cubic feet of gas per day. Although a highly specialized approach, it illustrates the potential for those situations where the selective partitioning or absorption of an important component allows efficient separation from complex mixtures.

Not all applications of preparative gas chromatography involve huge volumes; frequently the real purpose in preparative work is to acquire a small amount of highly purified material. The displacement method frequently provides selectivity for achieving extremely high levels of purity. Two specialized examples of sample purification have been cited by Scott and Phillips (23). In one of these *n*-heptane has been freed of olefinic materials by passing the sample through a column of alumina coated with 10% by weight of silver nitrate. The heptane obtained from this column is free of all unsaturated materials and illustrates a purification involving the simplest of preparative systems. The converse of the preceding purification is to free an olefin such as 1-octene from alkanes by using the same type of column. The commercial octene sample is introduced into the column; the latter then is purged of all volatile materials by passing nitrogen gas through the column for some time at room temperature. The column is subsequently raised to 120°C, causing the adsorbed 1-octene to be released and collected as a purified olefinic fraction.

The same authors have used a more sophisticated form of the displacement method for accomplishing some elegant preparative separations (46); two examples are summarized in Table VIII. The recovery levels and purities of the fractions indicated in Table VIII provide convincing evidence in support of more extensive use of the displacement technique for specialized preparative separations.

Another specialized example is the determination of trace quantities

TABLE VIII

Preparative Separations by Displacement Chromatography

Mixture	Column	Column temp., °C	Displacer	Purity, %	Per cent of total fraction with this purity
cis-3-Heptene, *trans*-3-heptene	10% w/w AgNO₃ on alumina, 1.5-g capacity	75	1-Octene	99+ 99+	∼91 ∼85
Ethyl acetate, ethyl propionate, isopropyl propionate	Carbon, Gutcliffe Speakman 207C, 5-g capacity [a]	75	*m*-Xylene	99.4 99.4 99.5	∼85 ∼70 ∼88

[a] This column, scaled up by a factor of 10, accomplished the same separation with 50-g samples.

of lower olefins in alkane solutions (23). By passing the sample through a column of alumina coated with silver nitrate, the lower olefins will be selectively adsorbed. These are subsequently displaced by purified 1-octene; the lower olefins will be displaced from the column just in front of the 1-octene breakthrough. This fraction is collected and subsequently injected into a conventional analytical elution column. The mixture of lower olefins will give discrete analytical peaks which will provide both qualitative and quantitative results for the analysis of the trace impurities in a large alkane sample.

One of the most common laboratory applications of preparative gas chromatography is the separation of a complex mixture using sufficient sample to provide adequate fractions for subsequent study by other analytical and instrumental methods, e.g., infrared and UV spectroscopy, mass spectrometry, and NMR spectroscopy. A representative example is the separation of the scent contained in the storage reservoir of the *Nezara viridula* (the green vegetable bug). Using preparative gas chromatography, 18 components were isolated which comprise 99.9% of the scent (47).

An example of a true preparative problem is the use of gas chromatography for the isolation of highly purified tetraethyl germanium (99.5% pure) (48).

Frequently the results obtained with analytical gas chromatography indicate the need for further identification by collection of pure fractions from a complex mixture. An example is the preparative isolation of the products of fatty acid metabolism, and their subsequent chemical identification through oxidative degradation followed by analysis using gas chromatography and spectrophotometry (49).

Often separations attempted by distillation are inadequate and lead to the application of preparative gas chromatography. An example is the separation of *cis–trans*-methylsilylcyclohexane using a 25-ft column, $\frac{1}{4}$ in. in diameter, filled with 30% DC-550 silicone oil on 30 mesh firebrick (50).

A mixture of chloropropanes and chloropropenes (consisting of 10 components) has been separated by preparative gas chromatography with the components subjected to high resolution NMR spectroscopy for complete identification (51).

A small-scale preparative separation of steroids and alkaloids has been accomplished by using extremely low loading of thermally stable liquid phases (0.75% w/w SE-30 silicone oil on Chromosorb P). By applying temperature programming to a 9-ft by $\frac{1}{2}$-in. glass column, five different steroids have been separated with almost complete recovery at a purity of approximately 99% (52).

Through the use of band-displacement chromatography, pure deuterium has been separated from deuterium–hydrogen mixtures using columns containing an inert support material coated with palladium. A 2-liter sample of 50–50 mixture of deuterium and hydrogen was separated completely in approximately 12 min. Another separation involved a hydrogen sample containing 32 ppm deuterium; after separation the sample contained less than 0.5 ppm deuterium. In yet another experiment, 99.3% pure tritium was prepared from a tritium–hydrogen mixture containing 6% tritium (53).

Both the Wilkins Instrument and Research Corporation and the F & M Corporation have cited a number of examples of interesting preparative-scale separations during the past five years. Some of the separations discussed include α- and β-pinene, components of Citronella Java (21 constituents in all), and the separation of six sugar derivatives (54). A range of samples has been separated by both long, narrow-diameter columns and short, wide-diameter columns (55). This same article discusses the economic factors involved in various approaches to preparative gas chromatography. In another trade release, some of the factors affecting preparative scale column performance are reviewed (56).

The *Aerograph Research Notes* give examples of a number of preparative separations with a critique of some of the claims for pre-parative separations (57). A later trade bulletin discusses the merits of long, narrow columns versus short, fat columns and cites as an example the separation of hop oil on a 100-ft by $\frac{3}{8}$-in. column (58). Another article weighs the problems of separation speed versus sample resolution versus capacity in preparative gas chromatography and applies these arguments to the separation of decalins, refined turpentine, fatty acid esters, and lavandin oil (59). A final trade article discusses the separation of styrene dimers as well as the separation of phenyl dodecanes (60).

V. SUMMARY OF COMMERCIAL INSTRUMENTATION

Although every instrument company engaged in the manufacture of analytical gas chromatographic equipment has considered prepara-tive-scale equipment, at the present time five companies are the major force in the development of practical preparative instrumentation. Both Varian-Aerograph and Hewlett–Packard/F & M Scientific Division specialize in laboratory scale equipment. The Aerograph equipment is designed for the use of long, small-diameter columns. Large through-puts are accomplished by automatic repetitive sample injection with automated sample collection. The general approach is modeled after the arguments presented by Verzele et al. (7–9). Columns 250 ft in length by $\frac{3}{4}$ in., or 100 ft by $\frac{3}{4}$ in. can be accommodated in the ovens of the Aerograph instrumentation.

The F & M Scientific Division tends to promote the use of large-diameter columns, although their instruments also are designed to accommodate long, small-diameter columns. Much of the F & M litera-ture refers to "flow homogenizers" to improve column efficiency. Through the use of such devices column efficiencies approaching 200 plates/ft are claimed for 4-in. diameter preparative columns using 1-ml liquid samples.

During the past two years there has been significant research and development to extend preparative gas chromatography such that plant-scale separations are feasible. A review of these efforts recently has been presented (61) which indicates that Abcor is developing truly large-scale preparative equipment. A major effort by this company is the engineer-ing of a variety of baffle systems for achieving radial mixing. The goal is development of preparative gas chromatography plants utilizing columns up to 16 ft in diameter with a production level of millions of pounds per year. Hewlett–Packard F & M Scientific also is engaged in engineering studies of plant-scale chromatography. However, at present their plans do not appear to be as ambitious as Abcor's. One other com-pany is working on the development of plant-scale gas chromatographic systems, Nester–Faust. Their approach is the use of concentric-cylinder columns to obtain uniform flow with large-diameter preparative columns; this is similar to the proposal of Giddings (6). Such columns permit heat transfer, not only from the outside wall of the column, but also from the inside wall of the inner tube. In plant-scale chromato-graphy heat transfer is a major problem and may well be best accommo-dated with the concentric column.

VI. CONCLUSION

The utility of preparative separations by gas chromatography has already been amply demonstrated. For most research chemists con-cerned with purification of volatile mixtures, this technique is becoming an essential part of their research facilities. In the near future a number of refinements undoubtedly will be made in preparative instrumentation such that higher through-puts and improved resolution will result. Instrument manufacturers in subsequent designs will have to take account of the theoretical limitations inherent in elution gas chromatography. Excessive sample sizes and crudely designed preparative columns have detracted from the realization of the ultimate preparative capabilities of gas chromatography. The gas chromatographic technique provides inherent efficiencies that far surpass other preparative separations. If this advantage is not maintained while scaling up the through-put for preparative separations, many other methods will compete in terms of convenience and through-put. The major utility of the method in the near future will be for laboratory-scale separations with the goal of extremely high purity for relatively small samples (1–25 ml).

Consideration of the merits of preparative gas chromatography relative to distillation is a useful comparison. Distillations are most appropriately applied to large volumes of two-component mixtures; for many-component mixtures the distillation method rarely can provide the separation efficiency and the through-put possible with a good preparative gas chromatograph. With gas chromatography, mixtures consisting of ten or more components may be separated simultaneously, which is absolutely impossible with distillation systems. A problem with distillation separations is that many important two-component mixtures form azeotropes; gas chromatography easily overcomes this difficulty. Another problem with distillation is that efficient resolution of mixtures requires a large sample in that the hold-up in the column should be less than 5% of the pot volume. Thus preparative gas chromatography for sample sizes of less than 50 ml almost always will provide distinct advantages relative to distillation, particularly for the research worker concerned with resolving reaction mixtures and with purification of starting materials.

Preparative gas chromatography at the laboratory scale is a well-established technique with many practical examples of its utility. A number of useful commercial instruments are available and improvements are being developed almost monthly. Beyond this, there is extensive research and development to perfect plant-scale preparative gas chromatographic systems. This is primarily a problem of chemical engineering in which fluid dynamics, heat transfer, and good cost accounting are essential if the resulting systems are to be economically competitive with existing separation plants. Clearly, less expensive materials of construction than are used in laboratory-scale preparative gas chromatography must be developed. A reasonable expectation is that plant-scale separations will be limited to separations involving exotic, expensive chemicals such as perfumes, essential oils, and flavorings.

One hopes to see increased consideration of the displacement and frontal methods with respect to preparative gas chromatography. Both of these approaches provide specific advantages in terms of inherent through-put and in terms of more effective utilization of the separating capabilities of a given column. In view of the impressive separations that have been accomplished by the direct scale-up of analytical columns, a more imaginative approach could provide remarkable improvements in the capabilities of preparative gas chromatography.

References

1. D. E. M. Evans, W. E. Massingham, M. Stacey, and J. C. Tatlow, *Nature*, **182**, 591 (1958).
2. D. E. M. Evans, *Gas Chromatography, 1958*, D. H. Desty, Ed., Butterworths, London, 1958, p. 286.
3. J. J. Kirkland, *Gas Chromatography*, V. J. Coates, H. Noebels, and I. Fagerson, Eds., Academic Press, New York, 1958, p. 203.
4. J. H. Purnell, *Ann. N.Y. Acad. Sci.*, **72**, 614 (1959).
5. E. Bayer, K. P. Hupe, and H. Mack, *Anal. Chem.*, **35**, 492 (1963).
6. J. C. Giddings, *Anal. Chem.*, **34**, 37 (1962).
7. M. Verzele, *J. Gas. Chromatog.*, **3** (6), 186 (1965).
8. M. Verzele, *J. Chromatog.*, **15**, 482 (1964).
9. M. Verzele, J. Bouche, A. De Bruyne, and M. Verstappe, *J. Chromatog.*, **18**, 253 (1965).
10. K. P. Dimick and E. M. Taft, *J. Gas Chromatog.*, **1** (3), 7 (1963).
11. J. H. Purnell, *J. Roy. Inst. Chem.*, **82**, 586 (1958).
12. D. Dinelli, S. Polezzo, and M. Taramasso, *J. Chromatog.*, **7**, 477 (1962).
13. S. Polezzo and M. Taramasso, *J. Chromatog.*, **11**, 19 (1963).
14. A. J. P. Martin, *Gas Chromatography*, V. J. Coates, H. Noebels, and I. Fagerson, Eds., Academic Press, New York, 1958, p. 237.
15. A. J. P. Martin, *Vapour Phase Chromatography*, D. H. Desty, Ed., Butterworths, London, 1957, p. 1.
16. R. S. Porter and J. F. Johnson, *Nature*, **183**, 392 (1959).
17. M. J. E. Golay, H. I. Hill, and S. D. Norem, *Anal. Chem.*, **35**, 488 (1963).
18. C. N. Reilley, G. P. Hildebrand, and J. W. Ashley, Jr., *Anal. Chem.*, **34**, 1198 (1962).
19. P. Benedek, L. Szepesy et al., *Acta Chim. Acad. Sci. Hung.*, **14**, 3, 19, 31, 339, 353, 359 (1958).
20. M. Freund, P. Benedek, and L. Szepesy, *Vapour Phase Chromatography*, D. H. Desty, Ed., Butterworths, London, 1957, p. 359.

21. P. Benedek, L. Szepesy, and S. Szepe, *Gas Chromatography*, V. J. Coates, H. Noebels, and I. Fagerson, Eds., Academic Press, New York, 1958, p. 225.

22. J. H. Purnell, *Gas Chromatography*, Wiley, New York, 1963, p. 410.

23. C. G. Scott and C. S. G. Phillips, *Nature*, **199** (**4888**), 66 (1963).

24. C. W. Skarstrom, *Ann. N.Y. Acad. Sci.*, **72**, 751 (1959).

25. D. T. Sawyer and H. Purnell, *Anal. Chem.*, **36**, 457 (1964).

26. R. P. W. Scott, *Anal. Chem.*, **35**, 481 (1963).

27. J. Peters and C. B. Euston, *Anal. Chem.*, **37**, 657 (1965).

28. F. H. Huyten, W. Van Beersum, and G. W. A. Rijnders, *Gas Chromatography, 1960*, R. P. W. Scott, Ed., Butterworths, London, p. 224.

29. J. C. Giddings, *Anal. Chem.*, **35**, 439 (1963).

30. J. C. Giddings and G. E. Jensen, *J. Gas Chromatography*, **2** (**9**), 290 (1964).

31. G. L. Hargrove and D. T. Sawyer, *Anal. Chem.*, **38**, 1634 (1966).

32. J. C. Giddings and E. N. Fuller, *J. Chromatog.*, **7**, 258 (1962).

33. C. E. Schwartz and J. M. Smith, *Ind. Eng. Chem.*, **45**, 1209 (1953).

34. C. L. Guillemin, *J. Chromatog.*, **12**, 163 (1963).

35. K. P. Dimick and E. Taft, *J. Gas Chromatog.*, **1** (3), 7 (1963).

36. J. M. Kauss, J. Peters, and C. B. Euston, *Develop. Appl. Spectry.*, **2**, 383 (1962) (Pub. 1963).

37. H. Wiegleli and H. Prinzler, *Chem. Tech.* (*Berlin*), **15**, 98 (1963).

38. S. Sideman and J. Gilladi, *Gas Chromatog., Intern. Symp., 1961*, 3, 339 (1962).

39. J. W. Frazer and C. J. Morris, University of California Radiation Laboratory Document No. 14359, 1965.

40. N. W. R. Daniels, *Chem. Ind.* (*London*), **1963** (26), 1078.

41. H. Schlenk and D. M. Sand, *Anal. Chem.*, **34**, 1676 (1962).

42. A. E. Thompson, *J. Chromatog.*, **6**, 454 (1961).

43. R. Teranishi, J. W. Corse, J. C. Day, and W. G. Jennings, *J. Chromatog.*, **9**, 244 (1962).

44. D. H. Volman, *J. Chem. Phys.*, **14**, 707 (1946).

45. R. Teranishi, R. A. Flath, T. R. Mon, and K. L. Stevens, *J. Gas Chromatog.*, **3** (6), 206 (1965).

46. C. G. Scott and C. S. G. Phillips, *Gas Chromatography, 1964*, A. Goldup, Ed., Elsevier, Amsterdam, 1965, p. 266.

47. A. R. Gilby and D. F. Waterhouse, *Proc. Roy. Soc.* (*London*), Ser. *B*, **162**, No. 986, 105 (1965).

48. J. I. Peterson, L. M. Kindley, and H. E. Podall, paper presented at Pittsburgh Conference on Analytical Chemistry and Applied Spectroscopy, March 4–8, 1963.

49. D. G. Bishop and J. L. Still, *J. Lipid Res.*, **4** (1), 81 (1963).

50. T. G. Selin and R. West, *J. Am. Chem. Soc.*, **84**, 1856 (1962).

51. Y. Mashiko, U. Kanbayashi, K. Nukada, T. Suzuki, I. Takeda, and H. Tomita, paper presented at Pittsburgh Conference on Analytical Chemistry and Applied Spectroscopy, March 4–8, 1963.

52. H. M. Fales, E. O. A. Haahti, T. Luukkainen, W. J. A. Vanden Heuvel, and E. C. Horning, *Anal. Biochem.*, **4**, 296 (1962).

53. F. Batter, P. Molinari, G. Dirian, S. Grunspan, F. Menes, E. Saito, J. Lirat, and E. Roth, *Comm. Energie At.* (*France*), *Rappt. CEA 2647*, 1964.

54. *Facts and Methods*, Hewlett–Packard, F & M Scientific Division, **6**, No. 1, 4, 11 (1965).
55. *Facts and Methods*, Hewlett–Packard, F & M Scientific Division, **6**, No. 5, 4 (1965).
56. *Facts and Methods*, Hewlett–Packard, F & M Scientific Division, **7**, No. 4, 8 (1966).
57. *Aerograph Research Notes*, Varian-Aerograph (Winter 1963).
58. *Aerograph Previews and Reviews*, Varian-Aerograph, 5 (July 1965).
59. *Aerograph Research Notes*, Varian-Aerograph, 2 (Summer 1965).
60. *Aerograph Previews and Reviews*, Varian-Aerograph, 2 (1966).
61. *Chem. Eng. News*, 46 (June 28, 1965).

AUTHOR INDEX

Numbers in parentheses are reference numbers and show that an author's work is referred to although his name is not mentioned in the text. Numbers in *italics* indicate the pages on which the full references appear.

A

Abdul-Karim, A., 96(3), 98(3), 100–102(3), 104–107(3), 109(3), 110(3), 119(3), *120*, 253, *269*
Abel, K., 38(84), 41, *87*, *88*
Adam, N. K., 115, 116(27), *120*
Albert, D. K., 65, *90*
Allen, R. R., 68(191), *90*
Altenau, A. G., 177(48), *205*
Altshuller, A. P., 50, *89*
Amaya, K., 242, *268*
Amy, J. W., 7, *86*
Anders, M. W., 72, 73(216), 74, *91*, 291(18), 317(18), *321*
Andreatch, A. J., 67(189), *90*
Andrejev, L. V., 179(81,83,85), 181(85), *206*
Andrianov, K. A., 312(76), 314(76), *323*
Annis, J. L., 56(150), *89*
Ashley, J. W., 212, *267*, 332(18), *357*
Ashworth, A. J., 226(30), 249(30), 266, *268*
Aubeau, R., 74(218), *91*
Ayers, B. O., 167(19), *204*

B

Bache, C. A., 61, *90*
Bachman, L., 233, *268*
Badger, R. F., 311(71), *322*
Badings, H. T., 11(23), *86*
Baitinger, W. E., 7(15), *86*
Baker, E. B., 294(28), *321*
Bakr, A. M., 100(9), *120*
Ball, D. H., 70(202), *91*

Ballard, W. P., 65(185), *90*
Bambrick, W. E., 67(189), *90*
Baney, R. H., 310(70), *322*
Banner, A. E., 53(136), *89*
Barney, J. E., 47, *88*
Baron, C., 23(47), *86*
Barr, J. K., 181(93), *206*
Barrall, E. M., 83(253), *92*, 250, 251, *269*, 307(63), 308(63), *322*
Barrer, R. M., 25, 65, *87*, *90*
Barrow, G. M., 113(26), *120*
Bartz, A. M., 57, 58(152), *89*
Bassette, R., 64(171), *90*
Bate, R., 264(95), *270*
Batter, F., 354(53), *358*
Bayer, E., 328(5), 350(5), *357*
Beaven, G. H., 34(72), *87*
Bechtold, E., 233, *268*
Bednarczyk, J., 83(254), *92*
Beggs, W. S., 53(140), 54(140), *89*
Bell, R. P., 296(36), 303(36), *321*
Bender, S. R., 4(5), *85*
Benedek, P., 336, 351(19–21), *357*, *358*
Berezkin, W. C., 179(82), 189(82), *206*
Beroza, M., 68, 69(197), 83, *90*, *92*
Bevan, S. C., 28, 33(61b), 49(61b), *87*
Biemann, K., 54(145,146), 55(145), *89*
Billeb, K., 193(145), 194(145), *208*
Bishop, C. T., 70(202), *91*
Bishop, D. G., 353(49), *358*
Black, D. R., 53(135), *89*
Blaha, J., 82, *92*
Blakeway, J. M., 17(29), 18(29), *86*
Blandenet, G., 177(51), *205*
Blaustein, B. D., 25(59), *87*
Blinn, R. C., 59(161), *89*
Blom, L., 76(221,222), *91*

361

Fales, H. M., 72, *91*, 354(52), *358*
Farrington, P. S., 64(173), *90*
Faubert Maunder, M. J. de, 47(116), *88*
Favre, J. A., 177(49), *205*
Feit, E. D., 66(188), 72, *90*
Fejes, P., 217(17), 233, 234(17), 236(17), *267*
Felgenhauer, R., 70(203), 71(203), *91*
Felt, L., 177(47), *205*
Fenimore, D. C., 195(146), *208*, 272(6), 283(6), *287*
Fiks, M. M., 177(61), 193(136), *205*, *208*
Fishbein, L., 315, *323*
Fisher, G., 318(97), 319(97), *323*
Fisher, R. L., 267(100), *269*, *270*
Flath, R. A., 59(160), *89*, 351(45), *358*
Flett, M. St. C., 59(156), *89*
Forman, P., 264(95), *270*
Fowlis, I. A., 52(134), *89*
Franc, J., 71, 82, *91*, *92*
Frazer, J. W., 351(39), *358*
Frederick, D. H., 182(95,99), *206*
Fredericks, E. M., 77(231), *91*
Freeman, G. G., 312(75), *323*
Freund, M., 336(20), 351(20), *357*
Friedel, G. D., 83(255), *92*
Friedel, R. A., 316(91), 317(91), *323*
Fries, I., 55(148), *89*
Fromm-Czaran, E., 217(17), 233, 234 (17), 236(17), *267*
Fuller, E. N., 347(32), 349, *358*

G

Gardiner, W. L., 21(41), *86*
Gardon, J. L., 300(46,47), 302(46,47), 303, 314, *322*
Garner, P., 72(215), *91*
Gaumann, T., 2(3), *85*
Genkin, A. N., 316, *323*
Gerlach, H. O., 178(78), 185, 186–188 (78), 199(78), *206*
Giddings, J. C., 177(55), 178(75,77), 181(92), 183(102), 189(118–120), *205–207*, 263(93), *270*, 328, 346, 347(32), 348, 349, 355, *357*, *358*

Gil-Av, E., 68(194), 74, 75(194), *90*, 258, *269*, 292(22), 294(22,29), 318 (96,97), 319, *321*, *323*
Gilby, A. R., 353(47), *358*
Giles, C. H., 314(85), *323*
Gilladi, J., 351(38), *358*
Giuffrida, L., 7(17), 44, 57(17), *86*, *88*
Glueckauf, E., 158(15), *204*, 215, 216, 220(12), 221(12), 223(12), 226, 232, 265, *267*, *268*, 299, *322*
Godden, T. W., 137(22), *151*
Goey, J. de, 191(127), *207*
Golay, M. J. E., 158(16), 173, 183, 191(31), 191(125), 192, 193(31), *204*, *205*, *207*, 331, *357*
Goldup, A., 21(44), 36(76), 65(177), *86*, *87*, *90*, 139(25), *151*, 158(7), 159(7), 169(7), 191(7), *204*, 237(41), 248(53), 261, 266, *268*, *270*
Goodwin, E. S., 47(114), *88*
Gordy, W., 302, *322*
Goulden, R., 47(114), *88*
Graham, W., 183(108), *207*
Grant, D. W., 49, 60, *89*, *90*
Grant, J. A., 76(228), *91*
Gray, G. M., 18(32), *86*
Gray, G. W., 252(66), *269*, 307, *322*
Green, G. E., 76(225), *91*
Green, L. E., 313(77), *323*
Greene, S. A., 24, *87*
Gregg, S. J., 216, 226, 230, *267*
Gribben, T., 36(74), *87*
Griffiths, J. H., 38(85), *88*
Grimes, M. D., 71(212), *91*
Grob, R. L., 36, *87*
Groennings, S., 65, *90*
Grossman, J. D., 67, *90*
Grubner, O., 177(47), *205*
Grunspan, S., 354(53), *358*
Gudzinowicz, B. J., 48, *89*
Guggenheim, E. A., 110, 113–115, 116(27), *120*, 248(55), 249(56), *269*
Guillemin, C. L., 350(34), *358*
Guiochon, G., 18(33), 23(33), *86*, 188 (116), *207*
Gump, B. H., 105, *120*
Gunther, F. A., 59(161), *89*

H

Haahti, E. O. A., 354(52), *358*
Haarhoff, P. C., 221, 222(21), 223, *267*
Haken, J. K., 317(92), *323*
Halász, I., 123, 143, 144, *151, 152,* 153, 156(3), 158(8–11), 160(8,12), 161(14), 163(10), 165(3), 168(22), 170(24,25), 173(3), 174(3), 176(34,35), 177(11,25, 64,65), 178(14,22,78), 179(22), 180 (22,65), 183(25,65), 184(25), 185(22, 78,114), 186(78), 187, 188(12,22,78, 117), 190(115), 191(22,114,115,121, 122,124,126), 192(126), 193, 194(140), 195(140), 196(64), 198(140), 199(3, 25,78,140), 202(124), *204–208*
Halpern, B., 256, *269*
Hamlin, A. G., 267(99), *270*
Hammond, E. W., 47(117), *88*
Hanneman, W. W., 177(70), *206*
Hansen, R. P., 17(30), *86*
Hardy, C. J., 222(25), *268*
Hardy, E., 37(80), *87*
Haresnape, J. N., 185(113), 188(113), *207*
Hargrove, G. L., 325, 347, *357*
Harkins, W. D., 99(6), 100(6), *120*
Harlow, G. A., 77(231), *91*
Harris, W. E., 68(192), *90*
Hart-Davis, A., 133(17), *151*
Hartmann, H., 50, 51(131), *89*
Hartmann, K., 156(3), 165(3), 166(100), 167(100), 173(3), 174(3), 182(100), 187(3), 199(3), *204, 207*
Harvey, D., 292(21), *321*
Hawke, J. C., 17(30), *86*
Hawkes, S. J., 263(93), *270*
Hayward, D. O., 252, *270*
Hazeldean, G. S. F., 191(129), *207*
Heilbronner, E., 74, *91*
Heine, E., 143, 144, *152,* 153, 156(3), 160(12), 165(3), 168(22), 173(3), 174(3), 178(22), 179(22), 180(22), 185(22,114), 187, 188(12,22), 190(115), 191(22, 114,115,124), 199(3), 202(124), *204, 207*
Helfferich, F., 217, 230(18), 234(39), *267, 268*

Henderson, N., 59(160), *89*
Henly, R. S., 310(69), *322*
Henne, A. L., 47(120), *88*
Henneberg, D., 55(147), *89*
Henniker, J. C., 113(24), 116(24), *120*
Herling, J., 258, *269,* 292(22), 294(22), *321*
Hersch, P. A., 29, 77, *87*
Herzberg-Minzly, Y., 68(194), 74, 75 (194), *90,* 294(29), *321*
Hesse, G., 121(3), *151*
Hewlett-Packard, 354(54–56), *359*
Hildebrand, G. P., 212, *267,* 332(18), *357*
Hildebrand, J. H., 291(19), 299, 300 (19), 302(51), *321, 322*
Hill, H. I., 331, *357*
Hillman, G. E., 29(65), *87*
Hines, W. J., 71(212), *91*
Hishta, C., 182(95,98), *206*
Hively, R. A., 57(151), *89,* 256, *269*
Hoare, M. R., 25, *87,* 210(3), *267,* 291(12), *321*
Hoff, J. E., 66(188), 72, *90*
Hollis, O. L., 123, 127(10), *151,* 177 (60,66), *205, 206*
Hopkins, R. L., 79(209), *91*
Hoppe, W., 177(46), *205*
Horning, E. C., 21(41,42), *86,* 310(68), 313(78), *322, 323,* 354(52), *358*
Hornstein, I., 6, *86*
Horvath, C., 123(9), *151,* 170(25), 177 (25,64,65), 180(65), 183(25,65,104), 184(25), 191(124), 193, 194(140), 195(140), 196(64), 198(140), 199(25, 140), 202(124), *204–208*
Huber, J. F. K., 231–233, *268*
Hughes, J., 59(156), *89*
Hunt, R. H., 56, *89*
Hunter, I. R., 70(199), *90*
Hupe, K. P., 22(46), *86,* 328(5), 350(5), *357*
Hurrel, R., 280, *287*
Hurst, G. S., 47, *88*
Huyten, F. H., 345(28), 346(28), 349 (28), *358*

SUBJECT INDEX

A

Abstraction techniques, 61–69
  by chemical removal, 66
  experimental arrangements for, 63
  followed by displacement, 69
  for physical removal, 64
  by precolumn partition, 68
Acetone, 105, 184, 301
Acetylacetone, 48
Acetylene, 351
Acids, 65, 72, 85, 293
  hard and soft, 293
Acrylonitrile, 301
Activity coefficient, 14, 100, 105, 108,
    225, 246–248, 291, 296, 300,
    304–307, 319
  at infinite dilution, 248
  measurement of, 248
  use in correcting for gas imperfection,
    247
Adjusted retention time, see Net
    retention time
Adsorbent, preparation of, 130
  see also Gas–solid chromatography
Adsorption, 93–122, 246, 252, 263–264
  at gas–liquid interface, 93–119
  isotherm, 122, 246, 252
  on liquid phase surface, 96
  on polar liquid phases, 94
  on solid support, 93, 263–264
Aerogel, see Column, aerogel
Aerosil, 185, 197
Alcohols, 15, 28, 65, 67, 71–72, 82–85,
    102, 105, 127, 143, 235, 298,
    301–302
  abstraction of, 67
  dehydration of, with boric acid, 67
  esterification of, 72
  gas–solid chromatography of, 127
  partition coefficients for, 235

Aldehydes, 65, 68, 83
  abstraction of, 68
  see also Carbonyl compounds
Alkadienes, 19, 67, 74, 123, 131–133, 140
  abstraction of, 67
Alkaloids, 72, 82
Alkanes, 19, 60, 100–101, 117–118, 123,
    126, 133–138, 179, 181, 187–188,
    235, 266, 298, 306, 352
  desorption of normal from molecular
    sieve, 65
  gas–solid chromatography of, 135–137
  see also Hydrocarbons
Alkenes, 5, 19, 65, 71, 79, 123–124, 127,
    130–133, 140–141, 144, 148–150,
    179, 181, 186–188, 258–259,
    294–298, 351–352
  gas–solid chromatography of, 127
  hydrogenation of, 71
  postcolumn hydrogenation of, 19
  separation of cis–trans isomers, 124
  silver complexes of, 258–259
  trace analysis of, 69, 148–150
  trapping of, 5
Alkylbenzenes, see Aromatic hydro-
    carbons
Alkyl bromide, abstraction of, 68
Alkyl halides, see Halogen com-
    pounds
Alkynes, 19, 35
Alumina, 11, 122, 127–130, 140, 160,
    177–179, 190–193
  on glass beads, 183
  modifiers for, 130
  preparation of, 130–131
  salt-modified, 136, 140–142
  with silver nitrate, see Silver nitrate/
    alumina
  surface area of, 130
  water-modified, 131
Aluminum complexes, 48

F

G

Advances in Analytical Chemistry and Instrumentation

CUMULATIVE INDEX, VOLUMES 1–6

Author Index